Preparing for the
# New Jersey
# GEPA
# SCIENCE

# Preparing for the
# New Jersey
# GEPA
# SCIENCE

**PAUL S. COHEN**
Former Assistant Principal, Science
Franklin Delano Roosevelt High School
Brooklyn, New York

**JERRY DEUTSCH**
Chemistry Teacher
Edward R. Murrow High School
Brooklyn, New York

**ANTHONY V. SORRENTINO, D.Ed.**
Former Director of Computer Services
Former Earth Science Teacher
Monroe-Woodbury Central School District
Central Valley, New York

AMSCO

AMSCO SCHOOL PUBLICATIONS, INC.
315 HUDSON STREET, NEW YORK, N.Y. 10013

The publisher wishes to acknowledge the helpful contributions of the following consultants in the preparation this book:

ANDREA BLAKE-GARRETT
Supervisor of Science
Jersey City Public Schools
Jersey City, New Jersey

DANIEL MONIGLE
Science Teacher
Academy I Middle School
Jersey City, New Jersey

CAROLINE H. MURPHY
Science Teacher
Southern Regional Middle School
Manahawkin, New Jersey

Please visit our Web site at: *www.amscopub.com*

Text and Cover Design: Merrill Haber

Composition: Northeastern Graphic, Inc.

Artwork: Hadel Studio

When ordering this book, please specify: *either* **R 786 W** *or*
PREPARING FOR THE NEW JERSEY GEPA: SCIENCE

ISBN: 0-87720-942-1

# To the Student

 This book provides a complete review of intermediate-level science to help you prepare for your New Jersey Grade Eight Proficiency Assessment (GEPA) in Science.

The text is made up of ten chapters. These chapters cover topics in life, physical, earth and space science, the scientific method, and the history and interactions of science, technology, and society. Each chapter opens with the GEPA *Macro Statements* and *Knowledge Statements* and includes a *Chapter Outline*.

The text presents the major ideas of each topic in a manner that is easy to read and understand. The many illustrations that go with the text help explain the concepts. Each chapter is divided into several topic sections. Each major section is followed by a *Question Set*, which is composed of multiple-choice and open-ended questions. These questions, which are similar to the types you will see on the GEPA exam, reinforce and test the main points covered in the section and help you apply your scientific knowledge.

In addition, special features called *Skills Activities* appear at intervals throughout the text. The purpose of these features is to teach you a particular process- or laboratory-oriented skill, such as making measurements, organizing data, predicting an experimental result, interpreting data in a table, graph, or diagram, and so on. Each feature guides you through the skill and then ends with several follow-up questions that test your ability to apply the data or skill on your own.

Throughout the book, important vocabulary terms are printed in **bold italic** type. These terms are defined in the text and appear with formal definitions in the *Glossary* at the back of the book. Terms that are less important or that may be unfamiliar to you are printed in *italic* type. These terms do not appear in the *Glossary*, but are listed in the *Index*.

Finally, the book includes three *Practice Tests*. These tests (modeled after the GEPA sample test items and based on GEPA test specifications) cover the major concepts, understandings, and skills that are included in New Jersey's intermediate-level science curriculum. We wish you success in your studies and on the GEPA science examination.

# Contents

# Chapter **1**

# Problem Solving and Mathematics

**Macro Statements:** (*Problem Solving*) Develop problem-solving, decision-making, and inquiry skills. (*Mathematics*) Integrate mathematics as a tool for problem solving in science, and as a means of expressing and/or modeling scientific theories.

## KNOWLEDGE STATEMENTS

### Problem Solving

**A.** Inquiry is a multifaceted activity involving making observations; posing questions; examining sources of information to see what is already known; planning investigations; reviewing what is already known in light of experimental evidence; using tools to gather, analyze, and interpret data; proposing answers, explanations, and predictions; and communicating results.

**B.** A control and a single variable are essential in an experimental design.

### Mathematics

**A.** Science uses mathematics as a tool to determine and support conclusions.

## CHAPTER OUTLINE

**Problem Solving in Science**

**Scientific Procedures**

**Mathematics in Science**

# PROBLEM SOLVING IN SCIENCE

Welcome to the world of science! You may be wondering what you are likely to find in this world. You are probably familiar with many of the different fields of science, such as biology, chemistry, physics, and geology. But, what do we mean when we refer to a field as a "science"? Many dictionaries describe science as a body of knowledge systematically obtained. This knowledge is obtained through a system of inquiry that is common to all branches of science. Inquiry includes making observations, posing questions, examining reference materials, planning investigations, gathering and interpreting data, proposing explanations, and making predictions. Scientists then share their results with other scientists, who may want to verify or improve on the previous work.

In trying to understand the natural world, scientists focus on certain scientific *systems*. A system is a group of components working together to form a unified whole. For example, the human body is a biological system. It contains the many components necessary to keep you alive. One of those components is the circulatory system, with its components (blood, the heart, and blood vessels) working together. The components of a system may be systems themselves. Other systems that we will be exploring in this text include ecosystems and the solar system. Understanding how the components of a system interact with one another, and how systems work together, is an important part of the study of science.

 ## Observations

One way in which we study the natural world is to make careful observations. An *observation* is anything we perceive through one of our five senses. We draw conclusions or make predictions based upon an observation or a series of observations. We are constantly making observations and drawing conclusions in everyday life. In addition to the five senses, scientists use tools that extend or improve the senses. A microscope, for example, improves our ability to see objects too small to be seen with the naked eye. A telescope enables us to see objects that are too far away to be seen otherwise.

Suppose you walk into a room and notice an unpleasant odor. You say, "It stinks in here!" You have just made an observation. "What is causing that horrible smell?" You have just stated a *problem*. A problem is always stated in the form of a question. You might now say, "Something must have died in here." You have now made a guess as to the solution to your problem. You observed a foul odor, and you suspected that the cause of the odor was a dead animal. Your suspicion was based not on one observation, but on several. A possible answer to a problem, based on observations or prior knowledge, is called a ***hypothesis***. If you had never smelled a dead animal before, you would not have been able to guess the cause of the odor. The best hypotheses are those that are based on a large number of careful observations. Once a hypothesis has been posed, it is generally tested through further observations and experimentation. In the case above, you would probably want to find the dead animal before you could conclude that your hypothesis was correct. This organized, step-by-step approach to problem solving in science is known as the ***scientific method***.

## Question Set 1

*Multiple Choice*
Base your answers to questions 1 through 4 on the following paragraph.

On the first warm day in March, Jennifer takes out her bicycle, which she has not ridden all winter. She finds it very difficult to pedal. She also is not able to ride as fast as she used to, even though the wind is behind her.

1.  Jennifer *observes* that
    A.  she is out of shape
    B.  the bicycle needs oil
    C.  she is traveling unusually slowly
    D.  she needs to ride more often

2.  What *problem* might Jennifer pose based on her observations?
    A.  Why can't I ride as fast as I used to?
    B.  I am not riding as fast as I used to.
    C.  My chain needs oil.
    D.  I am out of shape.

3.  One possible *hypothesis* Jennifer can draw is that
    A.  the wind is behind her
    B.  she finds it difficult to pedal
    C.  she cannot go as fast as she used to
    D.  she is out of shape

4. Which procedure would be *least* helpful to Jennifer if she wishes to find out the cause of her difficulties?

   A. trying to ride against the wind

   B. oiling the bicycle and then riding the same route again

   C. asking several of her friends to try riding her bicycle and listening to their observations

   D. putting the bicycle upside down and turning the pedals with her hands, to see if the wheels can turn freely

## Open Ended

Base your answers to questions 5 through 7 on the following paragraph.

A poultry farmer was worried because his turkeys were underweight. The farmer had noticed a fox near his farm, which was upsetting the turkeys. He trapped and relocated the fox, and observed that the turkeys became calmer. Weeks later, he noticed an increase in the number of mice in the area where the turkeys were kept. Even though he continued to give the birds the same amount of food, the farmer saw that his turkeys continued to be underweight.

5. What was the original hypothesis formed by the farmer?

6. How would you revise that hypothesis based on the observation of the mice?

7. What should the farmer do to help increase the weight of his turkeys?

# SCIENTIFIC PROCEDURES

There are several procedures that scientists follow to make their hypotheses reliable. One of these is to make careful observations. In Question Set 1, Jennifer should have listened carefully to find out whether her bicycle was making any unusual noises. The sound of the wheel rubbing against the brake or an occasional squeaking sound might have helped her to locate the problem.

While studying a culture of bacteria in 1928, the Scottish bacteriologist Alexander Fleming noticed that there were no bacteria growing in one region of a particular sample. By examining this sample more carefully, he discovered that a mold was growing in the region where there were no bacteria.

## Research

After observing a natural phenomenon, such as bacteria not growing near a type of mold, scientists attempt to find out if other studies have been done on that phenomenon. Gathering facts, data, and other published opinions on a topic is called *research*. Today's scientists have a wide variety of research sources available to them. These include scientific journals (which publish the results of experiments), books, periodicals, and the news media. Nearly all of these are available on the Internet and in libraries.

## Forming a Good Hypothesis

It is important to base a hypothesis on a large number of observations. The greater the number of observations, the more likely the hypothesis is to be correct. For instance, Fleming might have hypothesized that the mold kills bacteria. He went on to test this hypothesis by performing hundreds of additional experiments. On the basis of just one experiment, he could not be sure that it was the mold, and not some other unknown factor, that had killed the bacteria. Fleming's careful observations eventually led to the discovery of penicillin, which has saved millions of lives.

## Variables

In performing valid experiments, it is important to limit the number of variables. *Variables* are the changeable conditions that can affect the outcome of an experiment. Refer back to Question Set 1. Jennifer's problem was probably caused by one or two variables: her physical condition and/or the condition of her bicycle. To make an accurate hypothesis, she needed to eliminate one of the variables. If she tried several well-maintained bicycles and found that she had difficulty riding all of them, then she could infer that the problem was with her and not with her bicycle. By eliminating a variable (the condition of the bicycle), she could pose a more reliable hypothesis.

Similarly, Fleming had to deal with such variables as food supply, light, temperature, and type of bacteria, any of which might affect bacterial growth. To limit these variables, he took two identical samples of bacteria under identical conditions, and then added penicillin to one of them but not to the other. In this way, he could confidently infer that it was the penicillin that was affecting the bacteria, and not some other variable.

## Controlled Experiments

An experiment that tests the effect of just one variable is called a *controlled experiment*. In Fleming's experiment, one sample of bacteria was treated with penicillin, while the other was not. All other conditions were kept the same in the two samples. The sample that was not treated—that is, the one that did not contain the variable—is called the *control*. The sample that was treated is called the *experimental sample*. Only by comparing an experimental sample to a control can we draw valid conclusions.

## SKILLS ACTIVITY **1**
### DESIGNING AND CONDUCTING AN EXPERIMENT

Sharon wishes to investigate whether a certain brand of fertilizer really produces larger flowers. She grows petunias, pansies, and marigolds, adding the same amount of fertilizer to each plant at the same time. The plants were grown under the same conditions of soil, light, and temperature. When the plants blossomed, Sharon measured the size of the flowers. She found that the petunias were larger than both the pansies and marigolds.

### Questions

1. Indentify the problem that Sharon was attempting to investigate.

2. Before doing her experiment, Sharon said, "Plants grown with fertilizer will produce bigger flowers." This statement is best described as a

   A. problem        B. hypothesis        C. conclusion        D. variable

3. What is the major error in the design of this experiment?

4. Sharon concluded that the fertilizer works best on petunias. Is her conclusion valid? Explain.

## Organizing Observations

When we wish to form a hypothesis based on a large number of observations, it is important to organize our observations in a logical fashion. Suppose that we are studying the rate of a chemical reaction occurring at various temperatures. The common household chemical hydrogen peroxide ($H_2O_2$) breaks down to produce water and oxygen gas ($2H_2O_2 \rightarrow 2H_2O + O_2$). We measure how long it takes to produce 50 milliliters (mL) of oxygen from identical hydrogen peroxide solutions at five different temperatures. In the first trial run, at 30°C, it takes 8.0 minutes. In the second run, at 50°C, it takes 2.1 minutes. In the third run, at 10°C, it takes 33.0 minutes. In the fourth run, at 20°C, it takes 16.0 minutes. Finally, in the fifth run, at 40°C, it takes 4.1 minutes.

Before we can make inferences about the effect of temperature on this reaction, we need to organize our data in a more logical fashion. Table 1-1 shows two possible ways (A and B) we could organize the data.

Which table is more helpful to us in forming a hypothesis about the effect of temperature on the time needed to produce a given amount of oxygen? Table A has more data, because it includes the order in which the observations were made. However, the extra data are neither helpful nor important! By listing the results in order of increasing temperature, as in Table B, we make it easier to observe a trend, and easier to draw a conclusion. Table B shows a better way of organizing the data.

Using Table B, we can easily note that as temperature increases, the time needed to collect 50 milliliters of oxygen decreases. In other words, as temperature increases, the chemical reaction proceeds more quickly. The speed at which a reaction proceeds is called the *rate of reaction*. In this case, as in most chemical reactions, an increase in temperature increases the rate of reaction.

**TABLE 1-1.    TIME NEEDED TO COLLECT 50 ML OF OXYGEN FROM IDENTICAL SOLUTIONS OF HYDROGEN PEROXIDE**

| | Table A | | Table B | |
|---|---|---|---|---|
| Trial Run | Temp. (°C) | Time (minutes) | Temp. (°C) | Time (minutes) |
| 1 | 30 | 8.0 | 10 | 33.0 |
| 2 | 50 | 2.1 | 20 | 16.0 |
| 3 | 10 | 33.0 | 30 | 8.0 |
| 4 | 20 | 16.0 | 40 | 4.1 |
| 5 | 40 | 4.1 | 50 | 2.1 |

There are further conclusions that can be drawn from Table *B*. Although we did not measure it directly, we can figure out how long it would take to collect 50 milliliters of oxygen at 25°C. We predict that it would take less than the 16 minutes needed at 20°C, but more than the 8 minutes needed at 30°C. We might even guess that it would take 12 minutes, which is halfway between 8 and 16. However, we can make a more accurate guess by using an important visual tool for organizing and comparing sets of data, called a ***line graph***.

 ## Using Line Graphs

In Figure 1-1, we have graphed the data given in Table *B*. We chose to plot temperature on the *x*-axis (the horizontal axis) and time on the *y*-axis (the vertical axis). We then entered our five measured points, and connected the points. Note that the lines connecting the points are *not* straight lines. Our five points do not lie on a straight line, so we draw a smooth *curve* to connect the points.

Line graphs are used to show the relationship between two numerical variables, the independent variable and the dependent variable. The variable you are controlling, the temperature in this case, is called the ***independent variable*** and is placed on the *x*-axis. The variable you measure, which depends on the value of the independent variable, is called the ***dependent variable*** and is plotted on the *y*-axis. In our experiment, time is the dependent variable. The amount of time (to collect 50 milliliters of oxygen) depends on the chosen tem-

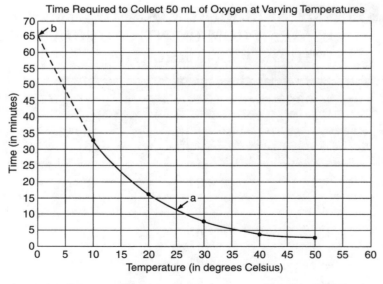

**Figure 1-1.** The line graph illustrates the effect of temperature on the rate of a reaction.

perature. When making a table of scientific data, as in Table *B* above, it is customary to list the independent variable first.

Our five measured points show our five observations. All other points along the curve on the graph are *inferences*. We infer that our measurements establish a trend, and that if we made other measurements they would follow the same trend. From our graph we can conclude that, at a temperature of 25°C, it should take about 11 minutes to collect 50 milliliters of oxygen (see point "a" on the graph). All our measurements were made between 10 and 50°C. On our graph, we extended the curve to show what might happen at a temperature of 0°C. By extending the graph, we can infer that it would take about 64 minutes to collect 50 mL of oxygen at a temperature of 0°C (see point "b" on the graph).

By graphing our observations, we are able to infer values that lie between and beyond our measured points. The greater the number of observations, the more reliable the inferences will be.

 ## Using Bar Graphs

**Bar graphs** are also used to help organize and illustrate observations. Suppose we wished to compare the weather in New Jersey to the weather in some other areas of the United States. One area of interest might be the amount of rainfall. Table 1-2 shows the average annual rainfall in eight U.S. cities, three of which are in New Jersey.

**TABLE 1-2. AVERAGE ANNUAL RAINFALL IN VARIOUS U.S. CITIES**

| City | Average Annual Rainfall (inches) |
| --- | --- |
| Cape May, New Jersey | 40.5 |
| Trenton, New Jersey | 45.5 |
| Newark, New Jersey | 44.0 |
| Cleveland, Ohio | 35.4 |
| Honolulu, Hawaii | 23.5 |
| Miami, Florida | 57.5 |
| Seattle, Washington | 38.9 |
| Los Angeles, California | 14.8 |

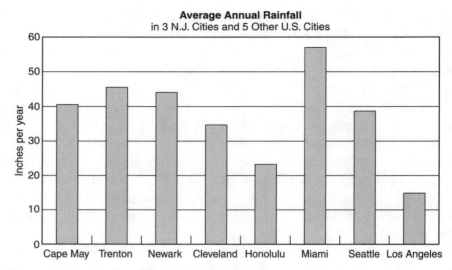

**Figure 1-2.** A bar graph makes it easier to compare observations, such as the average annual rainfall in several U.S. cities.

A bar graph can be used to compare these eight observations, as shown in Figure 1-2. Looking at the bar graph, you can quickly observe that of the eight cities, Miami has the most rainfall each year, while Los Angeles has the least. Bar graphs are used to make clear and dramatic comparisons. Notice that in a line graph (Figure 1-1), both the *x*-axis and the *y*-axis are quantitative (that is, they show amounts). In a bar graph (Figure 1-2), only the *y*-axis is quantitative.

Sometimes the information that a scientist needs to represent is not numerical in nature. In such cases, a picture really is worth a thousand words. For example, a scientist may draw a diagram that helps us understand the flow of blood through an animal's circulatory system, without attempting to draw an exact representation of what the circulatory system really looks like.

## Question Set 2

*Multiple Choice*

Base your answers to questions 1 through 4 on the following information.

When a gas is heated in a sealed container, the pressure of the gas increases. One unit commonly used to measure gas pressure is the *torricelli* (torr), named after the Italian scientist Evangelista Torricelli, the inventor of the barometer. At sea level, 760 torricellis is considered standard air pressure. Adam measured the pressure exerted by a gas in a sealed container at 10-degree intervals. Here are his data:

| Temperature (°C) | Pressure (torr) |
|:---:|:---:|
| 0 | 708 |
| 10 | 734 |
| 20 | 760 |
| 30 | 786 |
| 40 | 812 |
| 50 | 838 |
| 60 | 897 |
| 70 | 890 |
| 80 | 916 |
| 90 | 942 |

Adam graphed his data, as shown below.

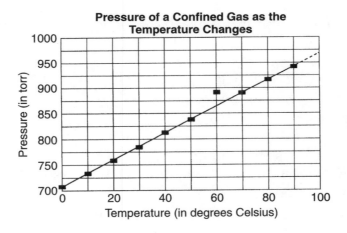

1.  In his experiment, Adam observed all the following *except*
    A. as the temperature increased, the pressure increased
    B. the pressure was 760 torricellis when the temperature was 20°C
    C. the pressure at 60°C was greater than the pressure at 70°C
    D. the pressure at 35°C was 800 torricellis

2. Which of the following is the most valid statement about the pressure of the gas at 100°C?
   A. Since Adam's measurements went up to only 90°C, no prediction can be made about the pressure at 100°C.
   B. Adam observed the pressure at 100°C to be about 970 torricellis.
   C. Adam can predict that the pressure at 100°C would be about 970 torricellis.
   D. The pressure at 100°C should be twice the pressure at 50°C.

3. Adam's graph does not go through the point he measured at 60°C. He predicts that if he repeats the experiment under the same conditions, he will get
   A. the same pressure at 60°C that he got the first time, 897 torricellis
   B. a different value for the pressure at 60°C, probably between 850 and 875 torricellis
   C. a completely different graph
   D. a different value for the pressure at 60°C, probably between 825 and 850 torricellis

4. In Adam's experiment, the temperature is the
   A. independent variable      C. control
   B. dependent variable        D. standard

Refer to the bar graph in Figure 1-2 on page 10 to answer questions 5 and 6.

5. Which city gets more annual rainfall than Trenton?
   A. Miami           C. Los Angeles
   B. Newark          D. Honolulu

6. Suppose we wanted to know which city has more rainy days, Seattle or Miami. Using our graph, we can definitely
   A. *observe* that Miami has more rainy days
   B. *infer* that Miami has more rainy days
   C. *infer* that Seattle has more rainy days
   D. *not* make any inference about the number of rainy days

## *Open Ended*

7. How can a line graph be used to predict points beyond the range of the measurements?

**8.** In one or two sentences, explain why a bar graph is more useful than a line graph to represent data.

# MATHEMATICS IN SCIENCE

 ## Making Measurements

How tall are you? If you can answer this question, it is because you have made a measurement. You probably used feet and inches to measure your height. In most parts of the world, however, your height would be measured in meters.

Scientists make many different kinds of measurements. To express these measurements, they all use the same set of units, called *SI units*, or *System of International Units*. Table 1-3 lists some of the many quantities that scientists measure and the units commonly used to express those quantities. Although they are commonly used, not all of these quantities are official SI units.

A standard set of prefixes is used to change the size of these units (see Table 1-4). For example, a kilowatt is equal to 1000 watts. A centimeter is 1/100 of a meter, and a millisecond is 1/1000 of a second.

**TABLE 1-3.  COMMONLY USED MEASUREMENT UNITS**

| Quantity | Unit | Abbreviation |
|----------|------|--------------|
| length | meter | m |
| mass | kilogram | kg |
| volume | liter* | L |
| time | second | s |
| temperature | degree Celsius* | °C |
| energy | joule | J |
| power | watt | W |
| force | newton | N |

*Units that are not part of the SI System.

## TABLE 1-4. PREFIXES USED IN THE METRIC SYSTEM

| | | |
|---|---|---|
| 1/1,000,000,000 | (0.000000001) | nano |
| 1/1,000,000 | (0.000001) | micro |
| 1/1000 | (0.001) | milli |
| 1/100 | (0.01) | centi |
| 1/10 | (0.1) | deci |
| 1000 | kilo | |
| 1,000,000 | mega | |
| 1,000,000,000 | giga | |

 ## Tools for Measurement

It is important that a scientist select the appropriate instrumentation to design and conduct investigations. Some of these tools are listed in Table 1-5.

## TABLE 1-5. TOOLS OF THE SCIENTIST

| Field of Science | Tool | Function |
|---|---|---|
| Biology | Compound microscope | Viewing small objects such as cells |
| Biology | Electron microscope | Viewing extremely small objects such as cell organelles and viruses |
| Biology | Micropipette | Transferring very small amounts of liquid |
| Astronomy | Telescope | Viewing distant objects |
| Astronomy | Spectroscope | Analyzing the colors of light from stars |
| Chemistry | Balance | Measuring mass |
| Chemistry | Graduated cylinder | Measuring volume |
| Chemistry | Burette | Delivering measured quantities of liquids |
| Physics | Spring scale | Measuring force |
| Physics | Electroscope | Detecting static electrical charge |

## SKILLS ACTIVITY **2**

## MAKING PRECISE MEASUREMENTS

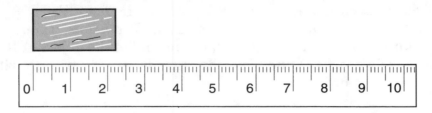

**Figure 1-3.**

Students were asked to measure the object illustrated in Figure 1-3. The following measurements were reported: (A) 2 centimeters; (B) 2.2 centimeters; (C) 2.22 centimeters; (D) 2.220 centimeters. Only one of these measurements is scientifically correct. Scientists have agreed to follow certain standard procedures when reporting measurements. On the ruler illustrated in Figure 1-3, each small line represents 1/10 (0.1) of a centimeter, or 1 millimeter (mm). The object being measured is larger than 2 centimeters but smaller than 3 centimeters. If we report the length as 2 centimeters, we are not using our ruler to its fullest capability. Measurement A is therefore inadequate. The end of the object is between the second and third small lines past the 2-centimeters mark, as you can see in the enlargement of the ruler shown in Figure 1-4.

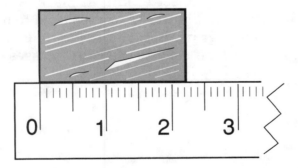

**Figure 1-4.**

Since each small line represents 0.1 centimeter, you can express the measurement as 2.2 centimeters. However, you can be even more precise. Note that the object is slightly longer than 2.2 centimeters; try to estimate how much longer than 2.2 centimeters it is. To do this, imagine 10 even smaller lines between 2.2 and 2.3 centimeters and estimate where the end of the object would be. One such estimate might be 2.22 centimeters. This is the correct expression of this measurement. Scientific measurements include one estimated place. Measurement D has two estimated places, the last 2 and the 0. Only one estimated place is permitted. Scientific measurements enable scientists to know the precision of the instruments used to make them. In summary, when making measurements, always "read between the lines."

Your height is actually a measurement of *length*—the distance between two points. Length is commonly measured with a ruler or tape measure. The standard unit of length is the **meter**, which is slightly longer than a yard. Smaller lengths are measured in *centimeters* (hundredths of a meter, cm) or *millimeters* (thousandths of a meter, mm), while long distances are measured in *kilometers* (thousands of meters, km). When using a ruler, place one end of the object at the zero (if it is clearly marked) and read the ruler where it lines up with the other end of the object.

 ## Mass

*Mass* is a quantity that measures the amount of material in an object. Scientists measure mass in metric units called *kilograms*. A kilogram (kg) is approximately equal to the mass of a quart of milk or a liter of soda. Your mass is probably between 40 and 70 kilograms. In the laboratory, you are usually measuring small quantities and therefore need a smaller unit for mass. The gram is 1/1000 of a kilogram and is about equal to the mass of a large paper clip.

Mass is measured with a *balance*, a device that compares the object being measured to an object of known mass. A triple-beam balance, like the one shown in Figure 1-5, can be used to measure masses to the nearest 1/100 of a gram. A modern electronic balance, as illustrated in Figure 1-6, can be used to measure masses even more precisely.

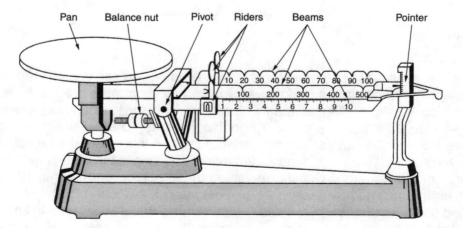

**Figure 1-5.** The triple-beam balance is used to measure mass; measurements are in metric units (grams).

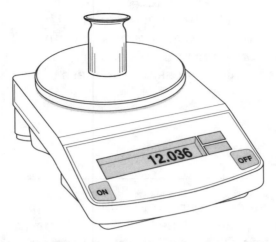

**Figure 1-6.** The single-pan electronic balance is used to measure mass; the object on this balance shows a mass of 12.036 grams.

 ## Weight

*Weight* is the force exerted when gravity pulls on an object. It depends on the mass of the object, and on the strength of gravity. Since the strength of gravity differs from place to place, an object's weight may change when it is moved. Its mass, however, does not change. For example, your weight on the moon would be 1/6 of your weight on Earth, because the pull of gravity felt on the moon is 1/6 of that felt on Earth.

Forces, such as weight, are measured with a *scale*, as illustrated in Figure 1-7. These scales contain springs, which are stretched or

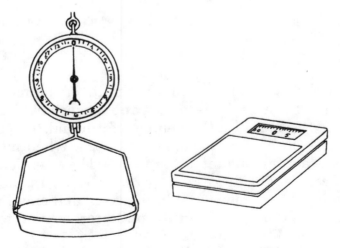

**Figure 1-7.** Scales such as these are used to measure weight; measurements are in English units (pounds).

pushed by the weight of the object. In the United States, weight is generally measured in ounces, pounds, and tons. The metric unit of weight is the *newton*. Since an object's weight is not the same everywhere, scientists prefer to measure the mass of an object, rather than its weight.

 ## Volume

***Volume*** is the amount of space an object occupies. The volume of a rectangular object is determined by multiplying the measurement of its length times its width times its height (volume = length × width × height).

The box in Figure 1-8 is 2.0 centimeters long, 4.0 centimeters wide, and 3.0 centimeters tall. You can determine its volume by multiplying 2.0 centimeters × 4.0 centimeters × 3.0 centimeters, which equals 24 cubic centimeters. The cubic centimeter, usually written as $cm^3$ or cc, is a unit of volume.

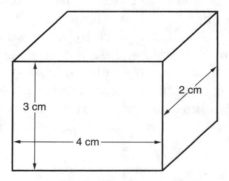

**Figure 1-8.** Multiply the measurements of length × width × height to find the volume of this box.

You are probably familiar with other units of volume, such as gallons, quarts, fluid ounces, tablespoons, and teaspoons. These units are commonly used to measure the volume of a liquid. The unit you use depends largely on how much liquid you need. When measuring liquids and gases, a common unit of volume used by scientists is the *liter*. *Note: One liter is equal to 1000 cubic centimeters*. In the metric system, large volumes are measured in liters (L) and small volumes are measured in milliliters (mL). Since a milliliter is equal to 1/1000 of a liter, it is also equal to 1 cubic centimeter.

To measure the volume of a liquid, you pour the liquid into a container of known volume. One such container is called a *graduated*

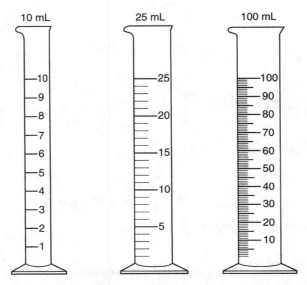

**Figure 1-9.** Graduated cylinders are used to measure the volume of a liquid; measurements are in milliliters (mL).

*cylinder.* A graduated cylinder, like those illustrated in Figure 1-9, has lines on it called *graduations*. Once the liquid has been poured into the graduated cylinder, the cylinder is placed on a level surface. As shown in Figure 1-10, you take the measurement by lining up your eyes with the liquid's surface. Water placed in any type of glassware forms a *meniscus*, a curve at the surface. You read the volume at the bottom of the curved water surface. In Figure 1-10, the volume should

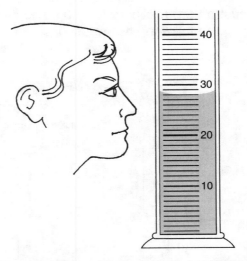

**Figure 1-10.** Always read the volume of a liquid at the bottom of the meniscus (*not* at the top of the curve).

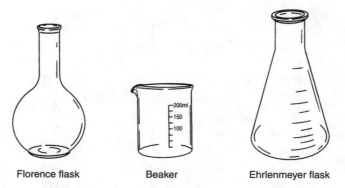

Florence flask    Beaker    Ehrlenmeyer flask

**Figure 1-11.** Three examples of laboratory tools that are used to hold and pour measured liquids.

be read as 28.5 milliliters. Remember, the numeral in the last place is an estimate, between the 28- and 29-milliliter lines. Figure 1-11 shows some other tools that are used for measuring volume.

## SKILLS ACTIVITY **3**

### MAKING MEASUREMENTS; PERFORMING CALCULATIONS

A graduated cylinder also can be used to determine the volume of small solid objects, as shown in the diagram below. When an object such as a glass marble or small rock is placed into the water inside the cylinder, the water level rises. The change in the volume of the water is equal to the volume of the object.

For example, the graduated cylinder in the following diagram contains 20.0 milliliters of water. When the marble is placed in the cylinder, the water level rises to 25.0 milliliters. The change in the water's volume is 5.0 milliliters, so the volume of the marble must be 5.0 milliliters (or 5.0 cubic centimeters). Study this procedure, then answer the following two questions.

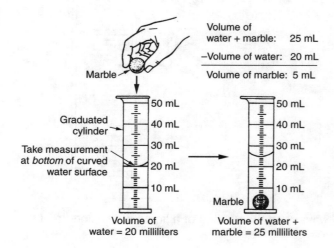

## Questions

1.  The diagram below indicates that the volume of the rock is, in milliliters,

    A. 30.0          B. 20.0          C. 10.0          D. 5.0

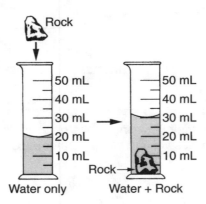

2.  A graduated cylinder contains 20.0 milliliters of water. If a stone with a volume of 12.0 milliliters and another stone with a volume of 5.0 milliliters are both placed into this cylinder, the water level will rise to show a total volume of, in milliliters,

    A. 32.0          B. 25.0          C. 17.0          D. 37.0

# Density

The quantity that compares the mass of an object to its size (or, more specifically, to its volume) is called *density*. **Density** is defined as the mass of an object divided by its volume (density = mass/volume). While the mass and volume of a piece of metal, for example, depend on the size of the piece, the density depends only on the nature of the metal (and its temperature). Let's compare the densities of lead and aluminum. At room temperature, the density of aluminum is 2.7 grams per cubic centimeter, which is abbreviated as 2.7 g/cm$^3$. Since density is mass divided by volume, the unit of density contains a mass unit, grams, divided by a volume unit, cubic centimeters. When we say that aluminum has a density of 2.7 g/cm$^3$, this means that a piece of aluminum with a volume of 1 cubic centimeter would have a mass of 2.7 grams. The density of lead at room temperature is 11.3 g/cm$^3$, so lead is about four times as dense as aluminum (see Figure 1-12).

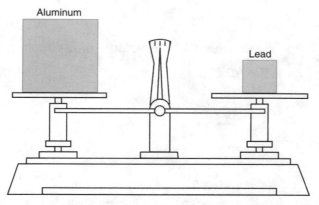

**Figure 1-12.** As shown by their positions on the balance, these metal cubes are of equal mass; the cube with less volume has a greater density.

 ## Measuring Temperature

*Temperature* is the measure of heat in a substance; that is, how hot or cold something is. You measure temperature with a tool called a *thermometer*. The thermometer contains a liquid (usually alcohol or mercury) that expands when it is heated. As the liquid expands, it moves up a thin, graduated tube. The height of the liquid in the tube tells us the temperature. As the liquid cools, it contracts and moves down the tube.

There are two scales commonly used to measure temperature: *Fahrenheit* and *Celsius*. The unit for measuring temperature is either the degree Fahrenheit (°F) or the degree Celsius (°C). Figure 1-13

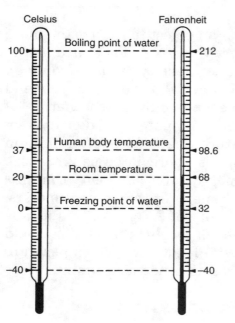

**Figure 1-13.** Some important readings on the Celsius and Fahrenheit thermometers are shown for comparison.

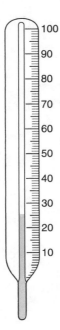

**Figure 1-14.** Reading between the lines: this thermometer shows a precise reading of 25.5° Celsius.

shows a Fahrenheit thermometer and a Celsius thermometer with several important temperatures indicated. Two important temperatures are the freezing point and the boiling point of water. Water freezes (turns to ice) at 0°C, which is the same as 32°F. Water boils (turns to steam) at 100°C, which is the same as 212°F. Two other temperatures that are important to know are standard room temperature (20°C or 68°F) and normal body temperature (37°C or 98.6°F.) When reading a thermometer, as with all measuring devices, you estimate between the lines. Figure 1-14 shows a thermometer with a temperature reading of 25.5°C.

## Question Set 3

*Multiple Choice*

Questions 1 and 2 refer to the diagram below.

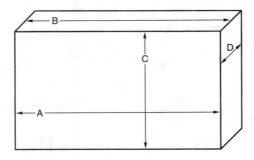

1.  Which two lines in the diagram indicate the same dimensions?
    A. $A$ and $B$               C. $B$ and $C$
    B. $A$ and $C$               D. $B$ and $D$

2.  Which mathematical calculation could be used to correctly determine the volume of this box?
    A. $A + B + C$               C. $B + D + C$
    B. $A \times C \times D$     D. $A \times B \times C$

Questions 3 through 6 are based on the diagrams below.

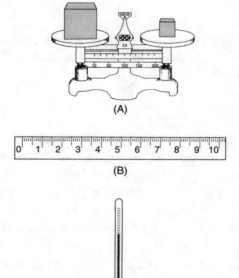

(A)

(B)

(C)

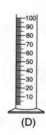

(D)

3.  Which of these measuring tools will give a reading in centimeters?
    A. tool $A$        B. tool $B$        C. tool $C$        D. tool $D$

4.  Which tool can be used to determine whether water is cool enough to freeze?
    A. tool $A$        B. tool $B$        C. tool $C$        D. tool $D$

**5.** A student has pieces of lead and aluminum of equal volume. Which tool could be used to help distinguish the lead from the aluminum?

   A. tool *A*      B. tool *B*      C. tool *C*      D. tool *D*

**6.** Which tool would be used to determine the volume of a liquid?

   A. tool *A*      B. tool *B*      C. tool *C*      D. tool *D*

## *Open Ended*

**7.** Volume can be measured in *all but one* of the following units: liters, quarts, grams, cubic centimeters. Which of these units is *not* used for measuring volume? What quantity is it used to measure, and what tool is used?

**8.** In several sentences, explain how you would measure the volume of an irregularly shaped rock.

**9.** The density of aluminum is 2.7 g/cm³ and the density of lead is 11.3 g/cm³. Which piece of metal would have a greater mass—aluminum with a volume of 10 cubic centimeters or lead with a volume of 2 cubic centimeters? Explain your answer.

## Statistical Analysis

Modern technology has changed the way scientists record, calculate, and present their data. Today's computers enable scientists to perform calculations and store information with a speed and precision that was never before possible. Among the vast array of computer programs now available, two of the most helpful to scientists are databases and spreadsheets. Both types of programs provide a way to store, sort, analyze, and present huge amounts of data.

Before a scientist can safely conclude that there is a significant difference between the control group and experimental group, a rigorous mathematical procedure called ***statistical analysis*** is used. Statistical analysis, also called *statistics*, is a mathematical method of examining data to determine whether the differences seen between groups are due to chance rather than to experimental conditions. For example, when a pharmaceutical company wants to determine the effectiveness of a new drug for the treatment of AIDS, the drug is tested on HIV-positive patients. The medication may appear to help some individuals, but statistics are used to determine whether their improvements are the result of the drug trial or due to chance alone. The more people there are in a study, the more reliable the results and the easier it is to draw a conclusion. Computers perform these analyses quickly and accurately.

# Range, Mean, and Median

Would you be happy with a grade of 82 on your next science test? That might depend on the range of scores in the class. The range, median, and mean are statistical tools commonly used to compare sets of data. The *range* is the difference between the top score and the bottom score. If the grades ranged from 57 to 85, you might be very happy with your 82. You might also want to know the mean grade on the test. The *mean* is the arithmetic average of the data. To calculate the mean, you add up all of the grades and then divide the sum by the total number of grades. The median is another statistical tool that can help you compare your score to that of the other students. The *median* is determined by listing all the scores in numerical order. The middle score (halfway down from the top) is the median.

## SKILLS ACTIVITY 4

### MAKING STATISTICAL CALCULATIONS

A gardener measured the heights of nine pea plants that were grown in full sunlight and obtained the following results:

**Pea Plants Grown in the Sunlight**

| Plant Number | Plant Height (cm) |
| --- | --- |
| 1 | 10 |
| 2 | 13 |
| 3 | 4 |
| 4 | 8 |
| 5 | 17 |
| 6 | 12 |
| 7 | 13 |
| 8 | 15 |
| 9 | 11 |

The gardener analyzed his results using the statistical tools of range, mean, and median. To know the range, you must find the lowest and the highest results. In this case, the plants' heights range from 4 to 17 centimeters. The mean is calculated by summing the heights, and then dividing by 9, the number of plants. The mean, in this case, is 11.4 centimeters. The median is found by listing the heights in order (from highest to lowest) and then finding the middle result. In this case, the heights from highest to lowest are 17, 15, 13, 13, 12, 11,

10, 8, and 4 centimeters. The middle height is 12 centimeters, the height that has four values above it and four values below it.

The gardener made these measurements to study the effect of amount of sunlight on the growth of pea plants. He measured the heights of another group of pea plants, grown in a shady part of the garden. Here is his second set of data:

**Pea Plants Grown in the Shade**

| Plant Number | Plant Height (cm) |
|:---:|:---:|
| 1 | 10 |
| 2 | 12 |
| 3 | 11 |
| 4 | 6 |
| 5 | 8 |
| 6 | 12 |
| 7 | 10 |
| 8 | 9 |
| 9 | 11 |
| 10 | 7 |
| 11 | 10 |

## Questions

1.  What is the *range* of heights among the plants grown in the shade?

2.  What is the *median* height of the plants grown in the shade?

3.  What is the *average* (mean) height of the plants grown in the shade?

4.  What conclusion can you draw about the effect of sunlight on the growth of pea plants?

5.  If you compared the data from only the first three plants in each group, which group of plants would have a greater average height?

6.  Which statistical analysis is more valid, the one that includes data for all 20 plants, or the one that compares only the first three plants from each group? Explain your answer.

# Chapter 2

# History of Science and Technology

**Macro Statements:** (*History of Science*) Recognize the historical origin of scientific theories; they are developed by people who live in their cultural/historical context. These theories are tested and may be replaced based on new information and investigative techniques. (*Technology*) Understand that technology is an application of scientific principles.

## KNOWLEDGE STATEMENTS

### History of Science

**A.** Technology is a response to needs within a cultural and historical context.

### Technology

**A.** The tools of technology assist scientific measurements and observations.

**B.** Scientific knowledge and technology are applied in the process of problem solving.

**C.** Technology is applied to space exploration.

## CHAPTER OUTLINE

**Relationship of Science, Technology, and Society**

**Tools Assist Scientific Measurement and Observation**

**Using Scientific Knowledge and Technology to Solve Problems**

**Technological Advances and Space Exploration**

# RELATIONSHIP OF SCIENCE, TECHNOLOGY, AND SOCIETY

## Science and Technology

Science and technology affect the lives of people all over the world. *Science* is the process of asking questions and seeking answers to gain an understanding of the natural world. For example, science attempts to answer questions about such topics as how the universe came into being, what the nature of matter is, and how life on Earth first evolved. By providing insight into the workings of nature, science helps us predict the outcome of physical events.

*Technology* uses scientific knowledge and other resources to develop new products and processes. These products and processes help people solve problems and meet the needs of individuals or society. Some problems that technology attempts to solve include how to increase gas mileage of cars, how to reduce pollution, and how to improve tools of communication.

While the emphasis in science is on gaining knowledge of the natural world, the emphasis in technology is on finding practical ways to apply that knowledge to solve problems. There are three major fields of science: life science, earth science, and physical science. Each of these fields contains a number of more specific sciences (see Figure 2-1). Biologists, chemists, and geologists are some types of scientists. Engineers, computer programmers, and medical technicians are examples of workers in the fields of technology.

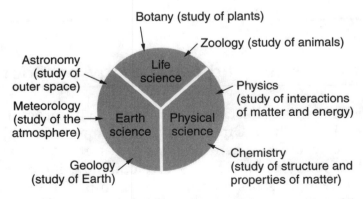

**Figure 2-1.** The three major fields of science each contain more specific areas of scientific study.

## Science and Technology Advance Each Other

Science and technology frequently help to advance each other. Scientific discoveries often lead to the development of new or better devices and processes. These technologies may, in turn, lead to new discoveries or to a better understanding of scientific principles. For instance, scientists discovered various properties of light, such as how light is bent when it passes through different types of lenses. This knowledge led to the invention of the telescope and the microscope. Using these devices, scientists have made many more discoveries about the natural world. Every technological advance is based in some way on scientific principles, as the examples in Table 2-1 suggest.

In fact, much technology involves knowledge from more than one field of science. For example, the artificial heart shown in Figure 2-2 involves knowledge from both life science (the structure of the human heart) and physical science (the mechanical principles of how the heart works).

**TABLE 2-1.** **RELATION OF SCIENTIFIC PRINCIPLES AND TECHNOLOGY**

| Scientific Principle | Technological Device |
| --- | --- |
| Low temperatures kill or reduce growth of microorganisms | Refrigerators and freezers |
| Sunlight contains energy | Solar-heating systems and solar cells |
| Splitting atoms of radioactive elements produces heat | Nuclear power plants |
| Every action produces an equal and opposite reaction | Rocket engines and jet engines |

## Effects of Science and Technology on Society

Science, technology, and society are constantly interacting with one another (see Figure 2-3). Often, a change in one area will affect the other two. For example, scientific discoveries about the structure of matter led to many technological developments, including the production of microprocessors on tiny silicon chips. These "microchips" made possible many new products that have affected society by improving health care, communications, and transportation.

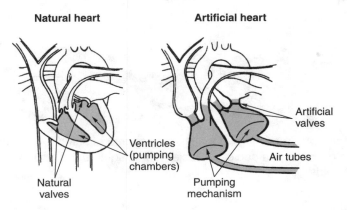

**Natural heart**          **Artificial heart**

Artificial valves

Ventricles (pumping chambers)

Air tubes

Natural valves

Pumping mechanism

**Figure 2-2.** The use of technology and knowledge from more than one field of science has made possible the development of the artificial heart.

Our culture, economy, and social systems are often affected by developments in science and technology. During the 1800s, the United States was transformed from a mainly agricultural society to a highly industrialized society. This period of cultural, economic, and social change was caused by the development of industrial machinery and new ways to power it. Some examples of other ways that science and technology have affected society are: health care products allow us to live longer, healthier lives; refrigerators and freezers eliminated the need for the ice-cutting industry; and communication systems, such as cell phones and the Internet, allow people separated by great distances to work together.

While science and technology have solved many problems, they have also created problems. Pollution of the environment and disposal of garbage and hazardous waste are problems caused, in part, by sci-

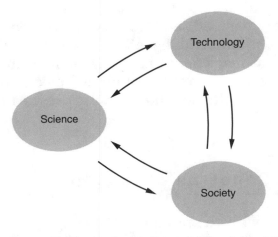

**Figure 2-3.** This diagram illustrates that science, technology, and society are constantly interacting and affecting one another.

**Figure 2-4.** Much of our garbage consists of products of science and technology. Disposal of the garbage is a societal problem that requires the efforts of people from many different fields.

ence and technology (see Figure 2-4). Solving such problems requires the cooperation of people working in government, industry, science, and technology.

## Effects of Society on Science and Technology

Society also affects science and technology in many ways. New technology is often developed in response to the needs of individuals or society. For example, the need to help people overcome diseases and disabilities has encouraged the development of new medical procedures, such as chemotherapy and laser surgery, and new devices, like artificial organs and limbs.

The attitudes of people in a society may influence the direction of scientific research and technological development. In our society, public opinion has encouraged research to find a cure for AIDS. In contrast, public attitudes have largely discouraged the use of animals to test the safety of new cosmetic products.

Acceptance and use of an existing technology can also depend on people's attitudes. An example is nuclear energy. Most people agree that nuclear energy has both benefits and drawbacks. However, people disagree about whether its benefits outweigh its dangers. Public attitudes against nuclear energy have led some countries to ban its use. Yet, other countries generate most of their electricity with nuclear energy. Public opinion will undoubtedly influence the future of nuclear energy (see Figure 2-5).

## Benefits and Concerns of Technology

Everyone interacts with the products of technology. In almost everything you do—wear clothing, sleep on a bed, watch television, eat with a knife and fork, ride on a school bus—you interact with the products

**Figure 2-5.** People's attitudes toward nuclear power will affect the acceptance and use of this technology in the future.

of technology. People use technology for a number of reasons. To extend or improve our abilities, we use radios and telephones, calculators and computers, binoculars and telescopes, and other devices. We use machines and appliances to help us do work that requires more than human strength and at faster speeds than are humanly possible. To overcome physical limitations, people use devices such as eyeglasses, hearing aids, and wheelchairs (see Figure 2-6).

Many products of technology are used to change our environment. As a result, our current lifestyle is much different from that of 50 years ago. In the 1950s, for example, most baseball games were played in the daytime. Now we can continue our activities after nightfall. Today, most baseball games are played at night under artificial lights. Few homes had television sets in the early 1950s, and there were only a few programs available. Today, many homes have two or more television sets, and there are many programs to be seen on dozens of channels.

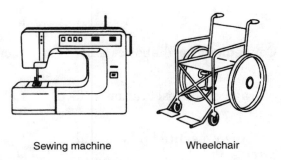

Sewing machine         Wheelchair

**Figure 2-6.** Some technological devices are used to extend human abilities or to overcome disabilities.

Every technological process or device affects the environment in some way. Some of these effects may be harmful. Lightbulbs and many other appliances require electricity. The production of electricity may use precious natural resources or cause pollution of the air and water.

Technology is also a concern because it is extending into morally sensitive areas, such as cloning and stem cell research. There are large segments of the population that are critical of this type of research. In addition, technology is responsible for the weapons of mass destruction that have many people concerned. The rapid development of technology sometimes makes it difficult to determine if the technology is beneficial or harmful. Scientists, politicians, and the public must constantly evaluate the worth of technology and make good decisions as to its use.

Table 2-2 lists some examples of benefits and concerns of technology.

**TABLE 2-2.** **BENEFITS AND CONCERNS OF TECHNOLOGY**

| Technological Process or Device | Benefits | Concerns |
| --- | --- | --- |
| Nuclear energy | Additional clean electricity | Risk of accidents; radioactive wastes |
| Painkilling drugs | Treat diseases, relieve pain | Addiction through abuse |
| Computers | Increased ability to process data | Loss of jobs; health problems from computer keyboards |
| Space travel | Increased knowledge | High financial cost; safety |
| Life-sustaining medical devices | Keep people alive | Decisions about when to use or remove them |
| Automobile | Increased mobility | Increased pollution; deaths and injuries |
| Chemical fertilizers | Increased agricultural yields | Harmful to lakes and streams; possible harm to humans |
| Artificial sweeteners | Convenient for diabetics and dieters | Increased risk of cancer |
| Refrigerants | Storage and preservation of food | Released into atmosphere, harmful to the ozone layer |
| Herbicides and pesticides | Destroy unwanted plants and insects | Upset natural food chain of some animals; possible harm to humans |

## SKILLS ACTIVITY 1

## TIME LINE LEADING TO WIRELESS RADIO COMMUNICATION

Guglielmo Marconi (1874–1937), an Italian physicist also known as the "father of radio," is credited with sending the first wireless transmission and reception in 1896. His discovery led to the development of radio transmission soon after. It took the discovery of many scientific principles and the development of many technological inventions before Marconi accomplished this monumental event.

Although it could be traced back further, many significant events occurred during the 150-year period before Marconi's discovery. Scientific knowledge regarding electricity, electromagnetic waves, and magnetism had to be discovered, and technological devices in the form of the telegraph, microphone, and transmitter had to be invented before wireless transmission and reception could occur. Even after Marconi accomplished wireless communication, further scientific and technological advancements such as vacuum tubes, transistors, and improved circuitry needed to be developed to produce the radio that we know today.

The time line below shows some scientific and technological advancements that led to wireless communication. Carefully examine the time line and answer the questions that follow.

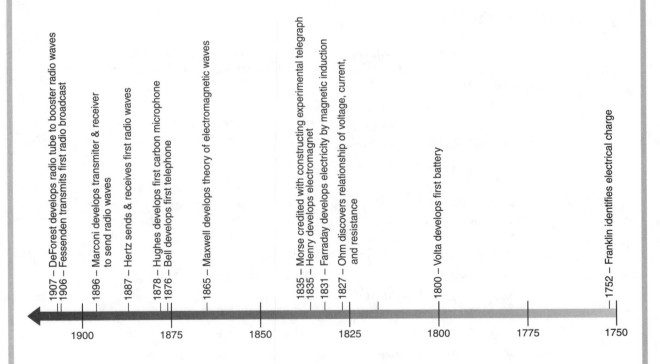

## Questions

1.  Using the time line provided above, list three scientists who contributed a scientific discovery and three scientists who contributed a technological invention before Marconi that helped lead to wireless communication.

2. What could be said about Marconi's achievement after 1896?

   A. Further scientific discoveries led to the radio.

   B. Further technologic inventions led to the radio.

   C. Further scientific and technological achievements led to the radio.

   D. No further improvements were made.

3. Answer the following questions based on this data: In 1883, Edison discovered that a hot filament emitted electrons; and in 1904, Fleming developed the radio tube from Edison's discovery. (a) Was Edison's achievement a scientific discovery or a technological invention? (b) Was Fleming's achievement a scientific discovery or a technological invention? (c) Where on the time line would the achievements of Edison and Fleming be placed?

## Question Set 1

*Multiple Choice*

1. Building the first electromagnet based on previously discovered scientific knowledge about magnetism and electricity is an example of

   A. a scientific discovery

   B. a technological development

   C. predicting future physical events

   D. observing the natural world

2. Based on scientific knowledge from many fields, engineers built a space probe and sent it to Jupiter in 1979. The probe sent data back to Earth, adding to our knowledge about Jupiter. Which statement best describes these events?

   A. New technology sometimes builds on past technology.

   B. Advances in technology cause some devices to become obsolete.

   C. Technology affects our natural environment.

   D. Science and technology help to advance each other.

3. An example of a political event that increased the need for science knowledge in the United States was the

   A. election of the U.S. president in 2000

   B. landing of a spacecraft on the moon

C.  invention of the television

D.  launching of *Sputnik 1* in 1957 by the Soviet Union

4.  The following graph shows how average life expectancy in the U.S. changed between 1910 and 1970. This change is most likely the result of

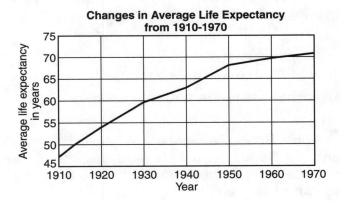

A.  advances in medical technology

B.  harmful effects of technology on the environment

C.  advances in educational technology

D.  advances in communication technology

5.  The functioning of which two instruments is based on similar scientific principles?
    A.  thermometer and ruler
    B.  thermometer and microscope
    C.  microscope and telescope
    D.  microscope and balance

6.  Developments in microelectronics and computer science are changing the United States from a largely industrial nation into a nation more dependent on information services. This is an example of
    A.  science helping technology to advance
    B.  society affecting science and technology
    C.  science and technology affecting society
    D.  science and technology solving society's problems

7.  Early space exploration started in the 1960s. It has progressed since then. For example, spacecraft first orbited Earth, then explored the moon, later reached Mars, and so on. The most likely reason for this progression is the
    A.  invention of faster rockets
    B.  increase in science knowledge only

   C. improvements in technology only

   D. increase in science knowledge and improvements in technology

8. The search for knowledge is an important issue for many people, especially scientists. An example of the search for science knowledge is

   A. building a telescope

   B. sailing a boat

   C. drawing a map of the moon

   D. exploring the ocean bottom

9. The Hubble Space Telescope was placed in orbit around Earth in the early 1990s. As people analyzed the pictures taken with the telescope, they learned more about the universe. This is an example of

   A. science improving our knowledge of technology

   B. technology improving our knowledge of science

   C. science improving our society

   D. technology improving our society

## Open Ended

10. Since about 1950, television technology has become an important part of our everyday activities. Explain how television is both beneficial to people and harmful to the environment.

11. The table below lists three technologies that affect our environment and three technologies that help people overcome disabilities. On a separate sheet of paper, list and describe three technologies that extend our abilities.

### VARIOUS USES OF TECHNOLOGY

| Affect Environment | Overcome Disabilities | Extend Abilities |
|---|---|---|
| Air conditioner | Hearing aid | _____ |
| Space heater | Wheelchair | _____ |
| Dam on a river | Eyeglasses | _____ |

# TOOLS ASSIST SCIENTIFIC MEASUREMENT AND OBSERVATION

## The Need for Instruments of Measurement

In society, there has always been a need for measuring length, mass, and time. Whether constructing a building or selling fruits and vegetables, people have always had a need for tools that could make these measurements.

Many of our early length measurements were based on the human body. The foot, for instance, is a unit of length that was based on the length of a human foot, and an inch was the distance across a thumb. However, such measurements varied from person to person and from time to time. Standardization became crucial as technology progressed and global trading increased. For example, it is important that the bolts made in one location fit the nuts made at another location. So, in 1960, an international conference developed the standardized system for measurement called the System of International Units, or SI units, as discussed in Chapter 1 (refer to Table 1-3).

A standard for each of the basic units was established. The standard for the length unit, the meter, is the length of the path traveled by light in a vacuum during a time interval of 1/299,792,458 of a second. The standard for the mass unit, the kilogram, is a platinum alloy cylinder kept in France. Subunits and multiple units of length are conveniently made in factors of 10. For example, a centimeter is 1/100 of a meter, and a kilometer is 1000 meters in length.

As studies in science progressed, it became essential that observations and experiments could be measured accurately. Scientists needed the ability to measure objects and record events with great precision in order to understand the principles of science. Using technology, tools of measurement were invented that provided the accuracy needed. Some common measuring tools, discussed in Chapter 1, are the ruler, thermometer, graduated cylinder, balance, hand lens, and compound microscope. The computer, electron microscope, telescope, and micrometer caliper are examples of sophisticated tools that measure objects with even greater precision (see Figure 2-7).

## Tools Improve Information Gathering

When solving a scientific problem, you usually need to gather some information. In some cases, the information is already known and need

Telescope

**Figure 2-7.** Sophisticated tools, such as the telescope, can measure objects with greater precision than common measuring tools can.

only be organized; in other cases, it is necessary to make measurements to gather information before it can be organized. Scientific tools provide a means of gathering quantitative data that can be organized into graphs and tables. Tools are used to measure objects and events, and provide quantitative data with varying degrees of precision and accuracy.

It is necessary to select the appropriate tool to precisely gather the information desired. For example, when making temperature measurements, it is necessary to use a thermometer. The thermometer used to measure air temperature need be capable of reading only whole-degree temperatures. However, when measuring small changes in temperature, such as the temperature of the human body, the thermometer should be capable of measuring tenths of a degree (see Figure 2-8).

Scientific information improves when scientific tools are more accurate. Line up a dozen identical thermometers and read the temperature of each. It is common to find that some of the thermometers will differ by a few degrees. A steel ruler will change the length of a cen-

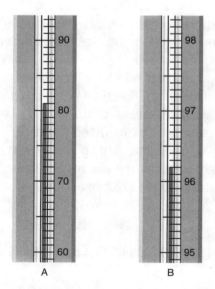

A                    B

**Figure 2-8.** Thermometer A shows a temperature of 81°F; thermometer B shows a temperature of 96.2°F. Thermometer B is more precise than thermometer A.

timeter based on differences in air temperature: the length of a centimeter will be slightly longer when the temperature is hotter, due to expansion of the steel! For most of our daily measurements these differences are insignificant, but the uncertainty of measurement can lead to problems when great accuracy is needed in science.

## Historical Development of the Microscope and the Computer

Tools for measurement have been essential to meet the needs of science and society. The early history of the microscope demonstrates how technology changed the microscope and assisted in increasing scientific knowledge. The history of the computer demonstrates how technology was affected by social needs.

*The Microscope.* Evidence shows that the magnifying lens was used as a spectacle (type of eyeglasses) to magnify objects more than 2000 years ago. During the late 1200s, the spectacle again became popular as a means of assisting people with visual problems. In the late 1500s, scientists first discovered the value of lenses for observing very small objects. A condensed history of early optical microscopes demonstrates how advances in magnifying lens technology and early scientific discoveries played important roles in the development of the microscope (see Figure 2-9 and Table 2-3).

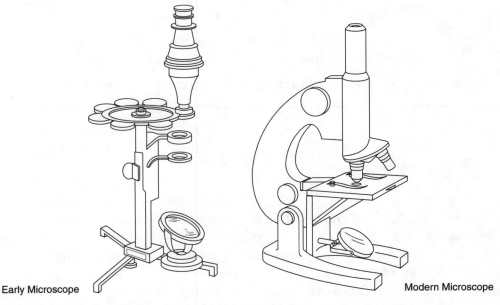

Early Microscope

Modern Microscope

**Figure 2-9.** The big difference between an early microscope and a modern microscope shows how advances in lens technology have improved the microscope over the past 250 years.

| TABLE 2-3. | ADVANCES IN THE DEVELOPMENT OF THE MICROSCOPE |
| --- | --- |

| Year | Development |
| --- | --- |
| 1595 | Zacharias Jansen is credited with the invention of the first compound microscope. |
| 1660 | Marcello Malpighi made early discoveries about respiration and the circulation of blood using a microscope. |
| 1665 | Robert Hooke discovered individual cells in cork tissue. |
| 1665 | Christopher Cock developed a single side mount that allowed the microscope to swivel between a vertical and a horizontal position. |
| 1670 | John Yarwell developed a tripod mount with a flat stage under the microscope. |
| 1670 | Anton van Leeuwenhoek produced high-quality lenses that allowed increased magnification; he was the first person to observe bacteria and protozoa. |
| 1704 | John Marshall created a microscope that had fine-focus adjustment and could slide up and down for better focusing. |
| 1700s | Mechanical improvements were made to the stage, below-stage lighting, up-and-down sliding of tube and stage, and fine-focus adjustment. |
| 1800s | Optical qualities of the lenses were improved by removing distortion and improving resolution. |
| 1900s | Quality of the image was improved considerably. |

*The Computer.* By the end of 2001, there were 182 million computers in the United States. The computer has become a major tool for personal tasks such as word processing, graphic design, and everyday calculations. It also provides scientists with the ability to perform complex calculations, refine images from space exploration, and make accurate temperature measurements of planets. A condensed history of the computer demonstrates how this tool was developed and became an important part of our society (see Figure 2-10 and Table 2-4).

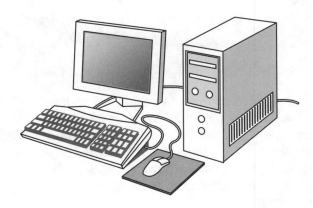

**Figure 2-10.** By the year 2001, there were more than 180 million computers in the United States of America. Many of these computers were in people's homes.

## TABLE 2-4.    ADVANCES IN THE DEVELOPMENT OF THE COMPUTER

| Year | Development |
|------|-------------|
| 1642 | Blaise Pascal invented a machine that could add and subtract. |
| 1790 | Joseph Marie Jacquard invented a system that aided the weaving loom. |
| Mid-1800s | Charles Babbage designed a mechanical computing machine. |
| 1890 | Herman Hollerith developed the punch-card tabulating machine for the 1890 U.S. census. |
| 1940 | George Stibitz invented the first electromechanical calculator. |
| 1941 | Konrad Zuse built a digital computer that was controlled by a program of instructions. |
| 1942 | John Vincent Atanasoff built the first vacuum-tube calculator. |
| 1946 | John Mauchly and J. Presper Eckert built the 30-ton ENIAC computer, capable of being programmed to do different tasks simultaneously. |
| 1951 | John Mauchly and J. Presper Eckert built the UNIVAC, the first commercially available computer in the United States. |
| 1975 | The first personal computer kit was made available for purchase by the public. |
| 1977 | Apple introduced the personal desktop computer for purchase by the public. |
| 1990 | Microsoft released Windows 3.0 operating system, simplifying home computer use. |
| 1996 | Palm Pilot introduced the first hand-held computer, capable of great mobility. |

## SKILLS ACTIVITY **2**

## GROWTH OF THE INTERNET

In 1969, the Internet began as a small network of computers organized so that a few research scientists could communicate. The network slowly grew, under the guidance of the U.S. Defense Department, for research and military purposes. In 1994, Internet browser software became available to many home computer users and allowed them to connect to the growing network. Today, the Internet has become an information system, communication system, and business system used by millions of people worldwide.

A vast amount of information is available on the Internet. From your personal computer, you can access information in the form of text, graphics, sound, and/or video on almost any topic. It is like having a large library of information available at your fingertips anywhere a computer can be attached to a telephone line.

You use the Internet as a communication system when you e-mail messages to other people. Pictures and video images can be attached to e-mail messages. "Chatting" on the Internet is a means of sending and receiving messages with someone who is on-line at the same time you are.

A large number of businesses sell products over the Internet. You can purchase books, flowers, rugs, paintings, cars, and much more. Consumer shopping over the Internet is an expanding business, accounting for billions of dollars in sales each year. Additional uses of the Internet include banking, auctions, travel planning, trading stocks, educational courses, and much more.

The graph below shows the growth of Internet host sites from 1989 to 1999. A host computer is the primary computer in a network of computers linked to the Internet. Use the graph and the information above to answer the following questions.

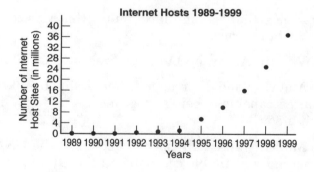

## Questions

1. What accounts for the sharp increase in Internet host sites between 1994 and 1995?

2. During which period of time was the increase of Internet host sites the greatest?

    A. 1994–1995    C. 1997–1998    B. 1995–1996    D. 1998–1999

3. How would the graph be modified to show that the number of host sites increased to 50 million in 2000?

## Question Set 2

*Multiple Choice*

1.  Which ruler would measure the diameter of a quarter most precisely?

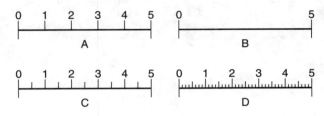

    A. ruler *A*     B. ruler *B*     C. ruler *C*     D. ruler *D*

2.  Scientific tools are more accurate today than they were years ago because
    A. technology has improved the tools
    B. scientists' skills have improved
    C. more scientific knowledge exits today
    D. problem-solving skills have improved

3.  Using seat belts in cars saves lives. This is an example of
    A. technology meeting the needs of science
    B. technology meeting the needs of society
    C. science meeting the needs of technology
    D. science meeting the needs of society

4.  Before 1500, early astronomers used crude instruments to make their star measurements and produce star maps. The Danish astronomer Tycho Brahe (1546–1601) built a 10-foot quadrant capable of improved star measurements. Brahe's quadrant was an example of
    A. a technological achievement
    B. a scientific achievement
    C. an instrument that measures time
    D. an instrument that measures mass

*Open Ended*

5.  Sir Isaac Newton is credited with saying, "If I have seen further than other men, it is because I stood on the shoulders of giants." What did Newton mean by this statement?

6.  Why is it important that countries use standardized units of measurement?

**7.** What are the fundamental SI units for length and mass? What are some subunits and/or multiple units of these standard units?

# USING SCIENTIFIC KNOWLEDGE AND TECHNOLOGY TO SOLVE PROBLEMS

## Strategies for Problem Solving

In science, most problems are presented in the form of questions. The scientist seeks answers to these questions. In the attempt to find answers, scientists may find themselves asking other, related questions. Some examples of questions that scientists seek to answer are: Is there life on Mars? How can we predict an earthquake? Can we prolong human life?

Many student problems come in a much simpler form. Typically, students have problems associated with math, logic, words, and/or mechanical devices. To solve these problems, it is most helpful to have an organized *strategy*, or plan. The strategy for solving any problem is similar whether it is a scientist's research problem or a student's simple math problem. Strategies for solving problems include the following steps:

- *Identify the Problem.* The initial step in solving most problems is to be sure you know exactly what the problem is. One way to identify the problem is by writing a clear and concise question that states the problem.

- *Organize Information.* Gather information and produce a list, chart, diagram, and/or graph of the information. This puts all known information into an orderly format.

- *Look for a Pattern.* Determine if the data are organized in some special way. The data may show positive or negative trends, may be linked to other data, or may be repetitious.

- *Trial and Error.* Take a logical guess to solve the problem and then check to determine if the guess fits the solution to the problem.

- *Solve an Easier Related Problem.* Reduce the problem to simple terms and determine a solution to the simpler problem. Then repeat the procedure with the more complex problem.

- *Change Your Focus*. Some ways of changing your focus on a problem are to: (a) look for smaller problems you can solve within the larger problem; (b) eliminate some information and try to solve the problem; and (c) work backward to make sense of the data.

Problem-solving skills can be improved with practice. The more problems you solve, the more likely it is that you will be able to recall a strategy to solve a new problem. Problem solving is an important life skill that can be beneficial in many areas beyond just science and mathematics.

## Scientific Knowledge Is Used to Solve Problems

Many common problems are solved using scientific knowledge and/or technology. In our daily routine, we are presented with many problems that we solve by using some scientific knowledge we already have. For example, you open a new bottle of ketchup and try to pour some on your fries. The ketchup does not come out of the bottle. So you thrust the bottle forward and then quickly pull it back. Eventually, the ketchup comes out. You are using Newton's first law of motion to get the ketchup out of the bottle; that is, an object in motion tends to stay in motion. The ketchup in the bottle has to continue moving forward even though you pull the bottle back (see Figure 2-11).

Perhaps, in another situation, you cannot open the metal cap on a bottle. So, you place the cap in hot water. After a short time, you try to open the cap again, and it unscrews easily. Why? Because, as you know, metal expands when it is heated. The metal cap has become a little larger, looser, and easier to open.

**Figure 2-11.** The ketchup comes out of the bottle when you thrust the bottle forward and then quickly pull it back. This illustrates how common problems are often solved using scientific knowledge. In this case, it is Newton's first law of motion—an object in motion (the ketchup) tends to stay in motion.

## Technology Is Used to Solve Problems

After clothes are washed in a washing machine, they are dried. People used to hang their wash outdoors and allow the air and sunshine to evaporate the water from them. Now, wet clothes can be placed in a dryer and tumbled with heat, which causes them to dry. The dryer makes it unnecessary to hang the wet clothing outdoors on a clothesline and wait for the items to dry (see Figure 2-12).

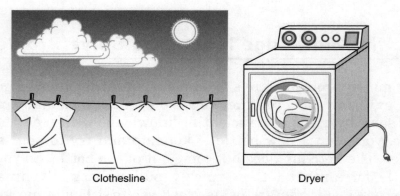

Clothesline                    Dryer

**Figure 2-12.** Less work is required to place clothing in a dryer than to hang it up on a clothesline to dry.

Years ago, the typical frying pan was made completely of metal. That is, the pan and the handle were both metal. When something was cooked in a pan, the handle got hot due to conductivity of the metal, and a potholder had to be used to move the hot frying pan from the stove. Today, the typical frying pan handle has been replaced with a synthetic material that is a poor conductor of heat.

## Scientific Principles and Simple Mechanical Devices

Some scientific principles can be demonstrated through a simple mechanical device. Many common tools found around the house are based on scientific principles and are designed to make our work easier. Many of these tools are found in the workshop, garage, and kitchen.

Try to loosen a tight nut on a bicycle with a wrench. If the nut does not move, you may try a wrench with a longer handle. The extra length of the handle, which functions as a *lever*, provides an increase in force on the nut.

A car gets a flat tire, and a car jack is used to raise the car so that the tire can be removed and replaced. The screw mechanism in a car jack can multiply a small force, so it is powerful enough to raise a car (see Figure 2-13).

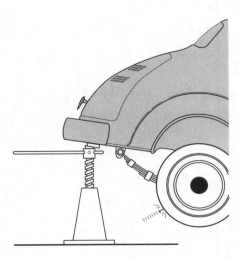

**Figure 2-13.** A car jack multiplies a small force so that it is powerful enough to raise a heavy car.

Opening the lid of a tightly covered jar can be difficult because your hand slips around the lid. Using a rubber pad between your hand and the lid increases friction, which can help you turn and remove the lid.

## Tools Based on Scientific Principles

Some tools that are used to measure and quantify science are examples of technology based on scientific principles. Three examples are described below.

*Barometer.* Air is a substance and it has weight. How can the weight of air be measured? Galileo presented this question to his young assistant, Evangelista Torricelli. To answer this, Torricelli took a tube of water 34 feet (10.4 meters) in length that was closed at one end and submerged the open end in a pool of water. The changing weight of the air on the water caused the water in the tube to rise and fall. By replacing water with denser liquid mercury, a tube just 3 feet (0.9 meter) in length can be used. The atmospheric weight of air on the pool of mercury supports the column of mercury in the tube (see Figure 2-14). When atmospheric pressure increases, the mercury in the tube goes up; and when atmospheric pressure decreases, the mercury goes down. Standard pressure at sea level is 29.92 inches (760 milliliters) of mercury in the tube. The barometer thus measures the weight of air.

*Thermometer.* Heat is a form of energy contained in a substance. The more heat present in a substance, the faster and farther apart its molecules move. Temperature is the measure of the vibrating molecules in a substance. Under normal conditions, most substances expand when they are heated. Therefore, if you measure the amount of expansion and contraction of a substance, you are measuring the temperature of the substance. Most substances expand and contract very little with a small increase or decrease in temperature. However, by placing a liquid such as mercury or alcohol in a very thin tube, a small increase or

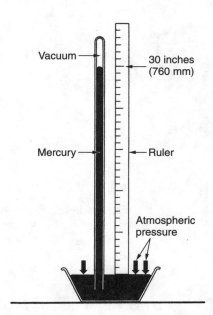

**Figure 2-14.** The mercury barometer is an example of technology based on scientific principles—atmospheric pressure supports the column of liquid mercury inside the barometer.

decrease in temperature will cause a noticeable movement of the liquid in the tube. Measurement of the liquid's length (or height) in the tube is an indication of the surrounding temperature (see Figure 2-15).

*Compass.* A compass consists of a magnetized metal needle that freely pivots above a circular dial, which is labeled with the major geographic directional points. Earth's iron-rich core acts much like a giant bar magnet. The magnetized needle of a compass aligns with

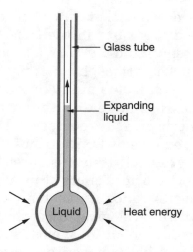

**Figure 2-15.** The thermometer is another example of technology based on scientific principles—liquids expand with an increase in temperature (and contract with a decrease in temperature). When heat energy is added to a thermometer, it causes the liquid inside to expand and move up the glass tube.

Earth's magnetic field and points toward the magnetic north pole. A compass operates because opposite poles of two magnetic objects attract each other. The magnetic north pole is close to the geographic North Pole, and a slight adjustment of direction may be necessary to determine true north.

## SKILLS ACTIVITY 3

### HOW TO BUILD A WATER THERMOMETER

A thermometer measures the temperature of a substance. Its use is based on the principle that most substances expand when heated and contract when cooled. Therefore, the volume of water in a glass will expand when a room gets warmer, and contract when the room gets cooler. This is difficult to observe because the change is slow, and the relatively large volume of water in the glass makes it difficult to see the small change in volume. However, if the water is placed in a narrow glass tube, the expansion and contraction is easily observed.

Robin wanted to build a water thermometer. Using a flask, a one-hole rubber stopper, and some colored water, Robin constructed her thermometer. She inserted the glass tube into the rubber stopper and placed the stopper on the flask so that the end of the tube was submerged in the flask's colored water (see diagram).

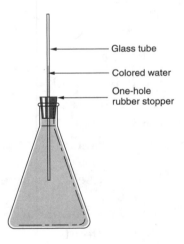

Glass tube

Colored water

One-hole rubber stopper

## Questions

1.  If Robin were to wrap her hands around the flask for several minutes, what would happen to the liquid in the glass tube?

2.  Why would it be a bad idea to heat the flask with a flame over a burner?

3.  How might Robin calibrate her thermometer using a Celsius thermometer?

## Question Set 3

*Multiple Choice*

1. Michael placed a glass tube and rubber stopper into the top of a flask. He held the flask over a beaker filled with water for several minutes, with his hands wrapped around the flask. Michael observed bubbles of air rising out of the water. What does this demonstrate?

   A. Air contracts when it is heated.
   B. Air expands when it is heated.
   C. Air contracts when it is cooled.
   D. Air expands when it is cooled.

2. The front door on Matt's house squeaks every time he opens it. Matt places a few drops of oil on the hinges of the door and it stops squeaking. This is an example of
   A. scientific knowledge applied to problem solving
   B. scientific knowledge applied to technology
   C. science affecting technology
   D. technology affecting science

3. Which of the following problems is solved using technology?
   A. opening a window
   B. pulling a nail out of the wall with a claw hammer
   C. drinking a glass of water
   D. melting butter on hot toast

**4.** Which scientific principle is demonstrated when the man in the diagram lifts the tree stump with the lever?

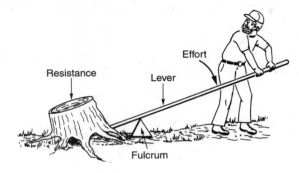

A. Work = force × distance.

B. A lever multiplies effort, making it easier to uproot the tree stump.

C. A lever multiplies work, making it easier to uproot the tree stump.

D. A lever multiplies distance, making it easier to uproot the tree stump.

**5.** Which mechanical device demonstrates the scientific principle that reducing friction produces easier and smoother motion?

A. using a ball bearing around a wheel's axle

B. using a wedge to cut wood

C. sliding a box upward on a ramp

D. cutting paper with scissors

**6.** The initial step in solving a problem is

A. stating the problem in the form of a question

B. gathering the data

C. taking a guess at the solution

D. drawing possible conclusions

**7.** When solving the following math problem, which problem-solving strategy is most helpful?

*Problem:* What is the next number in this sequence of numbers?
          1, 2, 3, 7, 8, 9, 15, 16, 17, 26, 27

A. trial and error            C. change your focus

B. organize information       D. look for a pattern

**8.** Squeezing the hand brakes on a bicycle causes a hard rubber surface to come into contact with the turning tire. Eventually, the bicycle will stop. What scientific principle is responsible for stopping the bicycle?

A. inertia                    C. gravitation

B. action and reaction        D. friction

*Open Ended*

9. Describe three ways that technology has improved our living conditions.

10. Answer the following items based on the diagram below, which shows the structure of a mercury barometer.

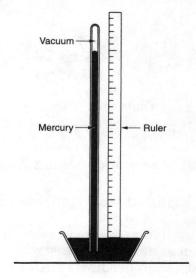

(a) Why is mercury used instead of water?
(b) Where would you place an arrow to show that atmospheric pressure is pushing the mercury?
(c) What scientific principle is the mercury barometer based on?

# TECHNOLOGICAL ADVANCES AND SPACE EXPLORATION

## The History of Space Science

Before 1957, space science was studied from the surface of Earth. The first observations were made with simple measuring instruments, and in the early 1600s, optical instruments aided the study of the night sky. Eventually, more elaborate instruments gathered light and other forms of radiation from space. Meteorites, pieces of rock from space that landed on Earth, were also studied to learn about space. People were limited in their study of space because they were stuck on the planet.

*The Space Exploration Program.* The new age of space exploration began in 1957 when the former Soviet Union placed *Sputnik 1* into

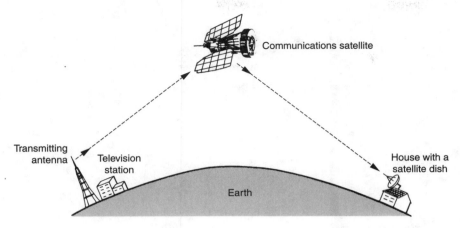

Communications satellite

Transmitting
antenna

Television
station

House with a
satellite dish

Earth

**Figure 2-16.** Advances in space technology enable us to view distant events on television (by means of communication satellites, such as the one shown here) as well as distant objects and events in our universe (by means of powerful telescopes, such as the Hubble).

orbit around Earth. Within a few years, the United States sent satellites around the sun and moon to gather information, and placed the first weather satellite into orbit around Earth. (See Figure 2-16.) During the 1960s, space probes explored the surface of the moon, Mars, and Venus. Starting in about 1980, further exploration continued with spacecraft investigating Mercury, Jupiter, Saturn, and Uranus. During the 1990s, spacecraft made detailed studies of Mars and comets, and the Hubble Space Telescope was placed in orbit around Earth. The Hubble Space Telescope has provided much-improved pictures of objects in our solar system and in deep space. Early in the twenty-first century, space probes were sent to study nearby asteroids, comets, and Mars.

*Astronaut-in-Space Program.* In the late 1950s, unmanned spacecraft were launched into suborbital flights to test the feasibility of manned space flights. The manned, or astronaut-in-space, program began in 1961 when the former Soviet Union and the United States each sent an astronaut into suborbital flight. During the next seven years, astronauts progressed from doing a single orbit to multiple orbits of Earth, studying the operating mechanics of space vehicles, docking procedures, and living in space. Then, in 1968, the first manned spacecraft orbited the moon and returned to Earth. In 1969, U.S. astronauts first landed on the moon. In 1973, the first U.S. space station, *Skylab*, was placed in orbit. In 1983, *Spacelab* provided astronauts with an orbiting lab on which they could do experiments and study how humans might live in space for an extended period of time. The former Soviet Union launched the first mission to construct the International Space Station in 1998 (see Figure 2-17). By the early 2000s, Russian and U.S. scientists were already living and working together on the space station.

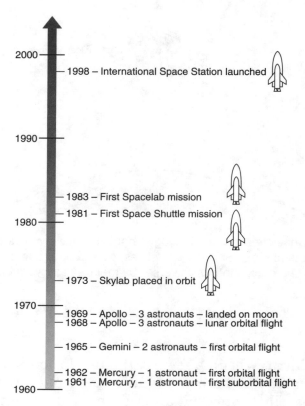

| | |
|---|---|
| 2000 — | |
| — 1998 – International Space Station launched | |
| 1990 — | |
| — 1983 – First Spacelab mission | |
| — 1981 – First Space Shuttle mission | |
| 1980 — | |
| — 1973 – Skylab placed in orbit | |
| 1970 — | |
| — 1969 – Apollo – 3 astronauts – landed on moon | |
| — 1968 – Apollo – 3 astronauts – lunar orbital flight | |
| — 1965 – Gemini – 2 astronauts – first orbital flight | |
| — 1962 – Mercury – 1 astronaut – first orbital flight | |
| — 1961 – Mercury – 1 astronaut – first suborbital flight | |
| 1960 — | |

**Figure 2-17.** The time line shows the progress made by astronauts in the space program.

## Space Technology Gains Knowledge About the Universe

Throughout history, people have had the desire to learn about the universe and the world around them. This search for knowledge is the essence of science and technology. It drives scientists to try to answer questions about who we are and where we are in this vast universe. It also provides an incentive to develop new technologies to answer some of the many questions related to understanding the universe. There are many examples of how space technology has improved our knowledge of the universe. Two examples of technologies that have helped gain knowledge about the universe are described below.

*Space Probes to Planets and Their Moons.* Space probes have been sent to other planets and their moons (natural satellites) to learn more about their physical characteristics (see Figure 2-18). On Earth, we are limited as to what we can observe and measure on other objects in the solar system. However, from space probes such as the *Voyager* we have discovered lightning on Jupiter, the ring structures of Jupiter, Uranus, and Neptune, and volcanoes on Jupiter's satellite Io.

*Hubble Space Telescope.* Scientific goals for the orbiting Hubble Space Telescope include learning more about the following topics: the

**Figure 2-18.** The *Voyager* spacecrafts were launched in 1977; they were used to explore the planets Jupiter, Saturn, Uranus, and Neptune.

history and structure of our solar system; the structure of our universe; and how stars evolve (see Figure 2-19). Deep space observations by the telescope have determined that the expansion of the universe seems to be occurring at an accelerating rate. Pictures of the birth and death of stars reveal information about how stars form, evolve, and die. Close-up pictures taken with the Hubble Space Telescope have provided information about the surface structure of Mars, the surface of Pluto and its satellite Charon, and the atmospheres of Uranus and Neptune.

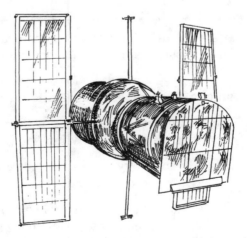

**Figure 2-19.** The Hubble Space Telescope helps astronomers gather more information about the universe.

**Figure 2-20.** Protective headgear and cordless power tools were originally developed as space technologies.

 ## Space Technology Affects Our Lives

Space technology has also added much to our personal lives (see Figure 2-20). The National Aeronautics and Space Administration (NASA) has designed and developed many technologies for the purpose of space exploration, and has made them available for commercial and consumer purposes. Since 1976, NASA has developed more than 1300 technologies that have been converted into products, systems, processes, or services. These technologies have benefited U. S. industry, created jobs, and improved our quality of life.

**TABLE 2-5.** **DEVICES FROM SPACE TECHNOLOGY THAT IMPROVE OUR LIVES**

| Item | Description |
|------|-------------|
| Carbon monoxide sensor | A small carbon monoxide sensor detects and alerts people to the exposure of deadly carbon monoxide gas. |
| Smoke and fire detector | A battery-powered device senses and alerts people about smoke and fires in homes and other buildings. |
| Kidney dialysis machines | Medical devices use a chemical process to remove toxic wastes from the human body when the kidneys are malfunctioning. |
| Artificial heart | Space technology used to design miniature fuel pumps is being converted into artificial hearts to be placed in humans. |
| Cordless power tools | Battery-operated power tools such as drills, saws, and screwdrivers make it easier to do jobs around the house. |

Some examples of space technology that are now used in our daily lives include: freezer-to-oven ceramic dishes; football masks equipped with radios; rechargeable cardiac pacemakers; hang gliders; and food-processing methods. Table 2-5 lists and describes five more devices that were developed from space technology and that help millions of people everyday.

## Question Set 4

*Multiple Choice*

1. When Galileo used a telescope to view Jupiter in 1609, he discovered four satellites orbiting Jupiter. This is an example of using
   A. technology to discover new technology
   B. technology to gain knowledge of the universe
   C. scientific knowledge to discover new technology
   D. scientific knowledge to improve technology

2. The astronaut-in-space program started in 1961. Some accomplishments of the program have been space walks, suborbital flights, orbital flights, and walking on the moon. Which of these accomplishments occurred first?
   A. space walks
   B. suborbital flights
   C. orbital flights
   D. walking on the moon

3. Technology used for the space program has contributed to the development of medical devices and safety products. Which of the following items was derived from space technology?
   A. automobile
   B. helmet for biking
   C. telescope
   D. rocket engine

4. Which technology allows scientists to learn about the birth and death of stars?
   A. space probes
   B. space rockets
   C. space stations
   D. Hubble Space Telescope

5. What information about space was discovered during the period of time from the development of the first telescope to the start of the space race?
   A. Lightning exists on the planet Jupiter.
   B. There are nine planets in our solar system.
   C. There is a ring structure around Uranus.
   D. Volcanoes exist on one of Jupiter's moons.

6. The manned space program has successfully placed a
   A. person on the moon
   B. person on Mars
   C. person on Venus
   D. person in orbit around Mars

7. In 1980, the U.S. spacecraft *Voyager 1* flew past Saturn and took the first close-up pictures of the planet. This event is an example of how
   A. scientific knowledge leads to new technology
   B. old technology leads to new technology
   C. technology gains knowledge about the universe
   D. technology is discovered through science

## Open Ended

8. One of the concerns people have about the space program is its very high cost. Yet the program has many benefits. Besides gaining knowledge about space science, what is another benefit of the space program?

9. During the 1960s, advancements in rocket technology took astronauts from suborbital flight to orbital flight and to the moon. Draw a diagram of the Earth–moon system and add a dashed line for each of the flight paths listed:
   (a) Draw an Earth-suborbital flight path and label it A.
   (b) Draw an Earth-orbital flight path and label it B.
   (c) Draw an Earth-to-moon flight path and label it C.

# Chapter 3

# The Structure of Living Things

**Macro Statement:** Recognize the similarities, differences, interdependencies, and basic structures of living things.

## KNOWLEDGE STATEMENTS

**A.** Cells carry on many functions needed to sustain life.

**B.** Important levels of organization in living systems for structure and function include cells, tissues, organs, organ systems, and organisms.

**C.** Organisms can be classified by external and internal characteristics, e.g., invertebrate/vertebrate and vascular/nonvascular.

**D.** Organisms have life cycles.

## CHAPTER OUTLINE

**Living Things Carry Out Life Functions**

**Organization in Living Things**

**Classification of Living Things**

# LIVING THINGS CARRY OUT LIFE FUNCTIONS

Living things, or **organisms**, share certain characteristics that set them apart from nonliving things. In particular, organisms carry out *life functions,* some of which are listed in Table 3-1.

## The Cell

Living things are made up of basic units called **cells**. Each cell of an organism carries out basic life functions. Most cells contain certain structures that help them carry out these functions. The **nucleus** controls cell activities. Surrounding the nucleus is a thick fluid called the **cytoplasm**, which is where most life functions take place. The cytoplasm is contained within the **cell membrane**, the "skin" of the cell, which regulates the flow of materials into and out of the cell. Figure 3-1 shows a typical animal cell.

## Cells and Life Functions

Living things are made up of one or more cells. Cells are considered the basic units of structure and function for all living things. For instance, an ameba consists of a single cell, while a human consists of

**TABLE 3-1. LIFE PROCESSES AND THEIR FUNCTIONS**

| Process | Function |
| --- | --- |
| Nutrition | Taking food into the body (*ingestion*), breaking it down into a form usable by cells (*digestion*), and eliminating undigested material (*elimination*) |
| Transport | Moving materials throughout the organism |
| Respiration | Releasing energy stored in food |
| Excretion | Removing waste materials produced by the organism |
| Regulation | Responding to changes in the organism's surroundings |
| Reproduction | Making more organisms of the same kind |

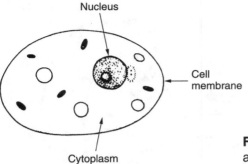

**Figure 3-1.** The basic features of a typical animal cell.

trillions of cells. Thus, an ameba is *unicellular*, while a human is *multicellular*, but they are both made up of either one or more cells. This is why cells are considered to be the basic unit of structure in living things. Since each cell carries out all of the basic life functions, cells are also considered to be the basic unit of function in living things. Smaller structures within the cell perform these life functions. Table 3-2 lists some of these structures.

Plant cells and animal cells have many structures in common, but they also have some important differences (see Figure 3-2).

Plant cells have a cell wall that encloses the entire cell, including the cell membrane. The tough cell wall gives support to the plant's structure. Animal cells do not have cell walls, but are enclosed only by the cell membrane. Structures called *chloroplasts*, which contain chlorophyll, are found only in plant (and algae) cells. Chloroplasts are the site of photosynthesis, the food-making process of plants. Centrioles, which participate in cell division, are found only within animal cells.

## TABLE 3-2.  SOME CELL STRUCTURES AND THEIR FUNCTIONS

| Structure | Function |
| --- | --- |
| Mitochondria | Respiration—in which food is "burned" (combined with oxygen) to produce energy. Called the "powerhouse of the cell." |
| Ribosomes | Synthesis—in which proteins are made. |
| Lysosomes | Digestion—in which digestive enzymes are stored. |
| Nucleus | Reproduction—in which genetic material is stored. |
| Vacuole | Digestion and excretion—in which digestion occurs or where excess fluid is stored. |
| Chloroplasts | Photosynthesis—in which glucose (sugar) is produced in green plants. (Present in plant cells only.) |

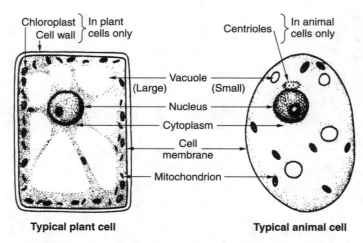

**Figure 3-2.** Comparison of typical plant cells and animal cells.

## Organisms and Their Environment

Living things are constantly interacting with their surroundings. These surroundings are called the *environment*, which includes both living and nonliving things. Organisms obtain food, water, and oxygen from the environment. In turn, they release wastes, such as carbon dioxide. Thus, there is a continual exchange of materials between an organism and its environment.

## Nutrition

Every organism needs food to stay alive. Food provides an organism with *nutrients*, which are used for producing energy as well as for growth and repair. Some important nutrients are listed in Table 3-3. The process of *nutrition* includes ingestion, digestion, and elimination. *Ingestion* is the taking in of food. *Digestion* is the physical and chemical breaking down of nutrients into a usable form. *Elimination* or egestion is the removal of undigested materials from the body.

## Transport

Water is necessary for *transport*, the moving of materials throughout an organism. For instance, blood, which is mostly water, carries nutrients to the cells of your body. Blood takes away wastes from the cells, too. Most of the chemical processes in living things can take place only in a watery environment. In addition, water is necessary for plants to make food. For all of these reasons, life is not possible without water.

**TABLE 3-3.  NUTRIENTS AND THEIR USES**

| Nutrient | Use |
| --- | --- |
| Proteins | Supply materials for growth and repair |
| Carbohydrates (sugars and starches) | Provide quick energy |
| Fats and oils | Provide stored energy |
| Vitamins | Assist life processes; prevent disease |
| Minerals | Supply materials for growth and repair; help carry out life processes |

## Respiration

Organisms release the energy stored in food through a process called *respiration,* which occurs in all cells. During respiration, many nutrients in food combine with oxygen. This chemical process releases energy and forms carbon dioxide and water as waste products. Scientists use the term "burning" to describe changes in which a substance combines with oxygen and releases energy. Therefore, respiration is a form of burning without flames. All living things, including plants, obtain energy from food through some form of respiration.

## Excretion

Carbon dioxide is a waste material produced by cells during respiration and must be removed. In humans, carbon dioxide and other waste materials are carried away by the blood. These wastes are filtered out of the blood and then removed from our bodies through exhaling, perspiring, and urinating. The process of removing wastes from the organism is called *excretion*.

## Regulation

Why do you perspire when it is hot? Your body perspires to cool off. Why do you drink more when it is hot? Your body knows that it must replace water used to keep you cool. Being thirsty is a response to the heat. Organisms respond to changes in their internal and external environments. This process, called *regulation*, helps an organism maintain *homeostasis*, the preservation of a constant internal environment.

## Reproduction

Living things come from other living things. **Reproduction** is the process by which an organism produces new individuals called *offspring*. Each particular kind of organism that can reproduce fertile offspring is called a **species**. For example, lions are a species of big cat; tigers are a different big cat species. Since every individual organism eventually dies, reproduction ensures the continuation of the species.

## Growth and Development

A puppy resembles an adult dog. A young elephant looks like a small version of its parents. As these young animals mature, they will increase in size. This increase in size is called *growth*. However, some organisms, such as a frog or a butterfly, have a very different type of growth and *development*. In fact, frogs and most insects change so dramatically during their lives that the young may not resemble the adults at all. A dramatic change in development such as this is called **metamorphosis**.

The changes an organism undergoes as it develops and then produces its own offspring make up its **life cycle**. Figure 3-3 illustrates the very different life cycles of a frog, a butterfly, and a human.

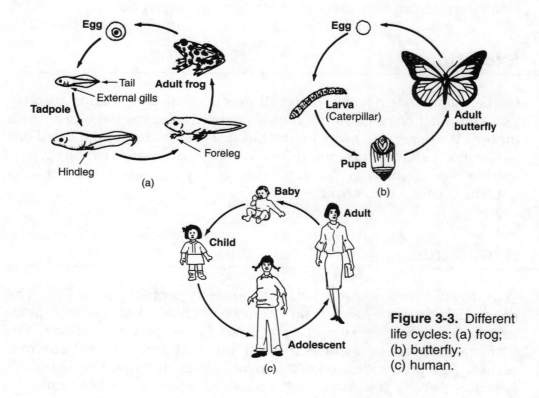

**Figure 3-3.** Different life cycles: (a) frog; (b) butterfly; (c) human.

We have summarized some of the basic functions necessary to sustain life. Many of these involve complex chemical reactions, such as those found in respiration and nutrition. Cells provide the framework that supports these complex chemical reactions.

## Question Set 1

*Multiple Choice*

1.  Which of the following functions occurs in plants but not in animals?
    A. obtaining energy from food
    B. responding to changes in the environment
    C. synthesizing food from carbon dioxide and water
    D. producing new individuals

2.  The process of "burning" food inside an organism's cells to release energy is called
    A. excretion        C. digestion
    B. growth           D. respiration

3.  Which statement is true of *all* living things?
    A. They are exact copies of their parents.
    B. They come from other living things.
    C. The young look like small adults.
    D. They always have two parents.

4.  Which of the following statements is *most* correct?
    A. The cell is the basic unit of structure in living things but not the basic unit of function.
    B. The cell is the basic unit of function in living things but not the basic unit of structure.
    C. The cell is both the basic unit of structure and the basic unit of function in living things.
    D. The cell is neither the basic unit of function nor the basic unit of structure in living things.

5.  Mitochondria are known as the "powerhouse of the cell" because they make energy available by carrying out the life function of
    A. excretion        C. digestion
    B. growth           D. respiration

**6.** Suppose that you are a piece of sugar just eaten by a horse. Which best represents the correct sequence of life functions that you would be a part of?

A. respiration → digestion → transport

B. transport → digestion → respiration

C. digestion → transport → respiration

D. transport → respiration → digestion

## Open Ended

**7.** Identify and describe the process that is shown in the diagram below.

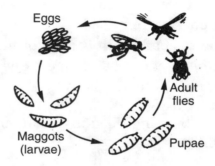

**8.** What two features can be used to easily distinguish between animal cells and plant cells?

**9.** The following diagrams represent cells from two different organisms. Which one is from a plant and which one is from an animal? Explain your answer.

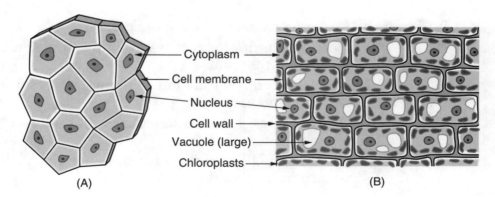

**10.** Which life process is *not* necessary in order for an individual organism to survive but *is* necessary in order for the organism's species to survive? Explain.

## SKILLS ACTIVITY **1**

### INTERPRETING AN EXPERIMENT

About 300 years ago, the Italian scientist Francesco Redi wondered where maggots (small, wormlike organisms) came from. The popular belief at the time was that rotting meat turned into maggots. This idea—that living things could come from nonliving material—was called *spontaneous generation.* Redi designed an experiment to test this belief. He placed meat into eight jars. Four jars were left open; four were tightly sealed.

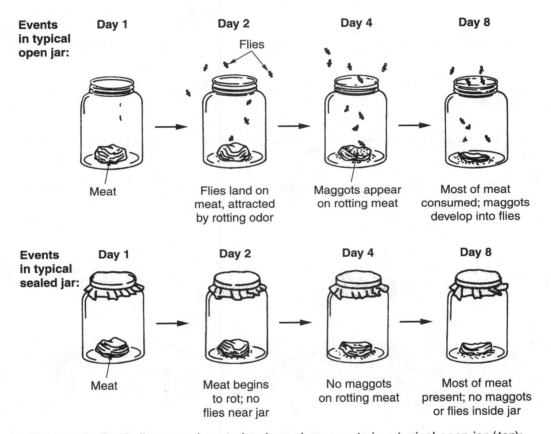

**Events in typical open jar:**

| Day 1 | Day 2 | Day 4 | Day 8 |
|---|---|---|---|
| Meat | Flies land on meat, attracted by rotting odor | Maggots appear on rotting meat | Most of meat consumed; maggots develop into flies |

**Events in typical sealed jar:**

| Day 1 | Day 2 | Day 4 | Day 8 |
|---|---|---|---|
| Meat | Meat begins to rot; no flies near jar | No maggots on rotting meat | Most of meat present; no maggots or flies inside jar |

**Diagram 1.** Redi's first experiment: drawings show events in a typical open jar (*top*); and in a typical sealed jar (*bottom*).

As you can see, no maggots appeared on the rotting meat in the sealed jars. However, not everyone was convinced that Redi's experiment had disproved spontaneous generation. Some people claimed that fresh air was needed for spontaneous generation to occur. Therefore, Redi performed a second experiment. This time the jars were covered by fine netting, which allowed fresh air into the jars but prevented flies from entering and landing on the meat. Diagram 2 illustrates what Redi observed in his second experiment. Study both diagrams and then answer the following questions.

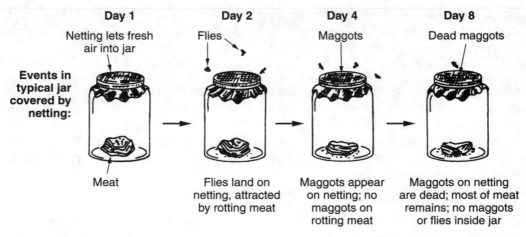

| Day 1 | Day 2 | Day 4 | Day 8 |
| --- | --- | --- | --- |
| Netting lets fresh air into jar | Flies | Maggots | Dead maggots |
| Events in typical jar covered by netting: | | | |
| Meat | Flies land on netting, attracted by rotting meat | Maggots appear on netting; no maggots on rotting meat | Maggots on netting are dead; most of meat remains; no maggots or flies inside jar |

**Diagram 2.** Redi's second experiment: the netting lets fresh air—but not flies—enter the jar.

## Questions

1. Based on Redi's experiments, where do you propose maggots really come from?

2. What conclusion can be drawn about spontaneous generation from these experiments?

# ORGANIZATION IN LIVING SYSTEMS

Many organisms are unicellular. In these organisms, all life functions must be carried out within the single cell. In complex multicellular organisms, however, the needs of the organism cannot be met by millions of cells working independently. Instead, the cells are organized into systems to meet the needs of the whole organism. Multicellular organisms contain a number of different systems. Each system carries out a specific life function and thereby contributes to the operation of the body as a whole.

In addition, all body systems are interdependent and work with one another to keep the organism alive. For instance, the respiratory system brings much-needed oxygen into the body; the circulatory system then transports the oxygen throughout the body.

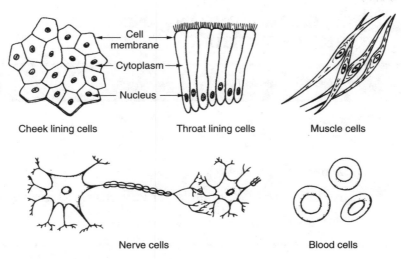

**Figure 3-4.** Different kinds of animal cells.

## Levels of Organization in Multicellular Organisms

*Cells.* Living things are made up of basic units called ***cells***. An organism contains many types of cells, each one designed to perform a different function. Figure 3-4 shows several kinds of animal cells. The cell's size, shape, and structure generally contribute to its function. For example, a nerve cell carries messages throughout the body. The long shape and fingerlike extensions enable these cells to receive messages from many cells and transmit them to a target organ. Muscle cells have a long, thin flexible shape so that they are able to contract and stretch.

*Tissues.* A single muscle cell working alone cannot move your arm. Many muscle cells must work together to perform this task. A group of similar cells working together to perform the same function is called a ***tissue***. Muscle tissue produces body movements. Skin tissue covers and protects the body. Table 3-4 lists some types of human tissues.

**TABLE 3-4.** **TYPES OF HUMAN TISSUE AND THEIR FUNCTIONS**

| Tissue | Function |
|--------|----------|
| Blood | Transports materials throughout the body |
| Bone | Supports and protects body and organs |
| Muscle | Helps body to move; aids in circulation, digestion, and respiration |
| Nerve | Carries messages |
| Skin | Covers and protects body; excretes wastes |

### TABLE 3-5. IMPORTANT ORGANS AND THEIR FUNCTIONS

| Organ | Function |
| --- | --- |
| Heart | Pumps blood |
| Kidney | Removes wastes from blood |
| Lung | Exchanges gases with the environment |
| Stomach | Breaks down food by physical and chemical means |
| Brain | Controls thinking and voluntary actions |

*Organs.* A group of tissues working together forms an ***organ***. Organs may even contain several different types of tissue. For example, the heart is an organ that pumps blood throughout the body. The heart is composed mainly of muscle tissue, but it also contains blood tissue and nerve tissue. The more complex an organism is, the greater its need for specialized organs and tissues. Table 3-5 lists some important organs of the human body.

*Organ Systems.* A group of organs working together to carry out a specific life process makes up an ***organ system***. The circulatory (or

### TABLE 3-6. HUMAN ORGAN SYSTEMS

| System | Function | Examples of Organs or Parts |
| --- | --- | --- |
| Skeletal | Supports body, protects internal organs | Skull, ribs |
| Muscular | Moves organs and body parts | Arm and leg muscles |
| Nervous | Controls body activities; carries and interprets messages | Brain, spinal cord |
| Endocrine | Regulates body activities with hormones | Adrenal glands |
| Digestive | Breaks down food into a usable form | Stomach, intestines |
| Circulatory | Carries needed materials to body cells and waste materials away from cells | Heart, arteries, veins |
| Respiratory | Exchanges gases with the environment | Lungs, bronchi |
| Excretory | Removes wastes from the body | Kidneys, skin |
| Reproductive | Produces offspring | Ovaries, teste |

transport) system carries out the process of transport, moving materials throughout the body. Table 3-6 lists the human organ systems. The health of a person depends on the ability of these organ systems to work together successfully.

## Question Set 2

### Multiple Choice

1. A group of organs working together to carry out a life process is called
   A. a cell          C. an organ
   B. a tissue        D. an organ system

2. A group of similar cells working together makes up
   A. a cell          C. an organ
   B. a tissue        D. an organ system

3. The type of tissue that carries messages throughout the body is most likely to be
   A. skin        B. muscle        C. nerve        D. bone

4. Going from the simple to the complex, which order correctly represents the organization of the human body?
   A. organ system → organ → cell → tissue
   B. cell → tissue → organ → organ system
   C. tissue → cell → organ → organ system
   D. organ → organ system → cell → tissue

5. Which body system supports and protects the other body systems?
   A. skeletal        C. reproductive
   B. endocrine       D. digestive

6. Which body system is mainly responsible for the movement of the body?
   A. digestive        B. circulatory        C. muscular        D. endocrine

### Open Ended

7. An outer layer of hard material called chitin covers the body of an insect. This material supports, protects, and gives the insect its shape. Which system in humans carries out a similar function? Explain.

8. Suppose you are a molecule of oxygen just inhaled by a person. Name each organ system you encounter as you travel through the body—for example, from the lungs, to a muscle in the arm (to be used to make energy), and then out of the body (as a waste product). Briefly describe what happens to you in each organ system.

9. Describe how cells, tissues, and organs in a multicellular organism are related to one another.

# CLASSIFICATION OF LIVING THINGS

Since there are millions of different species of organisms (both living and extinct), scientists must classify them in order to keep track of them and to understand the relationships among them. A classification system groups things together by certain chosen properties. This is an important technique used by scientists in all areas of science.

## Classifying Organisms

If you were asked to classify the items shown in Figure 3-5 into two groups, you might separate them as living things and nonliving things. If you look closely at the living things in the picture, you might separate them further into two smaller groups: plants and animals.

**Figure 3-5.** All things are classified as either living or nonliving. Identify the living and nonliving things in this illustration.

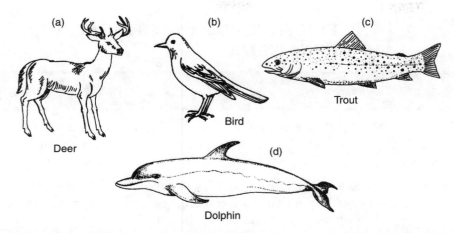

**Figure 3-6.** Scientists classify animals into different groups, such as mammals, birds, and fishes. Where do you think the dolphin would be placed?

Similarly, when you look at Figure 3-6, you might separate these animals into three types. This classification at first may seem obvious, but sometimes it can be very difficult. Even scientists are not always sure how to classify a newly discovered life-form.

The three groups you might have chosen are mammals, birds, and fish. Where did you put the dolphin? The dolphin is a mammal but, like the trout, it lives in the water. So, if the three groups you chose were animals that walk, animals that swim, and animals that fly, how would your classification be different? In which group would you place a penguin, or a bat? Scientists must carefully define the groups they use, so that there is agreement on how to classify an organism.

## Five-Kingdom Classification

In 1737, the Swedish scientist Carolus Linnaeus devised a classification system for living things. He grouped them based on internal and external structures and other shared characteristics. Linnaeus called the largest group a ***kingdom***. Scientists now recognize at least five kingdoms of living things. The two kingdoms you are probably most familiar with are plants and animals. One difference between plants and animals is the structure of their cells, as described earlier in this chapter (refer to Figure 3-2).

Animalia includes multicellular animals. They have cells with centrioles. Organisms in Plantae are multicellular plants. They have cells with cell walls and chloroplasts. Fungi are organisms whose cells have cell walls but do not have chloroplasts. They do not make their own food as plants do. The kingdom Protista is made up mostly of one-celled plantlike and animallike organisms. Organisms in the kingdom Monera have cells that do not contain an organized nucleus. Such

| TABLE 3-7. | **THE FIVE-KINGDOM CLASSIFICATION OF LIVING THINGS** | |
|---|---|---|
| **Kingdom** | **Description** | **Examples** |
| Animalia | Multicellular animals | Insects, fish, birds, mammals, reptiles |
| Plantae | Multicellular plants that have cells enclosed by a cell wall and that contain chloroplasts (to make their own food) | Trees, shrubs, grasses, mosses |
| Fungi | One-celled and multicellular organisms that have cells enclosed by a cell wall but they do not contain chloroplasts | Yeasts, molds, mushrooms |
| Protista | One-celled plantlike and animallike organisms | Algae, protozoa (e.g., ameba, paramecium) |
| Monera | One-celled organisms that lack an organized, membrane-enclosed nucleus | Bacteria, blue-green algae |

organisms are commonly called bacteria. Examples of organisms in each of the five kingdoms are listed in Table 3-7.

Each kingdom is broken down into subgroups called *phyla* (singular, *phylum*). An example of a phylum in the animal kingdom is chordates. All members of this phylum have a spinal cord. Most chordates are *vertebrates*. In all vertebrates, the spinal cord is protected by a set of connected backbones, or vertebrae. Animals such as dogs, birds, fish, frogs, and lizards would fall into this classification group. Animals such as sponges, clams, grasshoppers, spiders, and octopuses would not. These animals are called *invertebrates*, meaning they do not have a backbone.

Each phylum is broken down into *classes*. Some classes of chordates are aves (birds), mammalia (mammals), and reptilia (reptiles). Each class is broken down into *orders*, and each order is broken down into *families*. Each family is broken down into *genera* (singular, *genus*), and each genus is broken down into *species*. This may seem confusing at first, and you might wonder why we need so many different groups.

Think about how you address a letter. You include a person's country, state, city, zip code, street, and number. The country contains the largest number of locations. As you progress from state, to city, and eventually to street number, the areas get smaller and smaller. The system used by biologists works the same way. A kingdom contains an enormous number of different living things. As you progress down to

**TABLE 3-8.   EXAMPLES OF CLASSIFICATION OF LIVING THINGS**

| Group | House Cat | Red Maple | Lion | Human | Sugar Maple |
|-------|-----------|-----------|------|-------|-------------|
| Kingdom | Animalia | Plantae | Animalia | Animalia | Plantae |
| Phylum | Chordata | Tracheophyta | Chordata | Chordata | Tracheophyta |
| Class | Mammalia | Angiosperm | Mammalia | Mammalia | Angiosperm |
| Order | Carnivora | Dicotyledonae | Carnivora | Primates | Dicotyledonae |
| Family | Felidae | Aceraceae | Felidae | Hominidae | Aceraceae |
| Genus | *Felis* | *Acer* | *Panthera* | *Homo* | *Acer* |
| Species | *catus* | *rubrum* | *leo* | *sapiens* | *saccharum* |

species, the number of different kinds of living things in each group gets smaller and smaller.

## Scientific Naming of Organisms

Kingdom, phylum, class, order, family, genus, and species are assigned to every living thing (see Table 3-8). Scientists usually use only the last two names, the genus and species, to identify a living thing. The first letter of the genus is capitalized; the first letter of the species is not. Both are generally written in italics or are underlined. Together, the genus and species make up the scientific name. By using this system, scientists from different countries, who speak different languages, can still be sure they are referring to the same organisms in scientific papers and discussions.

The scientific name for a lion is *Panthera leo;* for a house cat it is *Felis catus.* A lion and a house cat are both felines; they are similar enough to be classified within the same family, felidae. But they are two different species and are dissimilar enough to be placed within two different genera.

## Question Set 3

*Multiple Choice*
The table below gives the scientific classification for a variety of animals. Look at the information in the table below and in Table 3-8; then answer questions 1 through 4.

| Group | Wolf | Dog | Horse | Grasshopper | Chimpanzee |
|-------|------|-----|-------|-------------|------------|
| Kingdom | Animalia | Animalia | Animalia | Animalia | Animalia |
| Phylum | Chordata | Chordata | Chordata | Arthropoda | Chordata |
| Class | Mammalia | Mammalia | Mammalia | Insectae | Mammalia |
| Order | Carnivora | Carnivora | Ungulate | Orthoptera | Primates |
| Family | Canidae | Canidae | Equidae | Locustidae | Pongidae |
| Genus | *Canis* | *Canis* | *Equus* | *Schistocerca* | *Pan* |
| Species | *lupus* | *familiaris* | *caballus* | *americana* | *troglodytes* |

1. Which animals are classified in the same genus but in different species?
   A. dog and chimpanzee
   B. horse and grasshopper
   C. wolf and dog
   D. wolf and horse

2. What is true about all the organisms in the table above?
   A. They all belong to a different kingdom.
   B. They all belong to a different phylum.
   C. They all belong to the same kingdom.
   D. They all belong to the same phylum.

3. Which group generally contains the largest number of different species?
   A. phylum     B. class     C. order     D. genus

4. A particular species of grasshopper would be most closely related to another organism that is in
   A. the same phylum, but a different class
   B. the same class, but a different order
   C. the same order, but a different family
   D. the same family, but a different genus

*Open Ended*

5. Based on the information presented in the tables above, which animal is most closely related to humans? Explain.

6. Before an exam on classification, a student was repeating to himself, "King Philip Crossed Over from Germany to Spain." How would this sentence help him on his classification exam?

## SKILLS ACTIVITY **2**
### ORGANIZING AND INTERPRETING DATA

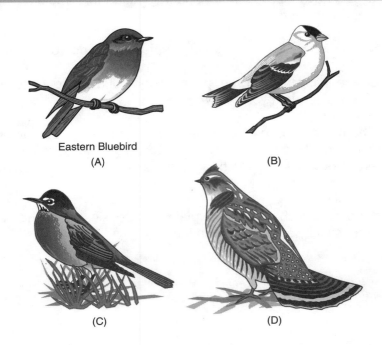

Eastern Bluebird
(A)

(B)

(C)

(D)

The state bird of New Jersey is the American goldfinch. It is in the class Aves (as are all other living birds), order Passeriformes, family ploceidae, genus *Carduelius,* and species *tristis.* The state bird of New York is the Eastern bluebird (see figure). It is in the order Passeriformes, family turdidae, genus *Sialia,* and species *sialis.* The state bird of Connecticut is the American robin. It is in the order Passeriformes, family turdidae, genus *Turdus*, and species *migratorius.* The state bird of Pennsylvania is the ruffed grouse. It is in the order Galliformes, family tetraonidae, genus *Bonasa*, and species *umbellus.*

| Classification | American Goldfinch (NJ) | Eastern Bluebird (NY) | American Robin (CT) | Ruffed Grouse (PA) |
|---|---|---|---|---|
| Kingdom | | | | |
| Phylum | | | | |
| Class | | | | |
| Order | | | | |
| Family | | | | |
| Genus | | | | |
| Species | | | | |

## Questions

1. Copy the table on page 79 into your notebook. Based on the data given, and what you have learned in the chapter, fill in the complete classification for each of the four state birds.

2. Which two birds are the most closely related? How do you know?

3. Based on the information given, predict which bird would least resemble the other three. Explain your answer.

4. Look at the pictures of the four state birds. The Eastern bluebird is identified for you. Based on the classifications given and the similarities in their overall body shapes and beak shapes, identify the remaining three birds.

5. Using this example about birds, explain how physical structure can be the primary basis for species classification.

# Chapter 4

# Diversity of Living Things

**Macro Statement:** Understand the effects of heredity and environment on the variation, survival, and evolution of a species.

## KNOWLEDGE STATEMENTS

**A.** In some organisms, all genes come from a single parent. In organisms that have sexes, typically half of the genes come from each parent, resulting in variations.

**B.** In nature, individual organisms with certain traits are more likely to survive and reproduce.

**C.** Changes in environmental conditions can affect the survival of a species.

**D.** Some characteristics are inherited and others result, or are acquired, from interactions with the environment.

## CHAPTER OUTLINE

**Genetic Material**

**Evolution**

**Adaptations**

# GENETIC MATERIAL

## Genes

All living things come from other living things through reproduction. During this process, offspring inherit from their parents a set of operating instructions called **genes**. Genes give the cell, or the organism it belongs to, its individual characteristics, or traits. Some traits in fruit flies, for example, are eye color, antenna length, and wing type (see Figure 4-1). This genetic information is contained in threadlike structures called *chromosomes*, found in each cell's nucleus. The number of chromosomes is specific for a species. For example, fruit flies have 8 chromosomes in each cell, while human beings have 46.

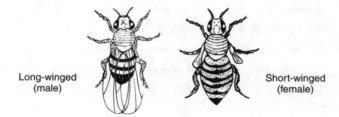

Long-winged
(male)

Short-winged
(female)

**Figure 4-1.** Two fruit flies (male and female, enlarged) that have different wing types.

## Asexual Reproduction

There are two types of reproduction: asexual and sexual. **Asexual reproduction** involves only one parent. The offspring produced are identical to the parent. Figure 4-2 shows some examples of asexual reproduction.

In asexual reproduction, the chromosomes, which carry the genes, are duplicated exactly. Therefore, all the genes of the offspring are identical to the genes of the parent. Since the genetic material is exactly the same in parent and offspring, the characteristics of the offspring are identical to those of its parent. Figure 4-3 illustrates how the chromosomes duplicate themselves before the cell divides.

## Sexual Reproduction

**Sexual reproduction** involves two parents and produces offspring that are not identical to either parent. The female parent produces an

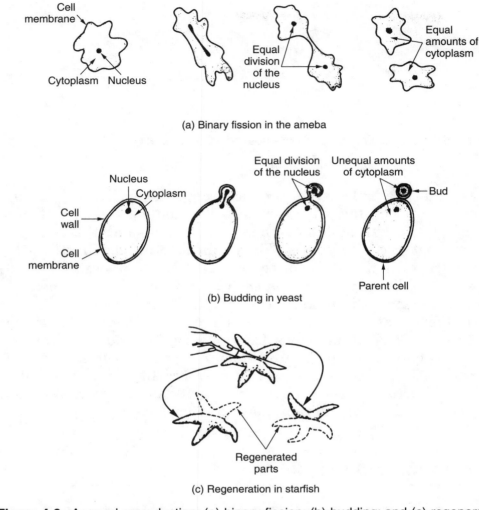

(a) Binary fission in the ameba

(b) Budding in yeast

(c) Regeneration in starfish

**Figure 4-2.** Asexual reproduction: (a) binary fission; (b) budding; and (c) regeneration.

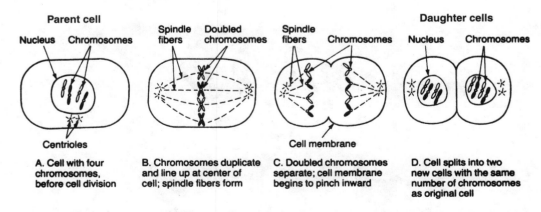

A. Cell with four chromosomes, before cell division

B. Chromosomes duplicate and line up at center of cell; spindle fibers form

C. Doubled chromosomes separate; cell membrane begins to pinch inward

D. Cell splits into two new cells with the same number of chromosomes as original cell

**Figure 4-3.** Cell division: Mitosis produces two new cells, each with the same number of chromosomes.

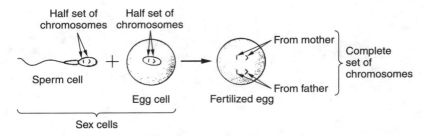

**Figure 4-4.** Fertilization occurs when a sperm cell and an egg cell unite.

egg cell, and the male parent produces a sperm cell. The egg cell and the sperm cell are known as sex cells. The joining together of these cells is called *fertilization*. Each sex cell contains half the number of a normal set of chromosomes. When joined during fertilization, they form one new cell with a complete set of chromosomes (see Figure 4-4). For example, human body cells each contain 46 chromosomes. The sperm and egg cells in humans contain 23 chromosomes each.

After fertilization, the cell develops into a new organism. Since half the genetic information comes from one parent and half from the other, the offspring is not identical to either parent. Typically, the offspring shows some traits of each of its parents. In this way, sexual reproduction leads to variation in the next generation. Figure 4-5 shows a possible result of sexual reproduction in chickens.

## Chromosome Pairs

Chromosomes come in pairs. Humans have 46 chromosomes or 23 pairs of chromosomes. Figure 4-6 shows a *karyotype*, which is a picture of the 23 pairs of chromosomes in a human. One chromosome of each pair comes from the mother and one from the father. Traits are

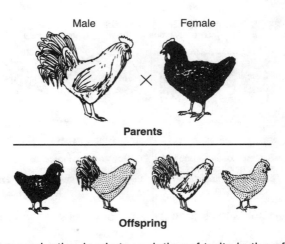

**Figure 4-5.** Sexual reproduction leads to variation of traits in the offspring.

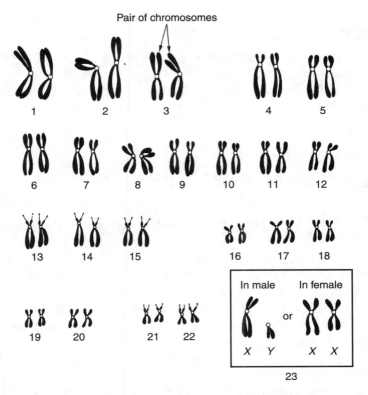

**Figure 4-6.** A karyotype for a human shows the 23 matching pairs of chromosomes.

controlled by the combination of genes from the two matching chromosomes. There are many genes on each chromosome.

When the pairs of chromosomes separate during egg cell and sperm cell formation, a large number of variations may occur. The process that determines which chromosome of each pair, and therefore which genes, each sex cell will receive is random. As a result, there is always variation in the genetic makeup of each sex cell produced.

This explains why brothers and sisters resemble each other but are not identical. By contrast, identical twins are formed after fertilization has occurred and therefore have identical genetic material.

## Other Methods of Reproduction

*Cloning* is the scientific technique by which organisms that normally reproduce sexually are reproduced asexually. This results in offspring that are genetically identical to their parents. Scientists have been able to clone several different species of plants and animals. Cloning of humans is not legal. There are differing viewpoints on the morality of cloning among members of the government, scientific community, and general population.

Some plants and animals can reproduce both sexually and asexually. Tulip plants, for example, can be grown by sexual reproduction from seeds or by asexual reproduction from bulbs. When a new variety of tulip flower is developed by sexual reproduction, a grower may wish to produce exact duplicates of that variety. This is accomplished by asexual reproduction. Since tulip bulbs are produced asexually, the grower can be fairly sure that the flower produced by the bulb will look just like the flower shown on the bulb's package.

## SKILLS ACTIVITY 1

### INTERPRETING DATA IN A TABLE

Most animals reproduce by the process of sexual reproduction. In sexual reproduction, sperm from the male joins with an egg from the female. This process, called fertilization, may take place either inside the female's body (*internal fertilization*) or outside the female's body (*external fertilization*). After the egg is fertilized, it develops into an *embryo*. This process may also take place either inside the female (*internal development*) or outside the female (*external development*).

For example, a chicken lays an egg, which is already fertilized. The chicken then sits on the egg to keep it warm as the embryo in the egg develops. Thus, chickens have internal fertilization and external development. The following table shows some different animals, their classes and habitats, and the types of fertilization and development they undergo. Study the table, then answer questions 1 through 5.

| Animal | Class | Habitat | Type of Fertilization | Type of Development |
|---|---|---|---|---|
| Goldfish | Osteichthyes (bony fishes) | Water | External | External |
| Bluebird | Aves (birds) | Land | Internal | External |
| Bee | Insecta | Land | Internal | External |
| Dog | Mammalia | Land | Internal | Internal |
| Frog | Amphibia | Water and land | External | External |
| Lizard | Reptilia | Land | Internal | External |
| Whale | Mammalia | Water | Internal | Internal |

## Questions

1. Based on the data in table, what is required for external fertilization?

   A. internal development

   B. a land habitat

   C. a water habitat

   D. having gills

2.  Which of the following is required for internal development?

    A. a land habitat          C. external fertilization

    B. a water habitat         D. internal fertilization

3.  A salamander belongs to the class Amphibia. What would you predict about salamanders?

    A. They live both on land and in water.

    B. They have internal development.

    C. They live in water only.

    D. They have internal fertilization.

4.  Alligators have internal fertilization and external development. Based on the table, which class do they most likely belong to?

    A. Amphibia      B. Reptilia      C. Bony fishes      D. Mammalia

5.  Based on the data in the table, what two generalizations can be made about mammals?

## Question Set 1

*Multiple Choice*

1.  Variation in a new generation of organisms is the result of
    A. sexual reproduction involving one parent
    B. sexual reproduction involving two parents
    C. asexual reproduction involving one parent
    D. asexual reproduction involving two parents.

2.  Which of the following diagrams illustrates sexual reproduction?
    A. 1            B. 2            C. 3            D. 4

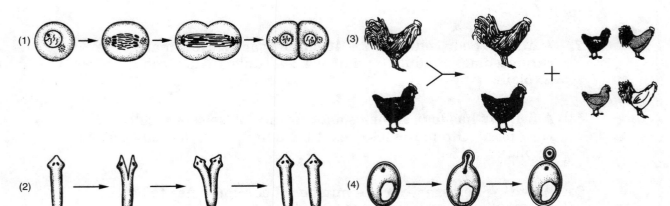

3. What process is illustrated by the following phrase:

    *egg + sperm → new cell (embryo)*

    A. growth     C. asexual reproduction
    B. budding     D. fertilization

4. Which of the following growers would most likely use asexual reproduction rather than sexual reproduction in his business?
    A. a dairy farmer developing a new breed of cow that produces more milk
    B. a farmer attempting to produce a new, sweeter variety of corn
    C. a grower attempting to guarantee his customers an identical strain of roses
    D. a farmer trying to combine the taste of a cherry tomato with the size of a beefsteak tomato

5. Bacteria reproduce by dividing in two. Which is an accurate description of the two new cells that are produced?
    A. Both cells are genetically different from the original cell.
    B. The new cells cannot reproduce because they were formed by asexual reproduction.
    C. The genes in the new cells are identical to the genes of the parent cell.
    D. Each new cell has twice as many genes as the parent cell had.

6. In a recent science fiction movie, cloning was used to create an army of identical soldiers. Cloning can best be described as
    A. a natural form of asexual reproduction
    B. an artificial form of asexual reproduction
    C. a natural form of sexual reproduction
    D. an artificial form of sexual reproduction

## Open Ended

7. A human body cell contains 46 chromosomes. How many chromosomes would a human egg cell (unfertilized) contain? Explain.

8. A fruit fly has four chromosomes in each of its sperm cells. How many chromosomes does it have in its regular body cells? Explain.

9. Why is it necessary for the number of chromosomes to be halved during sexual reproduction?

**10.** Explain why there is greater variation among living things that reproduce sexually than among living things that reproduce asexually.

Base your answers to questions 11 and 12 on the diagram below, which shows a form of reproduction.

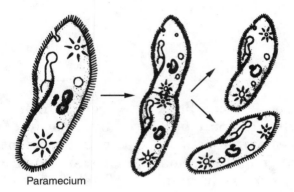

Paramecium

**11.** Which type of reproduction is shown in the diagram?

**12.** How does the genetic material of each daughter cell compare with the genetic material of the parent cell?

# EVOLUTION

If parents and offspring are genetically similar, why is there such diversity among living things? Several theories have been proposed to explain how living things have evolved over time.

## Acquired Characteristics

In 1809, the scientist Jean Baptiste de Lamarck suggested that if an organism developed certain traits during its lifetime that helped it survive, its offspring would inherit those same traits. For example, if a giraffe developed a long neck because it was always reaching for the topmost branches of trees, this trait would be passed on to the next generation. In fact, this does not occur. Lamarck's theory, called "the inheritance of acquired characteristics," was meant to explain the inheritance of new traits and the diversity of living things. However, it does not provide a reasonable explanation of how a new trait can be passed on to offspring.

In more recent times, the scientist August Weismann performed an experiment to test Lamarck's theory on the inheritance of acquired traits. Weismann cut off the tails of two mice and then let them reproduce. He continued to remove the tails of 20 generations of mice. Yet, in each generation, every mouse born had the same tail length as the original pair (before they were cut). This led Weismann to conclude that acquired characteristics are not inherited. Changes to body cells cannot be passed on to the next generation. Only changes to the sex cells can affect the inheritance of traits.

## Mutations

Genetic accidents do occur. Sometimes genetic material does not reproduce properly. This may be caused by a natural "accident" or by something in the environment. Such a genetic accident is called a ***mutation***. The new genetic information will cause a variation in the offspring. Mutations can be harmful, beneficial, or neutral (no noticeable effect). If the change is harmful, the organism will be less likely to survive and reproduce. If the change is beneficial, the organism will be better able to survive and reproduce. The new genetic information will then be passed on to each new generation. If these changes increase the likelihood that the organism will reproduce, they will become more common within the population.

## Natural Selection

In 1831, Charles Darwin set sail on a five-year voyage around the world to study nature. He made careful observations on the differences and similarities of organisms in isolated areas. He noticed that many organisms seemed to have changed over long periods of time in order to adapt to their particular environments. For example, on the Galápagos Islands (a group of isolated islands off the west coast of South America), Darwin found that the species of small birds called finches were different from one island to the next.

The finches were similar enough for Darwin to believe that they had a common ancestor. Yet the finches on one island had developed longer, thinner beaks that were useful in catching insects, whereas finches on another island had thicker beaks that were useful in cracking the shells of seeds (see Figure 4-7). Darwin concluded that, over time, the finches on each island had developed traits that helped them utilize the available food sources and survive. This change in a species is called ***evolution***.

Darwin's theory of how species change over time is referred to as "evolution by natural selection." Overpopulation, competition for food and space, and changes in the environment present a challenge to the survival of a species. Due to slight differences, or variations, among members of a species, some individuals are better adapted to

Catches insects with
beak and eats them

Seed eater                    Insect eater

**Figure 4-7.** Two different Galápagos finches—a seed eater and an insect eater—
show the variations in their beak types.

meet these challenges. The better adapted organisms are "naturally selected" by the environment to survive and reproduce, while the others die out. This process is called "survival of the fittest." After a long period of time and many changes, the members of a population may no longer resemble their ancestors; they are then considered to be a different species.

Darwin's theory did not account for the cause of the individual variations within a species. We now attribute these differences to mutations. Mutations, you will recall, are changes in the genetic material. (*Note:* In Darwin's time, scientists did not yet know about genes.) Changes that are harmful to an organism would be selected against, so they would not appear in generations that follow. The mutations that help an organism survive would be selected for, and would become more common in each succeeding generation. After many generations, and many mutations, the population of organisms may have changed enough to be considered a new species. This ongoing process of evolution can take millions of years to occur.

Evolution accounts for the great diversity among living things. The evolutionary process is dependent on the passing of genetic information, through chromosomes, from one generation to the next. As you learned, this occurs during reproduction.

# ADAPTATIONS

Living things have special characteristics called *adaptations* that enable them to survive under a given set of conditions. Organisms may be adapted for life in water, soil, or air. For example, a fish has gills that enable it to breathe underwater. An earthworm's body shape helps it move through the soil. A bird has feathered wings and light, hollow bones that let it fly. Many adaptations help an organism obtain

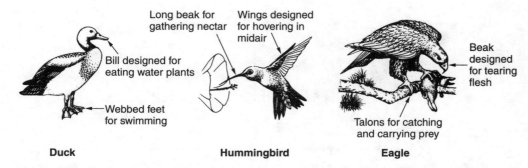

**Figure 4-8.** Differences in birds' beaks, wings, and feet show adaptations for survival in different habitats.

food or escape predators in its environment. Figure 4-8 illustrates how the features of certain birds aid their survival.

## Adaptations to Habitats

Earth's many environments include oceans, deserts, tropical rain forests, and the frozen Arctic tundra. Adaptations permit an organism to live in its own particular environment, or *habitat*. Organisms living in a dry, desert environment have adaptations that enable them to obtain and conserve water. For example, the cactus, a desert plant, has an extensive root system that helps it reach water and a thick stem for storing the water.

Animals living in the icy Arctic have adaptations that help them endure the region's very cold temperatures. For instance, polar bears have thick coats of fur; seals and whales have layers of protective fat called blubber. Table 4-1 lists organisms from various habitats and describes their special adaptations.

### TABLE 4-1. ORGANISMS AND THEIR ADAPTATIONS

| Organism | Habitat | Adaptation | Function |
|---|---|---|---|
| Arctic hare | Arctic | White fur in winter | Provides camouflage from predators |
| Monkey | Rain forest | Grasping tail | Acts as an extra hand to aid movement through trees |
| Cactus | Desert | Waxy skin | Reduces water loss from evaporation |
| Robin (bird) | Forest | Migration | Adapts to seasonal changes |
| Black bear | Forest | Hibernation | Adapts to seasonal changes |

## Seasonal Adaptations

Many environments change significantly with the change in seasons. Some organisms have developed adaptations that help them survive these drastic changes. Bears, for example, **hibernate** during the winter. They enter a sleeplike state of reduced body activity. This adaptation permits the bear to survive in the absence of available food. Other animals adapt by leaving the harsh winter environment in search of a warmer place. When the seasons change back again, they return. These animals are said to **migrate**. For example, the robin redbreast is common in New Jersey from March to October, but it is seldom seen here in the winter. The robin would not be able to find food such as worms and insects in the frozen ground, so it flies south for the winter and returns the next spring.

## SKILLS ACTIVITY 2
### TESTING A THEORY

A student wishes to test the theory of inheritance of acquired characteristics. He constructs a maze in which mice must turn left to receive food. After several tries, the mice learn to always make left turns when in the maze. When the mice are allowed to breed, the offspring are placed in the same maze. On entering the maze for the first time, some of the offspring turn left and some of the offspring turn right.

## Questions

1. Which conclusion can best be draw from these data?

   A. The learned behavior of the parent mice was inherited by their offspring.

   B. The learned behavior of the parent mice was not inherited by their offspring.

   C. Only the offspring that turned left inherited the learned behavior.

   D. Only the offspring that turned right inherited the learned behavior.

2. The student repeated the experiment several times and always got similar results. Does this experiment support Lamarck's theory of inheritance or not? Explain your answer.

3. After many trials in the maze, the offspring learned to turn left. What prediction can you make about the next generation of mice? Explain.

## Question Set 2

*Multiple Choice*

1. Birds that are adapted to live in a watery environment are most likely to have the type of feet shown in

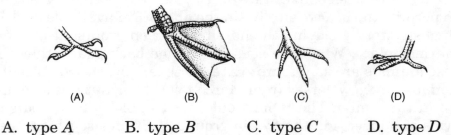

(A)    (B)    (C)    (D)

   A. type *A*    B. type *B*    C. type *C*    D. type *D*

2. Birds have light, hollow bones, which enable them to fly. This adaptation is the result of
   A. a diet of worms and seeds
   B. a series of genetic mutations over a long period of time
   C. a single genetic mutation that occurred recently
   D. a behavior learned from their parents

Refer to the paragraph below to answer questions 3 and 4.

   One of the most beautiful and common butterflies in our area is the orange-and-black monarch butterfly. Due to the diet of monarch caterpillars, the butterflies develop a taste that is unpleasant to birds. After a *taste*, birds usually learn not to eat this species of butterfly. Another species, called the viceroy butterfly, does not produce an unpleasant taste, but it has evolved a color pattern that is very similar to that of the monarch.

3. Which type of adaptation probably helps the viceroy butterfly survive?
   A. migration             C. imitating another species
   B. an unpleasant taste   D. camouflage

4. Which best accounts for the evolutionary development of the viceroy's color pattern?
   A. Dark wing patterns helped the viceroy camouflage and avoid birds.
   B. Natural selection favored viceroys that were most similar to the monarch.
   C. Orange-colored viceroy butterflies learned how to avoid birds.
   D. Viceroy butterflies have learned how to change their wing color.

5. All the following are challenges to the survival of a species *except*
   A. overpopulation
   C. changes in the environment
   B. competition
   D. adequate food supply

6. The arctic hare has white fur in the winter. This helps it survive because
   A. white fur is warmer than dark fur
   B. the hare is imitating the polar bear
   C. white fur provides camouflage in the snow
   D. the diet of the hare changes in the winter

7. Which of the following characteristics of the American goldfinch is acquired rather than inherited?
   A. They have bright yellow feathers in the spring and dull yellow feathers in the fall.
   B. The shape of their beak is well suited for cracking open seeds.
   C. They are often found near homes of people who put thistle seed in bird feeders.
   D. Their feet have three toes in front and one in back, which helps them perch.

8. Which of the following accounts for the diversity of traits among humans?
   A. Asexual reproduction involves the separation and recombination of genes, thus producing and maintaining variations.
   B. Asexual reproduction involves the duplication of genetic material, resulting in offspring with identical characteristics.
   C. Sexual reproduction involves the separation and recombination of genes, thus producing and maintaining variations.
   D. Sexual reproduction involves the duplication of genetic material, resulting in offspring with identical characteristics.

## Open Ended

9. Paul has a broken finger on his left hand, a scar above his right eye, brown eyes, and a good vocabulary. Which of these characteristics is most likely to be inherited by Paul's children? Explain your answer.

10. Darwin's theory of evolution explained that the individuals best suited to their environment are most likely to survive and reproduce. Darwin, however, could not explain how new adaptations might arise within a species. How do modern scientists explain the changes within a species that can lead to evolution?

# Chapter 5

# Matter: Atoms and Properties

**Macro Statements:** Describe the characteristic properties of matter and demonstrate how substances can be combined or separated. Explain how, in a closed system, when materials react with each other, many changes can take place but, in every case, the total amount of matter afterward is the same as before.

## KNOWLEDGE STATEMENTS

### Atoms

**A.** All matter is made up of atoms that may combine in groups to form molecules.

**B.** Symbols are used to represent atoms, and formulae are used to represent molecules.

**C.** In a chemical reaction, the total number of atoms after the reaction is the same as the total number of atoms before the reaction.

**D.** The motion of and distance between molecules determine the state of matter.

**E.** Over 100 different elements have been identified. They are grouped into three categories—metals, nonmetals, and noble gases—based on their similar properties.

### Properties

**A.** A mixture of substances may be separated using one or more of its characteristic physical properties.

**B.** Matter can be combined to form new substances with both chemical and physical properties that would be different from the original substances.

# CHAPTER OUTLINE

**Defining Matter: Atoms**

**Properties of Matter**

**Changes in Matter**

# DEFINING MATTER: ATOMS

Look all around you. The objects that you see, such as this book, your desk and chair, and the walls and ceiling, are all made of matter. The air (a mixture of gases) that surrounds you is also made of matter. In fact, every solid, liquid, and gas is a form of matter.

## What Is Matter?

*Matter* is defined as anything that has mass and takes up space. *Mass* is the total amount of material in an object. We measure mass with a triple-beam balance or an equal-arm balance, as shown in Figure 5-1. Notice that a balloon filled with air has a greater mass than an empty balloon, because air has mass. The amount of space an object occupies is called its *volume.* The air in the filled balloon in Figure 5-1 takes up space, giving the balloon a greater volume than the empty balloon.

Is there anything that is not made of matter? Is there anything that has no mass and takes up no space? Figure 5-2 shows that shining a light on a balance has no effect on the balance. This is because

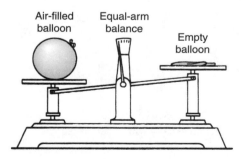

Air-filled balloon   Equal-arm balance   Empty balloon

**Figure 5-1.** The air-filled balloon is heavier (has mass) and takes up more space than the empty balloon because air is matter.

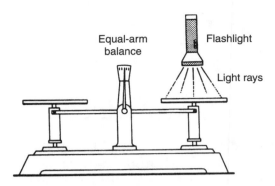

**Figure 5-2.** The balance is unaffected by the light shining on it because light is not matter.

light is a form of *energy*. Energy is not matter, since it has no mass and no volume. Some other forms of energy are heat and sound.

## Elements

The basic building blocks of matter are called ***elements***. All substances are made up of one or more elements. Oxygen, hydrogen, gold, and iron are examples of elements. Each element is represented by a symbol made up of one or two letters. For example, the symbol for hydrogen is H, oxygen is O, and gold is Au. The first letter of the symbol is always capitalized while the second letter, if any, is always lowercase. There are at least 115 known elements. (*Note:* The number of elements changes as new elements are created in research laboratories.) However, fewer than half of them occur commonly in nature. Table 5-1 lists the most common elements found in Earth's crust.

The smallest particle of an element that has the properties of that element is called an ***atom***. All atoms of a particular element are alike, but they are different from the atoms of any other element. For instance, all hydrogen atoms are alike, but they differ from oxygen

**TABLE 5-1.** **MOST COMMON ELEMENTS IN EARTH'S CRUST**

| Element | Chemical Symbol | Element | Chemical Symbol |
|---------|-----------------|---------|-----------------|
| Oxygen | O | Calcium | Ca |
| Silicon | Si | Sodium | Na |
| Aluminum | Al | Potassium | K |
| Iron | Fe | Magnesium | Mg |

atoms. If there are 115 different elements, there are 115 different kinds of atoms.

## Atomic Structure

All atoms are composed of smaller *subatomic* particles. These particles are called *protons, neutrons,* and *electrons.* Protons, neutrons, and electrons differ in their mass, electrical charge, and location in the atom. Protons and neutrons have roughly the same mass, while electrons are much lighter. Protons have a positive (+) charge, and electrons have a negative (−) charge. Neutrons have no electrical charge; they are electrically neutral.

Protons and neutrons are found in the center, or **nucleus**, of the atom. Electrons orbit the nucleus, moving very rapidly. The negatively charged electrons are attracted to the positively charged protons in the nucleus because oppositely charged particles attract each other. Since like charges repel and all electrons are negatively charged, electrons repel other electrons. Table 5-2 summarizes the properties of the subatomic particles.

The atoms of different elements have a different number of protons in their nucleus. Oxygen, for example, has 8 protons, while carbon has 6, and uranium has 92. The number of protons in the nucleus is called the *atomic number.* The Periodic Table of the Elements arranges the elements according to their atomic number.

## The Periodic Table of the Elements

Scientists organize the elements, based on their properties, in a chart known as the *Periodic Table of the Elements* (see Figure 5-3). On this

**TABLE 5-2. PROPERTIES OF THE SUBATOMIC PARTICLES**

| Particle | Mass (AMU)* | Charge | Location |
|----------|-------------|--------|----------|
| Proton | 1 | + | Nucleus |
| Neutron | 1 | 0 | Nucleus |
| Electron | 0.00054 | − | Outside the nucleus |

*The atomic mass unit (AMU) is a special unit created for measuring the mass of very small particles.

| 1 | | | | | | | | | | | | | | | | | 18 |
|---|---|---|---|---|---|---|---|---|---|---|---|---|---|---|---|---|---|
| **1**<br>**H**<br>1.008 | 2 | | | | | | | | | | | 13 | 14 | 15 | 16 | 17 | **2**<br>**He**<br>4.003 |
| **3**<br>**Li**<br>6.941 | **4**<br>**Be**<br>9.012 | | | | | | | | | | | **5**<br>**B**<br>10.81 | **6**<br>**C**<br>12.01 | **7**<br>**N**<br>14.01 | **8**<br>**O**<br>16.00 | **9**<br>**F**<br>19.00 | **10**<br>**Ne**<br>20.18 |
| **11**<br>**Na**<br>22.99 | **12**<br>**Mg**<br>24.31 | 3 | 4 | 5 | 6 | 7 | 8 | 9 | 10 | 11 | 12 | **13**<br>**Al**<br>26.98 | **14**<br>**Si**<br>28.09 | **15**<br>**P**<br>30.97 | **16**<br>**S**<br>32.07 | **17**<br>**Cl**<br>35.45 | **18**<br>**Ar**<br>39.95 |
| **19**<br>**K**<br>39.10 | **20**<br>**Ca**<br>40.08 | **21**<br>**Sc**<br>44.96 | **22**<br>**Ti**<br>47.88 | **23**<br>**V**<br>50.94 | **24**<br>**Cr**<br>52.00 | **25**<br>**Mn**<br>54.94 | **26**<br>**Fe**<br>55.85 | **27**<br>**Co**<br>58.93 | **28**<br>**Ni**<br>58.69 | **29**<br>**Cu**<br>63.55 | **30**<br>**Zn**<br>65.39 | **31**<br>**Ga**<br>69.72 | **32**<br>**Ge**<br>72.61 | **33**<br>**As**<br>74.92 | **34**<br>**Se**<br>78.96 | **35**<br>**Br**<br>79.90 | **36**<br>**Kr**<br>83.80 |
| **37**<br>**Rb**<br>85.47 | **38**<br>**Sr**<br>87.62 | **39**<br>**Y**<br>88.91 | **40**<br>**Zr**<br>91.22 | **41**<br>**Nb**<br>92.91 | **42**<br>**Mo**<br>95.94 | **43**<br>**Tc**<br>(98) | **44**<br>**Ru**<br>101.1 | **45**<br>**Rh**<br>102.9 | **46**<br>**Pd**<br>106.4 | **47**<br>**Ag**<br>107.9 | **48**<br>**Cd**<br>112.4 | **49**<br>**In**<br>114.8 | **50**<br>**Sn**<br>118.7 | **51**<br>**Sb**<br>121.8 | **52**<br>**Te**<br>127.6 | **53**<br>**I**<br>126.9 | **54**<br>**Xe**<br>131.3 |
| **55**<br>**Cs**<br>132.9 | **56**<br>**Ba**<br>137.3 | **57**<br>**La**<br>138.9 | **72**<br>**Hf**<br>178.5 | **73**<br>**Ta**<br>181.0 | **74**<br>**W**<br>183.8 | **75**<br>**Re**<br>186.2 | **76**<br>**Os**<br>190.2 | **77**<br>**Ir**<br>192.2 | **78**<br>**Pt**<br>195.1 | **79**<br>**Au**<br>197.0 | **80**<br>**Hg**<br>200.6 | **81**<br>**Tl**<br>204.4 | **82**<br>**Pb**<br>207.2 | **83**<br>**Bi**<br>209.0 | **84**<br>**Po**<br>(209) | **85**<br>**At**<br>(210) | **86**<br>**Rn**<br>(222) |
| **87**<br>**Fr**<br>(223) | **88**<br>**Ra**<br>226.0 | **89**<br>**Ac**<br>227.0 | **104**<br>**Rf**<br>(261) | **105**<br>**Db**<br>(262) | **106**<br>**Sg**<br>(263) | **107**<br>**Bh**<br>(262) | **108**<br>**Hs**<br>(265) | **109**<br>**Mt**<br>(266) | | | | | | | | | |

Key: 6 — Atomic number; C — Symbol; 12.01 — Atomic mass

| 58<br>**Ce**<br>140.1 | 59<br>**Pr**<br>140.9 | 60<br>**Nd**<br>144.2 | 61<br>**Pm**<br>(145) | 62<br>**Sm**<br>150.4 | 63<br>**Eu**<br>152.0 | 64<br>**Gd**<br>157.3 | 65<br>**Tb**<br>158.9 | 66<br>**Dy**<br>162.5 | 67<br>**Ho**<br>164.9 | 68<br>**Er**<br>167.3 | 69<br>**Tm**<br>168.9 | 70<br>**Yb**<br>173.0 | 71<br>**Lu**<br>175.0 |
|---|---|---|---|---|---|---|---|---|---|---|---|---|---|
| 90<br>**Th**<br>232.0 | 91<br>**Pa**<br>231.0 | 92<br>**U**<br>238.0 | 93<br>**Np**<br>237.0 | 94<br>**Pu**<br>(244) | 95<br>**Am**<br>(243) | 96<br>**Cm**<br>(247) | 97<br>**Bk**<br>(247) | 98<br>**Cf**<br>(251) | 99<br>**Es**<br>(252) | 100<br>**Fm**<br>(257) | 101<br>**Md**<br>(258) | 102<br>**No**<br>(259) | 103<br>**Lr**<br>(260) |

**Figure 5-3.** The Periodic Table of the Elements: Elements with similar properties are placed in the same group.

table, elements with similar properties are placed in the same vertical column, called a *group*. These groups are numbered from 1 through 18.

The majority of elements are shiny solids that conduct electricity. These elements are called ***metals***. (Mercury, which is a liquid at room temperature, is also considered a metal.) A smaller number of elements are poor conductors of electricity and lack the luster of the metals. These are called ***nonmetals***. Table 5-3 on page 102 lists other properties of metals and nonmetals. Metals and nonmetals behave differently when participating in chemical reactions. In many reactions involving elements, metals combine with nonmetals to form compounds. Nonmetals can also combine with other nonmetals to form compounds.

A still smaller group of elements, which are all gases at room temperature, seldom react with other elements. These are called the ***noble gases.*** The Periodic Table contains a zigzag line that separates the metals to the left from the nonmetals to the right. The last group of elements, group 18, contains the noble gases.

| TABLE 5-3. | THE PROPERTIES OF METALS AND NONMETALS |

| Metals | Nonmetals |
| --- | --- |
| Good conductors of heat and electricity | Poor conductors of heat and electricity |
| Shiny metallic luster | Dull luster |
| Solid at room temperature, except mercury (Hg)—(liquid) | All states, low melting points; for example: chlorine (Cl)—gas; bromine (Br)—liquid; sulfur (S)—solid |
| Silvery-gray color, except copper (Cu) and gold (Au) | Various colors; for example: chlorine—green; bromine—orange; sulfur—yellow |
| Malleable (can be hammered into sheets) and ductile (can be pulled into wires) | Brittle—break when hammered |

## SKILLS ACTIVITY 1

### READING FOR UNDERSTANDING

In a study called "The Tooth Fairy Project," scientists have asked parents to send them their children's baby teeth. These teeth are being tested for a radioactive form of the element strontium (symbol: Sr) called strontium-90.

Radioactive substances, such as strontium-90, are extremely dangerous when absorbed by the body. Scientists have linked exposure to radioactivity to an increased number of cancer cases.

Strontium-90 is an especially dangerous element because it is chemically similar to the element calcium. (Strontium is in the same group of elements as the element calcium: group 2.) The body—fooled by this similarity—mistakes the strontium-90 for calcium and deposits the radioactive element into the bones and teeth.

By measuring the amount of radioactive strontium in baby teeth, scientists are trying to determine our levels of radioactive exposure. They are looking to see if there is a link between areas of high radioactive exposure and areas with high cancer rates.

The Tooth Fairy Project has been going on for quite some time and has collected thousands of baby teeth for testing. The project will continue for many years to come.

### Questions

1. What are scientists in The Tooth Fairy Project looking for in baby teeth?
   A. calcium　　　B. strontium　　　C. cancer　　　D. tooth decay

**2.** The Tooth Fairy Project is trying to link

A. radioactive exposure to cancer rates

B. strontium-90 to calcium

C. tooth age to radioactivity

D. calcium to cancer rates

**3.** Referring to The Periodic Table of the Elements, explain why the body mistakes strontium for calcium.

## Compounds

Scientists know that there are millions of different substances. How is this possible if there are only 115 elements? Elements can combine to form new substances. A substance that is formed when two or more different elements combine is called a ***compound.*** Since many different combinations of elements are possible, many different compounds can exist. The common substance water is a compound that is formed when the elements hydrogen and oxygen combine.

A compound is represented by a *chemical formula* that indicates which elements have combined, and in what proportions. The chemical formula for water, $H_2O$, indicates that water contains two atoms of hydrogen to every atom of oxygen. Table 5-4 lists some common compounds and their chemical formulas.

The smallest particle of a compound is called a ***molecule.*** A water molecule is composed of two hydrogen atoms and one oxygen atom, as

**TABLE 5-4.    SOME COMMON COMPOUNDS AND THEIR CHEMICAL FORMULAS**

| Compound | Formula | Elements |
|---|---|---|
| Table salt | NaCl | Sodium, Chlorine |
| Water | $H_2O$ | Hydrogen, Oxygen |
| Sugar (sucrose) | $C_{12}H_{22}O_{11}$ | Carbon, Hydrogen, Oxygen |
| Quartz | $SiO_2$ | Silicon, Oxygen |
| Ammonia | $NH_3$ | Nitrogen, Hydrogen |

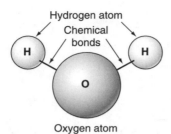

Hydrogen atom

Chemical bonds

H

H

O

Oxygen atom

**Figure 5-4.** The diagram shows the arrangement of atoms in a molecule of water.

shown in Figure 5-4. Atoms of the same element can also combine to form molecules. For example, two oxygen atoms combine to form a molecule of oxygen gas, $O_2$.

Atoms and molecules are extremely small. To get an idea of just how small, consider that one teaspoonful of water contains about 175 *sextillion* water molecules. (That would be written as $1.75 \times 10^{23}$, or 175 followed by 21 zeros!)

## Chemical Bonds

Atoms in a molecule are joined together by a special link called a ***chemical bond*** (see Figure 5-4). These bonds store chemical energy. Sometimes this energy can be released by a chemical reaction. Burning is one type of chemical reaction that releases energy. When wood is burned, energy stored in the chemical bonds within the wood is released as heat and light. Respiration is another chemical reaction that releases energy from chemical bonds.

## Mixtures

When two or more materials are put together without forming a new substance, a ***mixture*** is formed. Saltwater, for example, is a mixture of salt and water. Sand is a mixture of different minerals. Blood is a mixture of different cells, water, and other nutrients. Air is a mixture of several gases.

Unlike compounds, mixtures cannot be represented with a chemical formula. Table salt—a compound—is always NaCl (sodium and chlorine). However, saltwater—a mixture—can be more or less salty and still be saltwater. For example, salt in Utah is exactly the same as salt in New Jersey, but the saltwater in the Great Salt Lake in Utah is quite different from the saltwater in the Atlantic Ocean off New Jersey.

# PROPERTIES OF MATTER

## Physical Properties

Have you ever mistaken salt for sugar? They look very much alike. How might you tell them apart? Scientists faced with similar problems identify substances by examining their *properties*.

A difference in taste helps you distinguish salt from sugar. A difference in color (as well as taste) helps you distinguish salt from pepper. Taste and color are **physical properties**—properties that can be determined without changing the identity of a substance. All substances have unique physical properties by which they can be identified. Table 5-5 lists some physical properties often used to identify substances.

## States of Matter

One obvious physical property of a substance is whether it is a solid, a liquid, or a gas. These three forms of matter are called *states*. The arrangement and motion of the molecules within a substance determine its state.

TABLE 5-5.   **EXAMPLES OF PHYSICAL PROPERTIES OF SUBSTANCES**

| Property | Example |
|---|---|
| Phase | Mercury is a liquid at room temperature |
| Color | Sulfur is yellow |
| Odor | Hydrogen sulfide smells like rotten eggs |
| Density | Lead is much denser than aluminum |
| Solubility | Salt dissolves in water |
| Melting point | Ice melts at 0°C |
| Boiling point | Water boils at 100°C |

- In *solids,* the molecules are close together, move relatively slowly, and remain in fixed (unchanging) positions. The molecules in a solid do not flow (move from place to place); they vibrate within their fixed locations. Since the molecules do not change position, the shape of a solid is constant. A solid has a definite shape and volume, which do not depend on the container it is in.

- In *liquids,* the molecules are usually farther apart and moving faster than the molecules in solids. The molecules in a liquid can change position and flow past each other. Thus, a liquid has no definite shape; it takes on the shape of its container. However, liquids do have a definite volume. A given quantity of a liquid takes up the same amount of space regardless of the shape and size of its container.

- In *gases*, the molecules are much farther apart and move even faster than in liquids. The molecules of a gas can move anywhere within their container. A gas has no definite shape or volume but expands or contracts to fill whatever container it is in. Figure 5-5 shows how molecules are typically arranged in solids, liquids, and gases.

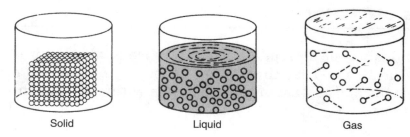

| Solid | Liquid | Gas |

**Figure 5-5.** The three phases of matter: solid, liquid, and gas.

The state of a substance depends on its temperature. At high enough temperatures, nearly all substances are gases (that is, their molecules move the most). At very low temperatures, nearly all substances are solids (that is, their molecules move the least).

## Changes in State

Since the state of a substance depends on the arrangement of its molecules, a change in this arrangement can cause a change in state. The changes in state are as follows:

- ***Melting*** is the change from a solid into a liquid. To change into a liquid, the solid's molecules must generally be moved farther apart, out of their fixed positions. Heat energy must be added to a substance to separate its molecules, so energy is absorbed during melting. (See Table 5-6.)

**TABLE 5-6.  EXAMPLES OF WATER PHASE CHANGES**

| Phase Change | Heat Flow | Examples |
|---|---|---|
| Liquid to gas | Water absorbs heat energy | Puddle evaporation; water boiling |
| Solid to liquid | Water absorbs heat energy | Snow melting on street; ice melting in soda |
| Gas to liquid | Heat energy is released | Cloud condensation; water condensing on cold window |
| Liquid to solid | Heat energy is released | Ice cubes forming in freezer; ice forming on lake surface |

- *Freezing* is the opposite of melting. When a liquid freezes into a solid, the molecules move closer together and bond more tightly into fixed positions. The process of freezing releases energy.

- *Boiling* or *evaporation* is the change of a liquid into a gas. This change requires that the molecules of the liquid be separated even farther apart. Therefore, energy is absorbed when a liquid changes into a gas.

- *Condensation* is the change from a gas to a liquid. During condensation, the molecules of a gas move closer together to form a liquid, and energy is released.

Figure 5-6 illustrates the energy changes that are associated with changes in state.

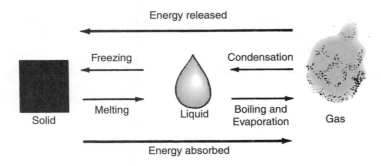

**Figure 5-6.** Energy changes occur during changes in phase.

For every substance, the change in state from a solid to a liquid occurs at a particular temperature, called its *melting point*. The melting point of ice (the solid form of water) is 0°C. The temperature at which a liquid freezes into a solid is called its *freezing point*. The freezing point of water is also 0°C. The freezing point and melting point of a substance are always the same.

The temperature at which a liquid boils and changes rapidly into a gas is called its *boiling point*. The boiling point of water is 100°C. This is also the temperature at which water vapor (the gas form of water), cooling from above 100°C, begins to condense into liquid water.

While a substance is changing state, its temperature remains constant. For example, while you are boiling water, the temperature remains at 100°C even though you are constantly supplying heat. The heat is used to cause the change in state rather than a change in temperature.

## SKILLS ACTIVITY 2

### INTERPRETING DATA IN A TABLE

By using melting point and boiling point information, we can determine what state a substance will be in at a given temperature. If the temperature of a substance is below its melting point, the substance is a solid. If the temperature is above its boiling point, the substance is a gas. If the temperature is between its melting and boiling points, the substance is a liquid. For example, at room temperature (20°C), water is a liquid, because 20°C is between the melting point and boiling point of water.

The table below lists the melting points and boiling points of some common substances. What state would table salt be in at a temperature of 1000°C? Since 1000°C is above the melting point of salt but below its boiling point, table salt would be a liquid at that temperature. Use the same kind of reasoning, based on data in the table below, to answer the questions that follow.

**Melting Points and Boiling Points of Some Common Substances**

| Substance | Melting Point (°C) | Boiling Point (°C) | State at 20°C |
|-----------|-------------------|-------------------|---------------|
| Water | 0 | 100 | Liquid |
| Alcohol | −117 | 78 | Liquid |
| Table salt | 801 | 1413 | Solid |
| Oxygen | −218 | −183 | Gas |

## Questions

1.  At a temperature of −190°C, oxygen is in the form of a

    A. gas                B. liquid              C. solid

2.  Alcohol would be a liquid at all the following temperatures except

    A. −100°C          B. 32°C              C. 100°C              D. 77°C

3.  The only substance listed that could be a liquid at a temperature of 90°C is
    A. table salt        B. water              C. alcohol            D. oxygen

## Question Set 1

*Multiple Choice*

1.  What does the diagram below show about matter?

    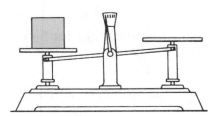

    A. Matter is made up of elements.
    B. Matter takes up space.
    C. Matter is a solid.
    D. Matter has mass.

2.  Which is *not* an example of matter?
    A. water          C. gold
    B. air            D. sound

3.  The amount of space an object occupies is called its
    A. volume         C. weight
    B. mass           D. length

4.  Atoms in a molecule are joined together by
    A. chemical bonds            C. electricity
    B. magnetism                 D. gravity

**5.** The circles in the closed jars shown below represent particles of matter. Which jar most likely contains a solid?

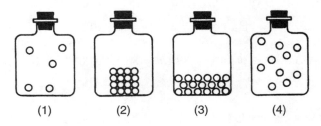

(1)      (2)      (3)      (4)

A. jar 1          B. jar 2          C. jar 3          D. jar 4

**6.** In which state of matter are the particles farthest apart and moving the fastest?

A. solid          B. liquid          C. gas

**7.** When you pour water from a beaker into a flask, there is a change in the water's

A. mass          B. volume          C. shape          D. density

**8.** Which statement best describes why atoms are electrically neutral?

A. Subatomic particles have no charge at all.

B. The number of negative electrons equals the number of positive protons.

C. Atoms contain only neutrons, which have no charge.

D. Protons are in the nucleus, while electrons are outside the nucleus.

**9.** Condensation refers to a change in state from a

A. solid to a liquid

B. liquid to a solid

C. liquid to a gas

D. gas to a liquid

**10.** The temperature at which a substance melts is the same temperature at which it

A. boils          B. freezes          C. condenses          D. evaporates

Refer to The Periodic Table of the Elements to answer questions 11 through 13.

**11.** Which of the following elements can be classified as a metal?

A. O (oxygen)                    C. Na (sodium)

B. He (helium)                   D. Cl (chlorine)

**12.** Which element would be a poor conductor of electricity?
  A. Fe (iron)          C. Au (gold)
  B. Cu (copper)        D. S (sulfur)

**13.** In which group of The Periodic Table would you place an element that has most or all of the following properties: solid; nonconductor of heat and electricity; forms a molecule with two hydrogen atoms?
  A. group 1            C. group 16
  B. group 2            D. group 18

## *Open Ended*

**14.** In two or more complete sentences, explain the differences between a mixture and a compound. Give two examples of each type.

**15.** A student opens a bottle of perfume in the back of a classroom. Although you do not see the bottle being opened, you become aware of the scent. In one or more complete sentences, explain how this effect happens.

**16.** Give an example of a change in state that releases energy.

**17.** The element sodium is very similar to the element potassium and very different from the element chlorine. Using The Periodic Table of the Elements as a guide, explain why.

 **Solutions**

How does a mixture of salt and water differ from a mixture of sand and water? When salt is placed in water, the particles of salt disappear, yet they can still be detected when tasting the mixture. A **solution** is a mixture in which the components remain evenly distributed. Saltwater is a solution. In a mixture of sand and water, the sand remains clearly visible settled at the bottom of the container. Sand and water is not a solution. The physical property that distinguishes the sand from the salt is called *solubility*. We say that salt dissolves in water to form a solution while sand does not dissolve in water. In other words, salt is **soluble** in water while sand is **insoluble** in water.

A solution generally has two parts, the **solute** and the **solvent**. The solute gets dissolved while the solvent does the dissolving. For example, when a solid such as salt gets dissolves in a liquid such as

**TABLE 5-7.  SOME SOLUTES THAT DISSOLVE IN WATER**

| Solution | Solute | Phase of Solute |
| --- | --- | --- |
| Seltzer | Carbon dioxide | Gas |
| Tea | Tea | Solid |
| Vodka | Alcohol | Liquid |

water, the salt (a solid) is the solute and the water (a liquid) is the solvent. Gases or other liquids may also dissolve in liquids to form a solution. Table 5-7 shows some common solutions with water as the solvent.

## Rate of Dissolving

What do you do after you add sugar to a cup of tea? You probably stir the mixture. Why? Stirring is one method of increasing the rate of dissolving. Which would dissolve faster, a sugar cube or a packet of granulated sugar? The smaller the particle size is, the faster the dissolving process will be. Therefore, granulated sugar dissolves faster than a cube of sugar does. Even granulated sugar dissolves quite slowly in iced tea. It dissolves much faster in hot tea, because an increase in temperature increases the rate of dissolving.

## Solubility

Not only does an increase in temperature dissolve sugar faster, it also allows more sugar to dissolve. In fact, it is possible to dissolve two cups of sugar in one cup of water if the water is hot enough (100°C).

In general, raising the temperature of a solvent increases the amount of solid solute that can dissolve in the liquid. The maximum amount of solute that can dissolve in a given amount of solvent is called the *solubility*. Generally, the solubility of a solid in a liquid increases as temperature increases. Gases, however, behave differently. The solubility of a gas in a liquid decreases when the solvent's temperature increases.

The solubility of a gas is also affected by pressure: the higher the pressure, the more soluble the gas. When you open a bottle of soda, you decrease the pressure on the solution. The carbon dioxide gas that was dissolved at the higher pressure comes out of the solution, forming bubbles.

## Choosing a Solvent

You have probably heard the expression, "Oil and water don't mix." A chemist might say instead, "Oil is not soluble in water." Oil is soluble in other solvents. We often need to choose a suitable solvent for a given solute. For example, nail polish does not dissolve in water. It does dissolve in acetone, a liquid often used as a nail polish remover. Grease and oil, which often stain clothing, do not dissolve in water. The "dry cleaners" use a liquid called "perc" that dissolves the grease without harming the fabric. The solubility of a given solute in a given solvent depends on the chemical bonds in the two substances.

## Density

Why are airplanes made of aluminum, and fishing sinkers made of lead? You might answer that aluminum is a light metal, while lead is a heavy metal. Yet an aluminum airplane has a much larger mass than a lead fishing sinker does. When we say that lead is heavier than aluminum, we really mean that if we have pieces of these two metals that are the same size, the lead piece will be heavier. (If the pieces are not the same size, we need another way to compare them.) As stated in Chapter 1, the quantity that compares the mass of an object to its size, or volume, is called *density*. Thus, density is defined as the mass of an object divided by its volume. At room temperature, lead (at 11.3 $g/cm^3$) is more than four times as dense as aluminum (only 2.7 $g/cm^3$). (Refer to Figure 1-12.)

## Why Do Objects Float?

A wooden log floats on water, while an iron nail sinks. Why? The answer to this question lies in the densities of these materials. A material will float if it is less dense than the liquid in which it is placed. From this information, we can conclude that iron is more dense than water, while wood is less dense than water. Water has a density of 1 $g/cm^3$. Any object with a density greater than 1 $g/cm^3$ will sink in water. The density of iron is 7.9 $g/cm^3$, and therefore it sinks in water.

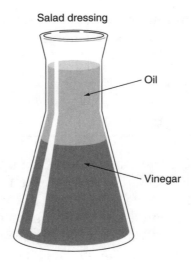

Salad dressing

Oil

Vinegar

**Figure 5-7.** The less dense liquid (oil) floats on top of the more dense liquid (vinegar).

Some liquids do not mix with each other. For example, the oil and vinegar in salad dressing form separate layers, as shown in Figure 5-7. What can you conclude about the density of oil compared with the density of vinegar? Since the oil floats on top of the vinegar, the oil must be less dense.

Helium balloons float on air in much the same way that wood floats on water. The density of a helium balloon is much less than the density of air. Some balloons use hot air instead of helium. Since hot-air balloons float, hot air must be less dense than cold air. When most materials are heated, they expand. This means that their volume increases while their mass stays the same. Since density is mass/ volume, an increase in volume will cause a decrease in a material's density. In general, an increase in temperature causes a decrease in density.

Objects that float are said to be *buoyant*. The **buoyancy** of an object in water depends on the density of the object relative to the density of the water. The less dense the object is, and the denser the water, the greater the buoyancy of the object.

## Question Set 2

*Multiple Choice*

1. Which one of the following materials is soluble in water?
   A. oil          B. salt          C. sand          D. grease

**2.** Which of the following combinations would dissolve the fastest?
   A. sugar cubes in iced tea
   B. granulated sugar in iced tea
   C. sugar cubes in hot tea
   D. granulated sugar in hot tea

**3.** When dissolving salt in water, the salt is considered to be the
   A. solvent      B. solute      C. mixture      D. solution

Use the information below to answer questions 4 through 6.

A student measures the mass and volume of four pieces of metal. The results are shown in the following table.

|         | Metal A | Metal B | Metal C | Metal D |
|---------|---------|---------|---------|---------|
| Mass    | 10.0 g  | 10.0 g  | 30.0 g  | 40.0 g  |
| Volume  | 2.0 cm$^3$ | 5.0 cm$^3$ | 5.0 cm$^3$ | 8.0 cm$^3$ |

**4.** Which metal is the densest of the four pieces measured?
   A. metal $A$      B. metal $B$      C. metal $C$      D. metal $D$

**5.** Which two pieces might be made of the same metal?
   A. $A$ and $B$      B. $B$ and $C$      C. $A$ and $D$      D. $C$ and $D$

**6.** The density of a 100.0-gram sample of metal A should be
   A. 5.0 g/cm$^3$      B. 10 g/cm$^3$      C. 50 g/cm$^3$      D. 100 g/cm$^3$

Questions 7 and 8 refer to the diagram below, which shows the relative densities of some liquids and solids at room temperature.

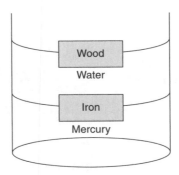

**7.** Which liquid in the diagram is least dense?
   A. wood          B. water          C. iron          D. mercury

**8.** Which solid in the diagram is most dense?
A. wood
C. iron
B. water
D. mercury

*Open Ended*

Refer to the diagram below, which represents a beaker of ice water, to answer the following question.

**9.** (a) This diagram indicates that the ice is
A. less dense than water
B. more dense than water
C. colder than water
D. warmer than water
(b) In one or more complete sentences, explain your answer.

**10.** What effect does an increase in temperature have on the density of air? Explain your answer. (Provide an example to support your answer.)

# CHANGES IN MATTER

We see change around us all the time. There are changes in us. There are changes in the weather. There are changes on Earth. Some of these changes involve physical aspects of matter. Other changes involve chemical aspects.

## Physical Changes

As you know, the chemical formula for water is $H_2O$ because each water molecule is made up of two atoms of hydrogen and one atom of oxygen. What is the formula for ice? When water freezes, the arrangement of its molecules changes, but the molecules themselves do not change. They are still $H_2O$. A change of state, such as freezing or melting, does not produce any new substances. A change that does not result in the formation of any new substances is called a ***physical change.*** All changes of state are physical changes. Crushing ice cubes into small pieces is also a physical change, since both crushed ice and ice cubes are still made of the same substance.

Similarly, when you dissolve sugar in water, the sugar still tastes sweet and the water is still wet. No new substances have been formed, so dissolving is a physical change. Figure 5-8 shows why boiling, melting, and dissolving are physical changes.

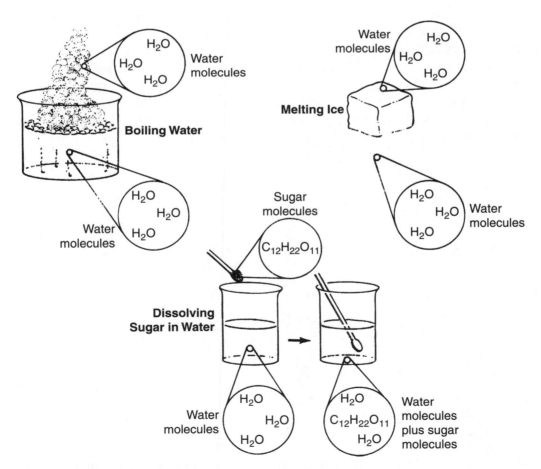

**Figure 5-8.** During physical changes, no new substances are formed.

## Separating the Parts of a Mixture

A mixture of two or more substances can be separated through physical changes. For example, a mixture of salt and water can be separated by evaporating, or boiling off, the water, thus leaving the salt behind. A mixture of iron and silver can be separated with a magnet. The iron will be attracted to the magnet, while the silver will not. How might a mixture of salt and sand be separated? This would involve a series of physical changes. First, the mixture could be added to water. The salt would dissolve, while the sand would not. This mixture could then be filtered, thus separating the undissolved sand from the salt-water solution. The dissolved salt particles are too small to be trapped on filter paper; instead, they would pass through the tiny openings in the paper. The sand particles are too large to pass through the openings in filter paper, so they would be caught. Finally, as stated above, we can boil off the water from the saltwater mixture, leaving just the salt behind. The sequence of steps is illustrated in Figure 5-9.

Density is another property that can be used to separate some mixtures. Fat-free milk is also called "skim milk." Fat is less dense than water, and insoluble in water. These physical properties enable the dairy industry to remove the fat from whole milk by skimming it off the surface. Some liquids form separate layers when mixed together, as shown in Figure 5-7. Such liquids also can be separated using differences in density.

Blood is a mixture that is often separated through the use of a *centrifuge*. A centrifuge is a device that spins material very rapidly. When mixtures are placed in a centrifuge, the denser material moves out-

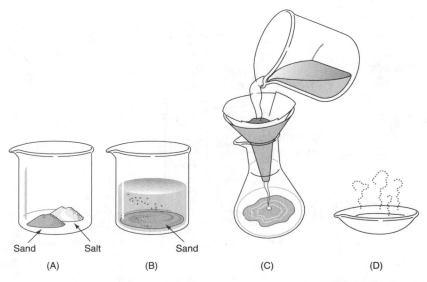

Sand  Salt  Sand
(A)  (B)  (C)  (D)

**Figure 5-9.** Separating the parts of a mixture: (A) making a mixture of salt and sand; (B) dissolving the salt in water; (C) separating the sand with a filter; and (D) evaporating the water (to get remaining salt).

ward, while the less dense material moves inward. In this way, denser blood cells are separated from the less dense blood plasma.

 ## Chemical Changes

What happens if you forget to put a carton of milk back into the refrigerator? First, the milk gets warm. This is a physical change. However, if you leave the milk out too long, it turns sour. The sour taste is caused by the production of a new substance called lactic acid. A change that produces one or more new substances is called a ***chemical change***. When a chemical change occurs, we say that a chemical reaction has taken place. For example, burning paper produces smoke and ash, both of which are new products. Thus, burning is always a chemical change.

Forming a compound always involves a chemical change, whereas forming a mixture involves only physical changes. Similarly, a chemical change is required to break apart a compound, whereas physical changes (such as boiling off saltwater to leave the salt behind or spinning blood in a centrifuge to separate its components) are sufficient to separate the parts of a mixture.

Chemical changes can be represented by chemical equations. A chemical equation uses formulas and numbers to keep track of a chemical change. The starting materials, called the *reactants*, are listed on the left side of the equation. The final materials, called the *products*, are listed on the right side. An arrow separates the two sides. The equation for the burning of coal, which is mostly carbon, would be written as: $C + O_2 \rightarrow CO_2$.

A chemist reads this equation as, "carbon plus oxygen yields carbon dioxide." In this reaction, carbon and oxygen are the reactants, and carbon dioxide is the product. Table 5-8 gives some examples of chemical changes.

**TABLE 5-8.** **EXAMPLES OF CHEMICAL CHANGES**

| Chemical Change | Reactants | Products | Equation |
| --- | --- | --- | --- |
| Burning coal | Carbon (C) + oxygen gas ($O_2$) | Carbon dioxide gas ($CO_2$) | $C + O_2 \rightarrow CO_2$ |
| Rusting of iron | Iron (Fe) + oxygen gas ($O_2$) | Rust ($Fe_2O_3$) | $4Fe + 3O_2 \rightarrow 2Fe_2O_3$ |
| Tarnishing of silver | Silver (Ag) + sulfur (S) | Tarnish ($Ag_2S$) | $2Ag + S \rightarrow Ag_2S$ |
| Photosynthesis | Carbon dioxide gas ($CO_2$) + water ($H_2O$) | Glucose ($C_6H_{12}O_6$); oxygen gas ($O_2$) | $6CO_2 + 6H_2O \rightarrow C_6H_{12}O_6 + 6O_2$ |

## Properties and Chemical Changes

The new substances produced by a chemical change have their own set of properties. These properties differ from those of the original substances that reacted, since those substances are no longer present as separate substances. For example, the element sodium is a soft metal that explodes on contact with water. The element chlorine is a poisonous, green gas. When sodium and chlorine combine in a chemical reaction, they produce sodium chloride, commonly known as table salt. The new substance that is formed has completely different properties from those of the original materials, which no longer exist separately. During a chemical reaction, the atoms are rearranged to form new substances. This involves the breaking of existing chemical bonds and the formation of new bonds.

Both physical and chemical changes occur in nature. The wearing away of a mountain by streams is an example of a physical change called **erosion**. Erosion is the physical wearing away of rock material at Earth's surface. The Grand Canyon in Arizona was formed over millions of years by this physical change.

The Statue of Liberty in New York City is made of copper but does not look copper-colored. This is due to a chemical reaction between the copper and the air, which produces a new, green-colored substance (patina). The chemical wearing away of a metal is called **corrosion**. Corrosion, which forms a new substance, is a chemical change. Erosion, which only moves substances around, is a physical change.

## Conservation of Matter

In a chemical change, no atoms are created and no atoms are destroyed. Every atom that is present before a reaction takes place is still there after the reaction takes place. What has changed is the way the atoms are arranged. Chemical reactions change only the way that the atoms are bonded to one another.

Figure 5-10 shows what happens when hydrogen and oxygen combine to form water in a chemical reaction. How many atoms of hydrogen are there before the reaction takes place? How does this compare with the number of hydrogen atoms after the reaction takes place? There are four hydrogen atoms both before and after the reaction. How are the starting substances (the reactants) different from the substances formed (the products)?

Before the reaction, each hydrogen atom was bonded to one other hydrogen atom; after the reaction, each hydrogen atom was bonded instead to an oxygen atom. This is an example of the **Law of Conservation of Matter**, which states that matter can be neither created

Hydrogen atoms    Hydrogen atoms    Oxygen atoms    Hydrogen atoms    Chemical bonds

H H    H H    +    O O    →    Chemical reaction

Hydrogen gas    Hydrogen gas    Oxygen gas    2 water molecules    Oxygen atom

$$2H_2 + O_2 \longrightarrow 2H_2O$$

**Figure 5-10.** In a chemical reaction, such as the formation of water molecules, there are the same numbers of atoms before the reaction as there are after the reaction.

nor destroyed in a chemical reaction. It can, however, be changed from one form to another.

## Conservation of Mass

How would the mass of the starting materials compare with the mass of the materials formed? The mass remains the same, since no atoms were created or destroyed. The ***Law of Conservation of Mass*** states that the mass of the reactants must equal the mass of the products. In other words, mass can be neither created nor destroyed.

Refer to the equation for the burning of coal shown in Table 5-8. It is quite obvious that one carbon atom and two oxygen atoms can be found in the reactants as well as in the product. Matter has been conserved. Examine the next equation, the rusting of iron. Iron (Fe) combines with oxygen ($O_2$) to form rust ($Fe_2O_3$). If we simply wrote the equation as $Fe + O_2 \rightarrow Fe_2O_3$, there would be more atoms after the reaction than there were before. This would violate the Law of Conservation of Matter and the Law of Conservation of Mass. Chemists use a procedure called *balancing* to ensure that the equation as written does obey these laws. The numbers in front of the formulas tell us that four atoms of iron react with three molecules of oxygen to form two molecules of rust: $4Fe + 3O_2 \rightarrow 2Fe_2O_3$. There are now four atoms of Fe and six atoms of O on both sides of the equation. The Laws of Conservation are obeyed.

When silver tarnishes, the mass of the tarnish must equal the mass of the silver and the sulfur that have combined together (refer to Table 5-8). If 108 grams of silver react with 16 grams of sulfur, the tarnish will weigh 124 grams. However, if we measure the mass of a silver spoon when there is no tarnish on it, and carefully weigh it again after it has tarnished, the mass will increase. This occurs because we are unable to weigh all of the reactants; we cannot account for the sulfur (which came from the air) in the initial weighing. It is important to remember to account for all the substances before and after a reaction. In particular, it may be easy to forget about gases, which either escape into or come from the air, since it is difficult to capture and weigh them.

## SKILLS ACTIVITY 3
## PREDICTING RESULTS

After studying Table 5-8, Maria performed an experiment on the rusting of an iron nail. She carefully measured the mass of the nail before rusting occurred and recorded her observation.

Initial mass = 3.0 grams    Final mass = ? grams

## Questions

1. What prediction should Maria make about the final mass of the iron nail after rusting?

   A. The mass will decrease because the iron is destroyed.
   B. The mass will stay the same because of the Law of Conservation of Matter.
   C. The mass will increase because rust combines iron atoms with oxygen atoms from the air.
   D. The mass will increase because iron atoms get heavier as they rust.

2. In another experiment, Maria measured the mass of a piece of wood before and after it was burned. The mass of the wood decreased after it was burned. What would be a possible explanation for this observation?

   A. Wood does not obey the Law of Conservation of Matter.
   B. Maria's measurements were incorrect.
   C. Atoms become lighter when heated.
   D. The burning wood produced gases that were not included in the final weighing.

3. How could Maria improve the experiment described in question 2?

   A. She should use a material that does not burn.
   B. She should perform the experiment in an open container.
   C. She should perform the experiment in a closed container.
   D. She should measure the mass of the heat released during the reaction.

**Energy and Chemical Changes**

As you have learned, new substances are formed during a chemical change. An example is making table salt from sodium and chlorine. However, simply mixing sodium and chlorine together does not produce table salt. Energy is needed to start the chemical reaction. Likewise, a match does not start to burn until you strike it. The friction caused by striking the match provides the heat energy needed to start the chemical reaction of burning.

Many chemical changes must be started by the addition of energy, in the form of heat, light, or electricity. However, some chemical changes do not require the addition of energy to get them started. The rusting of iron and the tarnishing of silver are examples of such reactions.

As a chemical reaction proceeds, energy is either absorbed or released. For example, the burning of a match releases energy in the form of heat and light. The chemical reaction that occurs in a battery releases electrical energy. On the other hand, when food is cooked, heat energy is absorbed by the chemical changes taking place. Table 5-9 gives some examples of chemical changes that absorb energy and chemical changes that release energy.

We can use chemical reactions to supply us with heat when we need it. For example, campers often use chemical hand warmers in cold weather. When they open the packet, the chemicals in the hand warmer react with oxygen in the air to release heat. Reactions that absorb heat are also useful. A cold pack, often used to treat minor bumps and bruises, contains two chemicals that absorb heat when they react with each other. To start the reaction, you simply break the seal that separates the two chemicals.

**TABLE 5-9. ENERGY AND CHEMICAL CHANGES**

| Chemical Changes That Release Energy | Type of Energy Released | Chemical Changes That Absorb Energy | Type of Energy Absorbed |
|---|---|---|---|
| Burning of wood | Light, heat | Cooking an egg | Heat |
| Battery powering a flashlight | Electricity | Recharging a battery | Electricity |
| Decomposing of organic matter | Heat | Photosynthesis | Light |

## Question Set 3

*Multiple Choice*

1. Which of the following processes could be used to separate a mixture of salt and water?
   A. burning the water
   B. evaporating the water
   C. filtering the salt
   D. using a magnet

2. Which is only a physical change?
   A. souring of milk
   B. burning of oil
   C. melting of ice
   D. rusting of iron

3. Which process involves a chemical change?
   A. photosynthesis
   B. boiling water
   C. freezing water
   D. melting ice

4. A chemical change always
   A. forms one or more new substances
   B. absorbs heat
   C. releases heat
   D. absorbs electricity

5. In making an omelet, which process involves a chemical change?
   A. melting butter
   B. chopping onions
   C. frying eggs
   D. adding salt

6. A chemist mixed sodium and chlorine, but no reaction took place. A probable explanation for this outcome is that
   A. the reaction only releases energy
   B. the reaction only absorbs energy
   C. these substances cannot react
   D. energy must be added to start the reaction

7. During a chemical change, energy is
   A. always released
   B. always absorbed
   C. either absorbed or released
   D. neither absorbed nor released

8. When making iced tea, Aidan noticed that there was less ice after he mixed the ice with the hot tea. On observing this, Aidan remembered that melting is a
   A. chemical change in which energy is absorbed
   B. chemical change in which energy is released

C. physical change in which energy is absorbed

D. physical change in which energy is released

9. Hydrogen gas is produced in a chemical reaction between zinc and an acid. Which setup below would most likely have the fastest reaction rate?

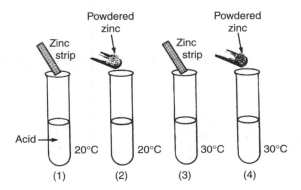

A. a zinc strip at 20°C

B. powdered zinc at 20°C

C. a zinc strip at 30°C

D. powdered zinc at 30°C

10. Food cooks faster at a higher temperature. This is because as the temperature increases, the rate of a chemical reaction usually

A. increases     B. decreases     C. remains the same

11. The diagram shows four samples of wood, each with a mass of 1 kilogram. Which sample would most likely burn the fastest?

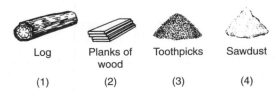

A. log

B. planks of wood

C. toothpicks

D. sawdust

12. Which change would be the most difficult to reverse?

A. melting an ice cube, because it is a physical change

B. dissolving sugar in water, because it is a chemical change

C. burning a match, because it is a chemical change

D. rusting an iron nail, because it is a physical change

13. George cracks open an egg and finds that it has a very bad smell. The egg has become rotten. This change is best described as

A. physical, because no new substances were formed

B. physical, because a new substance was formed

C. chemical, because no new substances were formed

D. chemical, because a new substance was formed

14. A molecule of carbon dioxide ($CO_2$) is made of one atom of carbon and two atoms of oxygen. Carbon dioxide can best be classified as

A. an element because it is made of one type of atom

B. an element because it is made of two types of atoms

C. a compound because it is made of one type of atom

D. a compound because it is made of two types of atoms

15. Which subatomic particles are found outside the nucleus of an atom?

A. positively charged protons

B. positively charged electrons

C. negatively charged neutrons

D. negatively charged electrons

16. The diagram below represents an atom of helium. Based on this diagram, which statement is true?

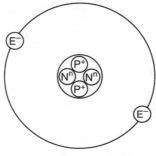

Helium atom

A. The positively charged protons are found outside the nucleus.

B. The positively charged protons are found inside the nucleus.

C. The negatively charged protons are found outside the nucleus.

D. The negatively charged protons are found inside the nucleus.

17. When 12 grams of carbon (C) react with exactly 32 grams of oxygen (O), carbon dioxide is formed. The mass of the carbon dioxide is

A. greater than 44 grams       C. less than 44 grams

B. equal to 44 grams            D. not determinable

18. Four grams of hydrogen react with oxygen from the air to form 36 grams of water. How many grams of oxygen were used?

A. 9          B. 40          C. 16          D. 32

## Open Ended

**19.** What is the difference between a physical change and a chemical change? Give one example of each.

**20.** Sulfur is insoluble in water, whereas sugar is very soluble in water. How might you separate a mixture of sulfur, sugar, and water?

To answer questions 21 and 22, refer to the table below, which shows two elements (zinc and sulfur) and their properties. The table indicates that the elements may combine in a physical change to form a mixture, or they can combine in a chemical change to form a compound.

| Element | Properties | Type of Change | Properties When Combined |
|---------|-----------|----------------|--------------------------|
| Zinc | Good conductor of electricity; gray | Physical | Zinc and sulfur mixture: moderate conductor of electricity; yellow and gray |
| Sulfur | Nonconductor of electricity; yellow | Chemical | Zinc sulfide compound: nonconductor of electricity; white |

**21.** What evidence indicates that a chemical change took place when the zinc and sulfur combined to form zinc sulfide?

**22.** During the chemical change, a bright white flash of light was observed. What does this indicate about the reaction between zinc and sulfur?

**23.** When writing a chemical equation, we sometimes indicate the state of matter following a compound's symbol, these being (s) for solid, (l) for liquid, and (g) for gas. The solid calcium carbonate ($CaCO_3$) decomposes when heated according to the reaction

$$CaCO_3 \text{ (s)} \rightarrow CaO \text{ (s)} + CO_2 \text{ (g)}$$

When 100 grams of calcium carbonate ($CaCO_3$) are heated and then reweighed, the weight of the (solid) product is 56 grams. Does this violate the Law of Conservation of Mass? Explain your answer.

# Chapter **6**

# Force and Motion

**Macro Statement:** Demonstrate and explain how the motion of an object is affected by one or more forces.

## KNOWLEDGE STATEMENTS

**A.** A body at rest remains at rest; a body in motion remains in uniform motion unless acted upon by an external force (Newton's First Law).

**B.** When more than one force acts on an object at the same time, the forces can reinforce or cancel each other, producing a net force that will change the speed and/or direction of the object.

**C.** Friction is a force that can retard motion.

## CHAPTER OUTLINE

**Force, Mass, and Motion**

**Newton's First Law of Motion**

**Newton's Second Law of Motion**

**The Force of Friction**

# FORCE, MASS, AND MOTION

 **Force**

A *force* is a push or pull (see Figure 6-1). To open a refrigerator door, you pull the door. To move a computer mouse across a mouse pad, you push or pull the mouse. To lift a log for the fireplace, you must pull the log up against the force of gravity. Table 6-1 lists examples of pushing and pulling forces.

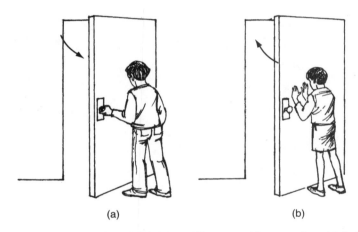

(a)                    (b)

**Figure 6-1.** Pulling (a) and pushing (b) forces illustrated by opening and closing a door.

A force can also stop an object's motion, change its speed of motion, or change its direction of motion, as the following examples show.

**TABLE 6-1.   PUSHING AND PULLING FORCES**

| Pushing Forces | Pulling Forces |
| --- | --- |
| Hitting a volleyball | Pulling a rope in a tug-of-war |
| Closing a refrigerator door | Lifting a shovel full of dirt |
| Hammering a nail | Climbing a rope |
| Wind knocking a tree down | Gravity pulling an apple to the ground |

*Force stops motion:* falling acorn striking the ground; glove catching a baseball.

*Force slows motion:* friction slowing a skateboard; car going from a flat road to an uphill road.

*Force changes direction:* tennis racket striking a tennis ball; wind causing a fly ball to curve.

 **Mass**

**Mass** is a measure of the amount of matter in an object. The mass of an object, unlike its weight, remains constant and does not change.

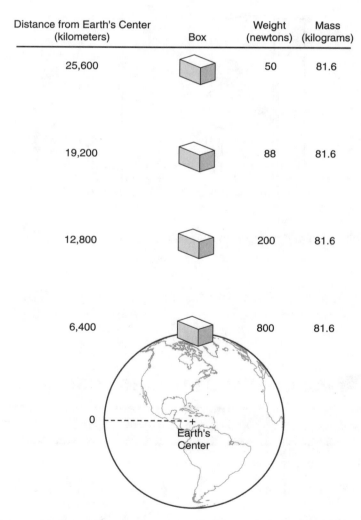

**Figure 6-2.** As an object moves away from Earth, its weight decreases, but its mass remains the same.

Figure 6-2 shows that although the weight of the box changes, its mass is unchanged as it moves away from Earth's center.

A bowling ball and a baseball have different masses. A bowling ball contains more matter and is more massive than a baseball. The greater the mass of an object, the greater the force necessary to move the object. Thus, a greater force is needed to throw a bowling ball than to throw a baseball.

 ## Motion

*Motion* is a change in the position of an object relative to another object, which is assumed to be at rest (see Figure 6-3). In other words, an object's motion is recognized in relation to a nonmoving object or reference point. For example, a school bus and its driver appear to be in motion when viewed by parents watching the bus drive down the street. The bus and driver change position relative to the nearby houses and trees. However, the bus driver does not appear to be in motion when viewed by the children on the bus. The driver does not appear to change position relative to the windows and seats on the bus.

An object has uniform motion when it moves in a straight line at a constant speed. A car traveling at a constant 80 kilometers per hour along a straight road is an example of an object in uniform motion. The car travels equal distances in equal periods of time in a single direction. If the car changes speed or changes its direction, then it does not have uniform motion.

**Figure 6-3.** An object's motion (the girl on a skateboard) is recognized in relation to a nonmoving object or reference point (the house, fence, or shrubs).

## SKILLS ACTIVITY **1**
### UNITS OF FORCE

A force that we are all familiar with is *gravity*. Gravity pulls objects down to Earth's surface, causing them to have weight. The basic unit for the force of gravity, or weight, is the *pound* (lb) in the English system and the *newton* (N) in the metric system. One pound is equal to about 4.5 newtons. Therefore, a girl who weighs 100 pounds is being pulled by Earth's gravity with a force of 450 newtons. The *kilogram* is the basic unit of mass. One kilogram is equal to about 9.8 newtons. So, it takes a force of 98 newtons to lift a box that has a mass of 10 kilograms.

We commonly think of weight in units of pounds, and mass in units of grams or kilograms. In your study of physical science, it is necessary to use newtons as the unit of force. The following questions provide practice in converting pounds and kilograms into newtons.

### Questions

1.  a. Write a word or symbols formula that will convert pounds to newtons.
    b. Write a word or symbols formula that will convert kilograms to newtons.

2.  Convert the following English units of force into newtons.

    a. 150 pounds

    b. 9 pounds

    c. 18.8 pounds

3.  Convert the following metric units of mass into newtons.

    a. 100 kilograms

    b. 17 kilograms

    c. 2.3 kilograms

## Question Set 1

*Multiple Choice*

1.  Which of the four different balls listed would require the greatest force to move?
    A. golf ball  C. basketball
    B. baseball  D. bowling ball

**2.** The mass of the Statue of Liberty would be
   A. greatest in New York City
   B. greatest at the North Pole
   C. greatest on the moon
   D. the same at all the above locations

Questions 3 and 4 refer to the following paragraph.

A force is a push or a pull. A force can start motion, stop motion, change the speed of motion, or change the direction of motion. In volleyball, the person serving a ball tosses it up to start the ball moving. The server then strikes the ball, changing its direction and increasing its speed toward the opposing team. When the ball reaches the other team, a player applies a new force, causing the ball to slow and go up. Then, a player applies a stronger force to change direction and send the ball back to the serving team. This continues until the point is won and the motion of the ball is stopped.

**3.** When serving in volleyball, the act of striking the ball is an example of applying
   A. a pushing force
   B. a pulling force
   C. no force at all
   D. both a pushing and a pulling force

**4.** The person returning a served volleyball attempts to
   A. change the speed and direction of the ball
   B. change the speed of the ball only
   C. change the direction of the ball only
   D. apply a force to stop the volleyball's motion

**5.** The front door of a house can be closed by use of
   A. a pushing force
   B. a pulling force
   C. either a pushing or a pulling force
   D. neither a pushing nor a pulling force

**6.** A person weighs less at the top of a mountain than at the base of a mountain because
   A. a person has less mass at the top of a mountain
   B. a person has more mass at the top of a mountain
   C. a person is farther from the center of Earth when at the top of a mountain
   D. there is less air pressure at the top of the mountain

7. The force of 1 pound is equal to 4.5 newtons and the force of 1 kilogram is equal to 9.8 newtons. Which force is the greatest?

    A. 10 pounds

    B. 10 kilograms

    C. 10 newtons

    D. 50 newtons

8. In a game of softball, the pitcher throws a ball toward the batter. If the batter swings and makes contact with the ball, a force is applied from the bat to the ball. What is the purpose of this force?

    A. The force stops the motion of the ball.

    B. The force slows the motion of the ball.

    C. The force changes the direction of motion of the ball.

    D. The force increases the speed of the ball.

## Open Ended

Questions 9 through 11 refer to the following description and diagram.

A thrown baseball will move in a straight line at a constant speed (uniform motion) until another force affects it. The application of other forces will cause the ball to eventually slow and stop.

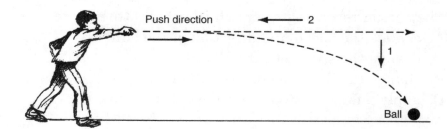

9. What force does arrow 1 represent?

10. What force is does arrow 2 represent?

11. Name another force that could also slow the ball and/or stop its motion.

Questions 12 and 13 refer to the following description.

Roberto threw a softball up into the air. It reached a height of 9 meters and then started to come down. He then threw the ball to a height of 12 meters.

**12.** What force pulled the ball down?

**13.** What is the most likely reason that the ball went higher on Roberto's second throw?

**14.** What two conditions are necessary for uniform motion?

# NEWTON'S FIRST LAW OF MOTION

 ## Newton's Laws of Motion

In the mid-1660s, British scientist Sir Isaac Newton studied the movement of objects. As a result of his studies, he formulated three laws that summarize the motion of objects. These laws deal with force, mass, and acceleration, and are referred to as Newton's (1) Law of Inertia, (2) Law of Acceleration, and (3) Law of Interaction. Even today, Newton's laws of motion remain the basis for understanding the motion of objects.

 ## The First Law of Motion

The **first law of motion** states that an object at rest will remain at rest and an object in motion will remain in motion, unless an outside force

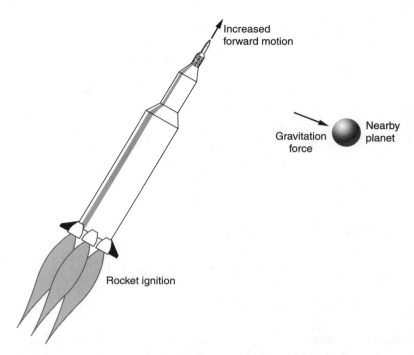

**Figure 6-4.** A rocket ship moving in space has uniform motion. The force of the booster rocket will increase the forward motion, while the gravitation force from a nearby planet can change the direction of motion.

acts on the object. There are two parts to this law. First, any object at rest will not move unless some force acts on it. For example, an empty garbage can will remain at the curb until some force moves it. The force that moves the garbage can may be a person or a very strong wind.

Second, any moving object will continue to move in the same direction, at the same speed, until a force acts on the object to change its speed or direction. A space probe will travel through the solar system in a straight line at a constant speed (uniform motion) until another force affects it. The force of a booster rocket or the gravitational pull of a nearby planet could change its direction or speed (see Figure 6-4).

 **Inertia**

The tendency of an object at rest to remain at rest or an object in motion to remain in motion is called *inertia*. In other words, inertia is the tendency of an object to resist any change in its motion. The more massive an object is, the greater its inertia, or the greater it will resist a change in motion. When you are riding in a moving car that stops suddenly, your body continues to move forward. Also, when you are seated in a parked car that suddenly accelerates, you feel your body move backward. When a car stops, your moving body resists the

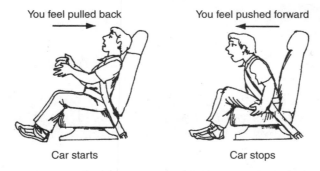

**Figure 6-5.** The first law of motion: Objects resist a change in motion—an effect you can feel in a starting or stopping car.

stopping action. When a car accelerates, your body resists being put in motion (see Figure 6-5).

## Mass: A Measure of Inertia

To overcome the inertia of either an object at rest or an object in motion, a force must be applied. The amount of force necessary to move the object is dependent on the mass of the object. The more massive an object is, the greater the force necessary to move the object.

An object's mass is a measure of its inertia. The greater the mass of an object, the greater the effort needed to start it in motion or to change its direction and/or velocity while in motion. Consider the effort needed to toss a bowling ball and a baseball so that they both travel at the same speed. It takes a greater effort to put a bowling ball in motion than to put a baseball in motion because the bowling ball has a greater mass. Likewise, it takes a greater effort to change the direction or velocity of a moving bowling ball than to do the same for a moving baseball. It also takes a greater effort to stop the bowling ball than to stop the baseball. The more massive bowling ball has a greater resistance to change in its motion (see Figure 6-6).

(a)           (b)

**Figure 6-6.** A greater force is needed to toss a large bowling ball (b) than to toss a small rubber ball (a). The bowling ball has a greater mass; therefore, it has a greater inertia.

## Question Set 2

*Multiple Choice*

1. Tarrence helped his dad push their car out of the garage to repair it. He pushed as hard as he could, but the car only moved very slowly. This example demonstrates the principle that

   A. a body at rest remains at rest unless a force affects it

   B. a body in motion remains in motion unless a force affects it

   C. a large mass requires a large force to move it

   D. every action has an equal but opposite reaction

2. On a breezy day, Esther pushed her model sailboat across the still water in a pond. According to Newton's first law, the sailboat should have continued across the pond and landed at Point *A*. However, it landed at Point *B*. The most likely reason for this was that

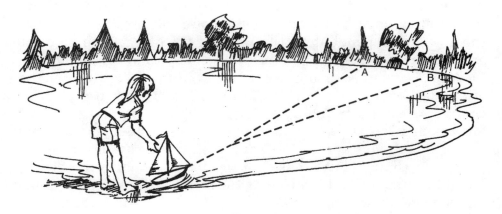

   A. the force of the wind changed the sailboat's direction of motion

   B. fish swimming near the sailboat changed its direction of motion

   C. the force of the moving water changed the sailboat's direction of motion

   D. the sailboat accelerated across the pond

3. What is the relationship between the mass and the inertia of an object?

   A. The greater the mass, the greater the inertia.

   B. The greater the mass, the less the inertia.

   C. The less the mass, the greater the inertia.

   D. The mass and the inertia are not related.

4. Which of the following objects would need the greatest force to be stopped?
   A. a baseball moving at 80 kilometers per hour
   B. a car moving at 80 kilometers per hour
   C. a train moving at 80 kilometers per hour
   D. an arrow moving at 80 kilometers per hour

Questions 5 through 7 refer to the following paragraph and diagram.

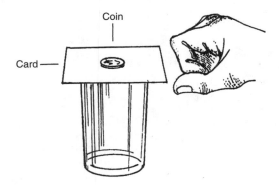

   Gail and Jared set up an experiment that they read about in their science textbook, which used a glass, several coins (penny, nickel, and quarter), and an index card. The students flicked the card from under each of the coins to see what would happen.

5. When they flicked the card from under each of the coins,
   A. the coins all stayed with the card and fell on the table
   B. the coins all dropped into the glass
   C. the quarter fell into the glass, and the other two coins fell on the table
   D. the penny fell into the glass, and the other two coins fell on the table

6. This experiment indicated that an object at rest will remain at rest and will resist being put into motion. What term best expresses what this experiment demonstrated?
   A. differences in mass        C. inertia
   B. acceleration               D. differences in forces

7. The quarter has the greatest mass of the three coins. Therefore, it would have the greatest
   A. resistance to change in motion
   B. acceleration
   C. change in direction
   D. distance to fall

*Open Ended*

8. The diagram shows (A) a parked car and (B) a car traveling at 80 kilometers per hour. Describe the type of inertia that each of these cars has.

9. If a bus and a car are both traveling at the same speed, why does it take longer for the bus to stop than for the car to stop?

10. Explain why a lead ball 5 centimeters in diameter has more inertia than a wooden ball 5 centimeters in diameter.

# NEWTON'S SECOND LAW OF MOTION

 ## Speed and Velocity

*Speed* and *velocity* are the two terms used to describe the motion of an object. **Speed** is the distance traveled per unit of time. It can also be described as the rate of change in position of an object. The following formula is used to determine speed:

Speed = distance/time, or $s = d/t$

A car travels from the Raritan Bridge on the Garden State Parkway to the Cape May ferry, moving a distance of about 200 kilometers (km) in 2 hours (hr). You can determine the car's average speed as follows:

$$s = d/t$$
$$= 200 \text{ km/2 hr}$$
$$= 100 \text{ km/hr}$$

*Note:* The abbreviation for kilometers per hour (km/hr) can also be written as kph. Other units that are used to label speed include feet/second, meters/minute, and centimeters/second.

Velocity and speed are similar. However, velocity also indicates direction; that is, it has a directional component. **Velocity** is the speed of an object in a specific direction. The direction is assumed to be a straight-line direction such as north, east, southwest, and so on. The formula below is used to determine velocity:

$$\text{Velocity} = \text{distance/time, or } v = d/t$$

An airplane travels from Milwaukee to New Orleans, moving a distance of 1400 kilometers in 2 hours. (*Note:* The units used to label velocity are the same as those used to label speed.) You can determine the airplane's velocity as follows:

$$v = d/t$$
$$= 1400 \text{ km/2 hr}$$
$$= 700 \text{ km/hr in a southerly direction}$$

 ## Acceleration

**Acceleration** is the rate of change in velocity. Although acceleration refers to either an increase or a decrease in velocity, the term *deceleration* is commonly used to describe a decrease in velocity. Acceleration occurs when a car increases its velocity; and deceleration occurs when a car decreases its velocity. The following formula is used to determine the rate of acceleration:

$$\text{Acceleration} = \frac{\text{final velocity} - \text{starting velocity}}{\text{time}}, \text{ or } a = v_f - v_s/t$$

A car increases its velocity from 10 km/hr to 30 km/hr in 2 seconds. The car's acceleration is determined as follows:

$$a = v_f - v_s/t$$
$$= (30 \text{ km/hr} - 10 \text{ km/hr})/2 \text{ sec}$$
$$= 20 \text{ km/hr/2 sec} = 10 \text{ km/hr/sec (or 10 kph/sec)}$$

Other units that are used to label acceleration include feet/second/second, meters/minute/second, and centimeters/second/second.

# The Second Law of Motion

The **second law of motion** states the relationship between force, mass, and acceleration. This law is commonly expressed by the following formula:

$$\text{Force} = \text{mass} \times \text{acceleration, or } F = m \times a$$

It could also be written as: $a = F/m$ and as $m = F/a$.

A large force that acts on a given mass will cause a greater acceleration than would a small force that acts on the same mass. For example, an adult (large force) pushing another adult (given mass) on a swing will cause a greater acceleration than would a child (small force) pushing an adult (same mass) on the swing (see Figure 6-7, Diagram A).

Also, a small mass acted on by a given force will have a greater acceleration than would a large mass acted on by the same force. For example, an adult (given force) pushing a child (small mass) on a swing will cause a greater acceleration than would an adult pushing another adult (large mass) on the swing (see Figure 6-7, Diagram B).

**Figure 6-7.** Acceleration is determined by the size of both force and mass.

## The Third Law of Motion

The ***third law of motion*** states that for every action there is an equal and opposite reaction. A simple demonstration of blowing up a balloon and letting it go shows how this law works. When the air is released from an opening in the balloon, the balloon moves (through the air) in the opposite direction. Other actions that produce an equal and opposite reactive force include kicking a soccer ball, walking (feet pushing against the ground), and hot gases shooting out of a rocket engine.

 ## Multiple Forces Acting on an Object

When a single force is great enough to move an object, it moves it in a single direction. For example, a man pushing a car with a force of 450 newtons moves the car in a single direction (see Figure 6-8). However, there is usually more than one force acting on an object. Then, the combination of forces act on the object as if a single force were present.

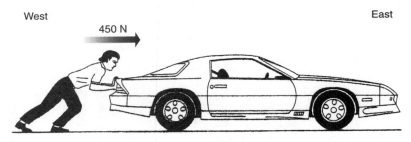

**Figure 6-8.** The diagram illustrates a man pushing a car in an east direction with a force of 450 newtons.

When two forces act on an object in the same direction, the force applied to the object is the sum of the two forces (see Figure 6-9). Two people pulling a cart in the same direction, one with a force of 270 newtons and the other with a force of 360 newtons, pull the cart with a total force of 630 newtons.

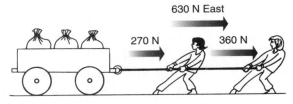

**Figure 6-9.** The diagram illustrates two forces pulling in the same direction. The total force on the cart is 270 newtons plus 360 newtons, or 630 newtons in an east direction.

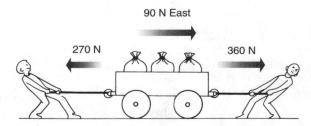

**Figure 6-10.** The diagram illustrates two forces pulling in opposite directions. The total force on the cart is 360 newtons minus 270 newtons, or 90 newtons in an east direction.

When two forces act on an object in opposite directions, the force applied to the object is the difference of the forces and in the direction of the stronger force (see Figure 6-10). Two people pulling a cart in opposite directions, one with a force of 270 newtons and the other with a force of 360 newtons, pull the cart with a force of 90 newtons in the direction of the higher force.

When two forces act on an object in an angular direction of less than 180°, the direction of movement lies between the two forces (see Figure 6-11). Two people pulling a cart at an angle, one with a force of 270 newtons and the other with a force of 360 newtons, pull the cart with a force somewhere between the sum and the difference of the two forces and in a direction between the two pulling forces.

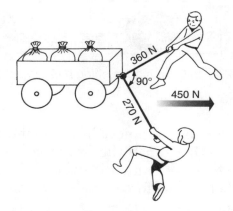

**Figure 6-11.** The diagram illustrates two forces pulling in an angular direction (having a 90° difference). The cart is moving in a direction between the two forces, with a force of 450 newtons.

When the forces acting on an object are equal and in opposite directions, the object remains at rest. A tug-of-war lacks motion when the pulling forces are equal (see Figure 6-12a). However, balanced forces become unbalanced when an additional force is introduced.

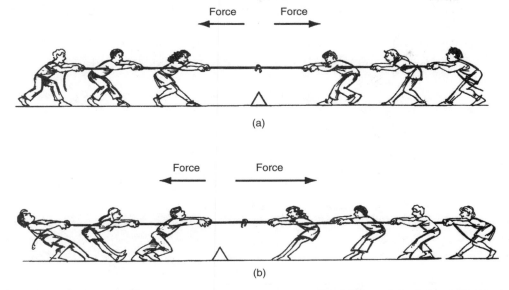

**Figure 6-12.** Illustration of a tug-of-war showing balanced forces (a) and unbalanced forces (b).

Thus, motion occurs when an additional force is introduced to one side of a balanced tug-of-war (see Figure 6-12b). Table 6-2 lists some examples of balanced and unbalanced forces.

### TABLE 6-2.  BALANCED AND UNBALANCED FORCES

| Balanced Forces | Unbalanced Force |
|---|---|
| Car parked in a driveway | Car pulling out of a driveway |
| Apple hanging on a tree | Apple falling to the ground |
| Roller coaster on top of a ride | Roller coaster coming downhill |

## SKILLS ACTIVITY 2
### ANALYZING DATA

Karen's science teacher set up a ramp that was 3 meters (300 cm) in length. The ramp had lines drawn across it at 10-centimeter intervals. (See diagram below.) A 2.5-centimeter solid metal ball was rolled down the ramp by the teacher and timed by a computerized clock during its first 5 seconds. Then

Karen rolled the ball down the ramp and the computer produced the following table of data.

Analyze the data in the table; then answer the following questions.

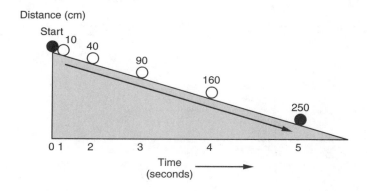

| Total Distance (cm) | Elapsed Time (sec) | Distance Each Second (cm) | Final Velocity (cm/sec) |
|---|---|---|---|
| 10 | 1 | 10 | 20 |
| 40 | 2 | 30 | 40 |
| 90 | 3 | 50 | 60 |
| 160 | 4 | 70 | 80 |
| 250 | 5 | 90 | 100 |

## Questions

1. (a) How far did the ball roll after 3 seconds? (b) How far did the ball roll between the second and third seconds? (c) What velocity did the ball reach after 3 seconds?

2. As the ball rolled down the ramp, it accelerated. What was the acceleration of the ball?

3. Predict the results if the ramp was longer and the ball were allowed to roll for 6 seconds. (a) What would be the total distance traveled? (b) How far would it travel between the fifth and sixth seconds? (c) What would be the ball's final velocity?

4. What is the relationship between the elapsed time and the final velocity?

## Question Set 3

*Multiple Choice*

1. Newton's second law of motion states the relationship between force, mass, and acceleration as $F = m \times a$. According to this law, an increase in force on a given mass will cause
   A. a decrease in acceleration
   B. an increase in acceleration
   C. a decrease in the mass
   D. an increase in the mass

2. A rocket traveling in space increases its velocity from 32,000 kilometers per hour to 40,000 kilometers per hour. To do this, the rocket must
   A. increase its mass
   B. decrease its mass
   C. increase the force acting on it
   D. decrease the force acting on it

Speed is determined by dividing the distance traveled by the time that it takes to travel that distance. The formula $s = d/t$ describes the relationship between the three factors. Use this formula to answer questions 3 and 4.

3. A boy on a bicycle rides 10 kilometers in one-half hour. At what speed did the boy travel?
   A. 20 kilometers per hour
   B. 40 kilometers per hour
   C. 1000 meters per minute
   D. 2 kilometers per hour

4. If instead the boy took 1 hour to travel the 10-kilometer distance, then the speed would have been
   A. doubled
   B. tripled
   C. quadrupled
   D. halved

5. Speed and velocity are similar, except that velocity has
   A. an acceleration component
   B. a distance component
   C. a time component
   D. a directional component

6. Newton's law of acceleration states the relationship between force, mass, and acceleration as $F = m \times a$. According to this law, a decrease in force on a given mass will cause
   A. a decrease in acceleration
   B. an increase in acceleration
   C. a decrease in the mass
   D. an increase in the mass

7.  The formula $v = a \times t$ (velocity equals acceleration multiplied by time) is used to determine the velocity of free-falling bodies. As the time increases, the velocity
    A. increases      C. remains the same
    B. decreases      D. increases, then decreases

8.  If one person pushes on a box with a force of 100 newtons and another person pushes on the same box in the opposite direction with a force of 90 newtons, the resulting force is equal to

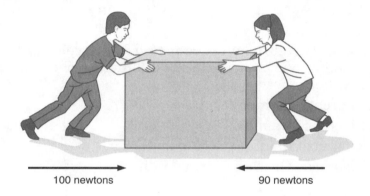

100 newtons        90 newtons

    A. the ratio of the two forces
    B. the product of the two forces
    C. the sum of the two forces
    D. the difference between the two forces

## *Open Ended*

Newton's second law of motion states the relationship between force, mass, and acceleration. This relationship is expressed by the formula $F = m \times a$ (or force = mass × acceleration). The following table shows six mathematical examples of how the formula is applied. Study the table; then answer questions 9 through 11.

|  | Acceleration (meters/second/second) | Force (newtons) | Mass (kilograms) |
| --- | --- | --- | --- |
| Example 1 | 1 | 1 | 1 |
| Example 2 | 2 | 20 | 10 |
| Example 3 | 1 | 10 | 10 |
| Example 4 | 1 | 20 | 20 |
| Example 5 | 0.5 | 10 | 20 |
| Example 6 | 2 | X | 50 |

9.  If the mass of a body remains the same and the force moving it is doubled, then the body's acceleration is doubled. Which two sets of examples in the table above demonstrate this?

10. If the force remains the same but the object is replaced by one that has twice the mass, what will happen to the acceleration?

11. How many newtons would the unknown force $X$ be equal to in Example 6 above? Explain.

12. A $CO_2$ cartridge was mounted on the top of a toy car with the nozzle of the cartridge pointing toward the rear of the car. When the compressed gas was released from the cartridge, the toy car moved 6 meters across the room and stopped. What can be changed so that the car will travel a shorter distance?

# THE FORCE OF FRICTION

 ## Friction Is a Force

*Friction* is a force that resists motion. It must be overcome to start an object moving and/or to keep the object moving. For example, the force needed to slide a book on a tabletop must be great enough to overcome frictional resistance. The book has to overcome more frictional resistance to start moving than to keep moving. Eventually, the frictional force between the moving book and the tabletop will cause the book to stop.

The rougher the surfaces and/or the heavier the object, the greater the frictional force and the more difficult it will be to move the object. A smooth tabletop provides an easier surface to push a book across than does a rougher surface. A less heavy book will travel farther on

**Figure 6-13.** Book *A* weighs 4 newtons and book *B* weighs 8 newtons. If both books are slid across the table with the same force, book *A* will travel farther.

a tabletop than will a heavier book if both are pushed with the same force (see Figure 6-13).

Friction also occurs when objects move through air and water. While flying, a plane must overcome the frictional force caused by air resistance. At a high altitude, a plane will encounter less dense air, so there will be less frictional resistance. Commercial planes that fly 8 kilometers above Earth's surface use less fuel overcoming frictional air resistance than do planes flying at a lower altitude in denser air.

Friction also causes a waste of energy during energy transformation. Electrical motors are made to transfer electrical energy into mechanical energy. But not all the electrical energy is converted into mechanical energy. The metal shaft within the motor turns on bearings, causing metal to rub against metal. Some of the energy is transformed into heat energy produced by the friction of the metal parts rubbing against each other.

 ## The Effect of Friction

We commonly think of friction as a hindrance to work and motion. When we try to move an object, the force of friction opposes the motion of the object. Sliding a heavy box across the floor may take a great amount of effort. If the friction between the bottom of the box and the floor is reduced, less effort is necessary to move the box. In a gasoline lawn mower, the chemical energy in gasoline is converted into mechanical energy in the rotating cutting blade. Much less gasoline would be used if the friction between the moving parts were reduced.

Friction is also a very desirable force. Car tires have irregular surfaces (treads) that increase their friction with the road. This provides the traction necessary to start a car's motion, and also the friction

Treads provide friction

**Figure 6-14.** Without friction between tire treads and the road surface, a moving car would slip and slide.

necessary to stop the car (see Figure 6-14). Consider how a car would start and stop on ice if there were no friction—starting would cause the tires to spin, and stopping would cause the car to slide a great distance. It is also friction that allows us to walk. Without friction between our shoes and the walking surface, we would slip and slide.

 ## Overcoming Friction

Sometimes we try to overcome friction to make work easier. Examples of ways to decrease friction include: (1) lubricating the area between two contact surfaces; (2) using ball bearings; (3) polishing the surface; and (4) using wheels.

Using a lubricant between two contact surfaces provides a thin fluid layer that replaces a solid friction with a fluid friction. Fluid friction is usually much less resistant to motion than is solid friction. Oil, grease, and graphite are examples of common lubricants that are used to decrease frictional resistance.

Using small, polished balls between two hard surfaces changes a sliding friction to a rolling friction. Rolling friction is less resistant to motion than is sliding friction. Ball bearings can be found in roller blades and in car wheels (see Figure 6-15).

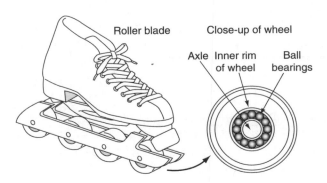

Roller blade        Close-up of wheel

Axle  Inner rim    Ball
      of wheel     bearings

**Figure 6-15.** Ball bearings in the wheel of a roller blade reduce friction as the wheel turns.

Polishing a surface makes it much easier to slide an object on it. A playground slide has a polished surface that enables children to slide down it more easily.

Sometimes, when it is difficult to move a heavy object, wheels are placed under it. The rolling wheel friction is less than sliding friction. For example, it is easier to move a refrigerator with a hand truck than to slide it across the floor. Likewise, the use of wheel carts makes it easier to move heavy boxes.

## SKILLS ACTIVITY 3

## INVESTIGATING FRICTION

Friction is a force that resists motion. It must be overcome to start an object moving and/or to keep the object moving in uniform motion on a horizontal surface. The amount of frictional force opposing the motion of an object is dependent on the weight of the object and on the type of surface over which the object is moving.

Science students Lena and Chin set up an apparatus to investigate how some factors affect the frictional force of a moving object. As shown in the diagrams, they attached a 40-newton metal block to a cord and a spring scale. In investigation 1, when the students started pulling the 40-newton block on the wooden board, they noticed that it took a force of 22 newtons to begin moving the block. In investigation 2, they noticed that it took a force of 15 newtons to continue the uniform motion of the block along the board. In investigations 3 and 4, the students made changes to the surface of the board; and in investigation 5, they changed the weight of the block. Data from the five investigations are recorded in the table below. Use the information in the diagrams and table to answer the following questions.

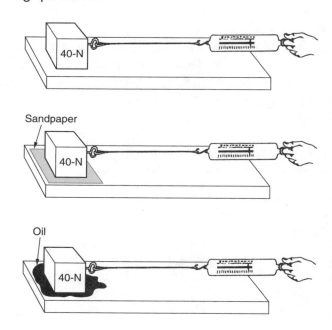

| Investigation | Block Weight/Motion | Type of Surface | Force Needed to Move Block |
|---|---|---|---|
| 1 | 40 N/Starts from rest | Wooden board | 22 N |
| 2 | 40 N/Uniform motion | Wooden board | 15 N |
| 3 | 40 N/Uniform motion | Sandpaper on wood | ? |
| 4 | 40 N/Uniform motion | Oil on wood | ? |
| 5 | 80 N/Uniform motion | Wooden board | ? |

## Questions

1. Why is the force needed to start the block moving from rest in investigation 1 greater than the force needed to keep the block going in uniform motion in investigation 2?

2. Describe the relative force needed to keep the block in motion in investigation 3. Explain.

3. Describe the relative force needed to keep the block in motion in investigation 4. Explain.

4. Explain why it took a greater force to keep the block in motion in investigation 5 than it did in investigation 2.

## Question Set 4

### Multiple Choice

1. According to Newton's first law, a penny pushed across a table will slide to the edge of the table and fall off. However, if the force applied is not great enough, the penny will stop on the table. What force stops the penny from falling off the table?

   A. gravity　　　C. air

   B. friction　　　D. the force of the table

Question 2 refers to the following paragraph and diagram.

Galileo determined that all objects fall at the same rate. That means that a penny and a crumpled piece of paper, when released from the same height at the same time, should hit the ground at the same time. An experiment was conducted by a teacher from a third-floor balcony of a school. The instructor released a penny and a crumpled sheet of paper and let them drop to the ground. The students observed that the penny hit the ground first.

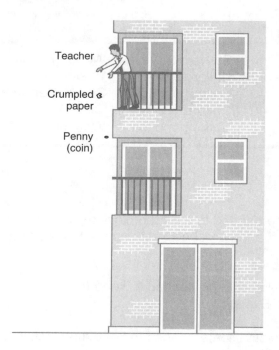

2.  Why did the penny hit the ground before the crumpled piece of paper did?

A. The penny has a greater mass.

B. The penny weighs more than the paper.

C. Frictional air resistance is greater on the crumpled paper.

D. Frictional air resistance is greater on the penny.

3.  Multiple forces act on a bicycle as it is ridden down the street, such as the force of gravity, the force applied to the foot pedals, and frictional force. In the following diagram of a child riding a bicycle, which arrow represents the force of friction?

A. arrow *A*     C. arrow *C*

B. arrow *B*     D. arrow *D*

Questions 4 and 5 refer to the following data and diagram.

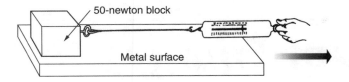

50-newton block

Metal surface

A 50-newton block is being pulled along a metal surface by a string, which is attached to a spring scale.

4. The force required to pull the block and make it slide along the surface is
   A. greater than 50 newtons
   B. less than 50 newtons
   C. exactly 50 newtons
   D. not possible to determine

5. How can the force of friction be decreased so that it is easier to move the block?
   A. Place sandpaper between the block and the metal surface.
   B. Apply oil between the block and the metal surface.
   C. Change the metal surface to a rubber surface.
   D. Chance the metal surface to a wooden surface.

## Open Ended

6. When you walk, your feet push against the ground, and the ground pushes back against your feet. What would happen if there were no friction between your feet and the ground?

7. Describe what it would be like to try to climb a rope if there were no friction present.

8. Give one example of how friction is advantageous and one example of how friction is a hindrance in our daily lives.

9. Explain what each of the following statements means:
   (a) Without friction, it would be unsafe to use a small throw rug on the floor.
   (b) Race cars need friction to start, turn, and stop; but less friction allows them to go faster.
   (c) Without friction, you could not eat with a fork and a knife.

# Chapter **7**

# Forms of Energy

**Macro Statement:** Demonstrate an understanding of the various forms of energy, including their transformations and interactions with matter.

## KNOWLEDGE STATEMENTS

A. Energy exists in various forms, e.g., heat, light, sound, mechanical, electrical, chemical, and nuclear. Energy cannot be created or destroyed, but can be changed from one form to another.

B. Heat can be transferred by the collision of atoms (conduction and convection) and by radiation.

C. Light interacts with matter by being reflected, refracted, or absorbed.

D. The sun is the major source of energy for Earth. The sun's energy arrives as light with a range of wavelengths, including visible light, infrared, and ultraviolet radiation.

E. Light from the sun is made up of a mixture of different colors of light, even though to the eye the light looks almost white. The light that an object reflects determines its color.

F. Vibrations may transfer energy through a medium as a wave, e.g., sound, earthquakes.

## CHAPTER OUTLINE

**What Is Energy?**

**Heat Energy**

**Sound Energy**

**Light Energy**

## WHAT IS ENERGY?

## Energy

*Energy* is the ability to do work. *Work* is done when a force moves an object over a distance. A flowing river has the ability to move a boat downstream. A moving car can carry people from one place to another. Therefore, both the river and the car possess some form of energy.

The origin of energy in the universe is unknown. However, most scientists think that all energy and all matter in the universe were created at the time of the big bang (that is, at the moment the universe formed). Scientists also believe that the total amount of energy and matter in the universe is constant.

## Forms of Energy

Energy exists in six different forms: mechanical, chemical, nuclear, heat, electrical, and light. Table 7-1 shows some examples of the different forms of energy.

*Mechanical energy* is the energy with which moving objects perform work. A hammer striking a nail, a jack lifting a car, and pedals turning the wheels of a bicycle are examples of things using mechanical energy. *Sound* is a type of mechanical energy.

### TABLE 7-1.  DIFFERENT FORMS OF ENERGY

| Form of Energy | Example |
| --- | --- |
| Mechanical | Spinning fan |
| Chemical | Burning candle |
| Nuclear | Nuclear reactor |
| Heat | Toaster |
| Electrical | Generator |
| Light | Lamp (bulb) |

*Chemical energy* is the energy stored in certain substances because of their chemical makeup. When these substances are burned, the energy is released. Coal, oil, propane gas, and foods are examples of substances that contain chemical energy.

*Nuclear energy* is the energy stored within the nucleus of an atom. This energy can be released by joining atoms together or by splitting atoms apart.

*Heat energy* is the energy produced by the molecular motion of matter. All matter contains heat energy. Rubbing your hands together, burning a match, or burning fuel oil in a home-heating system produces heat energy.

*Electrical energy* is produced by the flow of electrons through a conductor, such as a wire. Computers, televisions, and washing machines are all operated with electrical energy. A *generator* produces electrical energy.

*Light* is a form of radiant energy that moves in waves. Light as a form of energy can be demonstrated by using a magnifying glass to burn a hole in a leaf or by using a laser beam to burn a hole in a steel plate.

## Conservation of Energy and Matter

The *Law of Conservation of Energy* states that energy can be neither created nor destroyed. However, energy can be transformed from one type into one or more other types of energy. The *Law of Conservation of Matter* states that matter can be neither created nor destroyed. Energy and matter are related in such a way that they are interchangeable. That is, the total amount of energy and matter in the universe is constant, and each can be converted into the other. In the sun, large amounts of matter are being converted into light and heat energy. Scientists have been able to change matter into energy in nuclear reactors and energy into matter under special laboratory conditions.

## Energy Transformations

An energy transformation occurs when we convert one type of energy into another type of energy. Most of our daily activities involve the transformation of energy. For instance, when you take a bus to school each morning, chemical energy in gasoline is changed into heat energy and the mechanical energy that turns the vehicle's wheels. At school, when the bell rings between classes, electrical energy is transformed into sound energy. And at night, when you turn on a reading light,

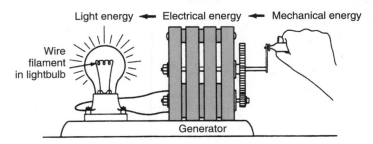

**Figure 7-1.** This hand-operated generator transforms mechanical energy into electrical energy, which is then transformed into light energy.

electrical energy is changed into light energy. Figure 7-1 illustrates two common energy transformations.

 ## Heat Energy: An Undesired Product of Energy Transformation

Very often during the energy transformation process, some heat energy is produced that is not desired. A car's motor is designed to change chemical energy within the gasoline into mechanical energy to move the car. The car's running motor eventually becomes hot due to the burning of fuel and the friction of the motor's moving parts rubbing against one another. In other words, some of the chemical energy is transformed into undesired heat energy instead of mechanical energy.

A vacuum cleaner is another item that produces undesired energy. A vacuum cleaner contains a motor that transforms electrical energy into mechanical energy. Run a vacuum cleaner for a few minutes and you can feel that it gets warm. The electrical energy entering the motor produces mechanical energy to operate the appliance, along with an undesired amount of heat energy. This process is illustrated in Figure 7-2.

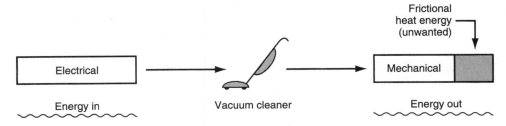

**Figure 7-2.** The Law of Conservation of Energy: An unwanted amount of energy may be released as heat during a transformation (electrical to mechanical), but no energy is lost.

## Question Set 1

*Multiple Choice*

1. What type of energy transformation is represented in the diagram below?

   A. chemical energy to sound energy
   B. electrical energy to light energy
   C. electrical energy to sound energy
   D. electrical energy to mechanical energy

Questions 2 and 3 refer to the following incident.

   In an effort to break apart a strip of aluminum metal, Charles bent it back and forth many times. He was surprised to notice the aluminum getting warm at the point of the bend.

2. What type of energy transformation does this activity represent?
   A. heat energy to mechanical energy
   B. chemical energy to sound energy
   C. chemical energy to heat energy
   D. mechanical energy to heat energy

3. The heating of the metal strip in this case is
   A. a gain of energy
   B. the creation of energy
   C. the loss of energy
   D. an undesired energy transformation

Questions 4 and 5 refer to the following data and diagram.

The lighting of matches in a matchbook illustrates several different energy transformations.

4.  When you strike a match on the rough strip of a matchbook cover, you transform
    A.  mechanical energy to heat energy
    B.  mechanical energy to chemical energy
    C.  mechanical energy to electrical energy
    D.  heat energy to chemical energy

5.  What type of energy transformation does the burning match represent?
    A.  chemical energy to light and sound energy
    B.  chemical energy to light and heat energy
    C.  chemical energy to heat energy, only
    D.  heat energy to light energy, only

6.  Which item transforms 100 percent of the energy it receives into useful energy?
    A.  window fan
    B.  hair dryer
    C.  battery-powered flashlight
    D.  no items transfer 100 percent into useful energy

## Open Ended

7.  For each item listed in the table below, write (on a separate sheet of paper) the type of energy input and the type of energy output that occur.

| Item | Energy Input | Energy Output |
| --- | --- | --- |
| Toaster | | |
| Window fan | | |
| Telephone | | |
| Chain saw | | |
| Kitchen stove | | |

8.  The Law of Conservation of Energy states that energy can be neither created nor destroyed. On a warm summer day, the sand on a beach is very hot; and at night, the same sand feels cool. What happens to the heat in the sand?

9. The Law of Conservation of Matter states that matter can be neither created nor destroyed. What happens to a log that burns and forms ashes in a fireplace?

10. Name one appliance or tool in a home that demonstrates the transfer from electrical energy to mechanical energy. Explain.

# HEAT ENERGY

 ## Heat Characteristics

***Heat*** is a form of energy produced by the vibrating motion of molecules. All matter is composed of molecules that are constantly vibrating; therefore all matter contains some heat. When heat is added to a substance, the molecules move faster and farther apart; and when heat is removed from a substance, the molecules move slower and closer together (see Figure 7-3).

The addition and removal of heat also cause most substances to expand and contract. Adding heat to a substance causes its molecules to move farther apart, which leads to an increase in size. Bridges, railroad tracks, and sidewalks have expansion spaces. This feature allows them to freely expand and contract in response to the temperature variations between summer and winter. Removing heat from a substance causes its molecules to move closer together, which leads to a decrease in size. The thermometer is an instrument that measures temperature by the amount of expansion or contraction of a substance such as mercury, alcohol, or even a metal spring (see Figure 7-4).

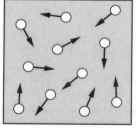
Molecules vibrating in a substance at 30°C

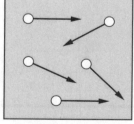
Molecules vibrating in a substance at 50°C

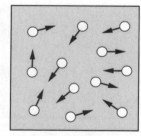
Molecules vibrating in a substance at 10°C

**Figure 7-3.** Adding heat energy to a substance causes the molecules to vibrate faster and move farther apart. Removing heat energy from a substance causes the molecules to vibrate slower and move closer together.

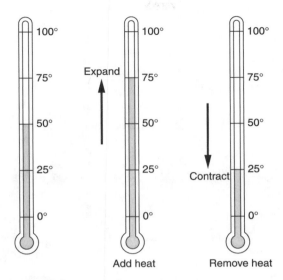

**Figure 7-4.** When the alcohol in a thermometer is heated, it expands and indicates a higher temperature. When heat is removed, the alcohol contracts and indicates a lower temperature.

Although most substances expand when heated and contract when cooled, water is an exception. In liquid form, water contracts as it cools. However, when water is cooled to 4°C, it starts to expand and continues expanding until it becomes ice at 0°C. That is why an unopened bottle of water or soda will crack if left outdoors during freezing weather. The force generated by the expansion of water changing to ice is so powerful that it can crack glass, rocks, concrete, and steel.

 ## Heat Transfer

Heat travels from warmer objects or places to cooler objects or places when a difference in temperature exists. The tendency is for heat to become equally distributed. Heat can move by conduction, convection, or radiation.

***Conduction*** is the transfer of heat by direct molecular contact. Metal objects conduct heat well (see Figure 7-5). A metal spoon placed

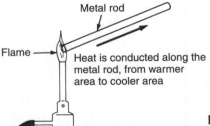

**Figure 7-5.** Heat is transferred by conduction along a metal rod.

**Figure 7-6.** Home-heating systems use convection currents to heat a room.

in a cup of hot water quickly becomes hot because heat is easily transferred from molecule to molecule within the spoon. A metal pot on a hot stove quickly distributes the heat throughout the pot by conduction. On the other hand, materials that do not transfer heat well can be used to insulate or reduce the flow of heat. The handle of a frying pan is usually made of plastic or wood, which reduces heat flow so you can grasp the handle without being burned.

*Convection* is the transfer of heat by the flowing action within a liquid or gas. Warm air added to a room rises, and the cooler air sinks. This causes a circular flow called a *convection current*, which distributes the heat within a room. Figure 7-6 demonstrates how a convection current occurs and eventually equalizes the temperature inside a room.

*Radiation* is the transfer of heat through space in the form of waves. The heat from the sun reaches Earth in the form of waves that travel through the vacuum of space. Place your hand several inches away from a lightbulb and you will feel the warmth of the bulb. The heat reaches your hand by means of radiation.

 ## Heat and Temperature

The terms *heat* and *temperature* are often confused. As stated above, heat is a form of energy that refers to molecular motion. The greater the molecular motion, the greater is the amount of heat energy in an object. The total heat energy in an object also depends on the mass of the object. The greater the mass of an object, the greater is the amount of heat energy it contains. For example, if two different quantities of water have the same temperature, the larger quantity will contain more heat energy.

If you take two quantities of water (100 grams and 1000 grams) that have the same temperature and heat both to the boiling point (in identical beakers above identical heat sources), the 1000 grams of water will take longer to boil (reach 100°C) than will the 100 grams of water. More heat is needed because of the greater quantity of water. Therefore, 1000 grams of water contains more heat energy than does 100 grams of water, even though they both have a temperature of 100°C (see Figure 7-7).

**Temperature** is a measure of the average molecular motion of a substance and is *not* related to the mass of the substance. A thermometer is an instrument that measures the temperature of a substance. One type of thermometer consists of a closed glass tube with mercury inside. When, for example, the tube is placed in hot water, the mercury molecules vibrate faster and expand. This causes the mercury to move up the tube, indicating a rise in temperature. When the tube is placed in cold water, the mercury molecules vibrate slower and contract. The mercury moves down the tube, indicating a decrease in temperature.

Scientists prefer to measure the temperature of substances in degrees Celsius (°C), but in some areas the Fahrenheit (°F) scale is still used. (Refer to Figure 1-13 for a comparison of important temperature readings on Celsius and Fahrenheit thermometers.)

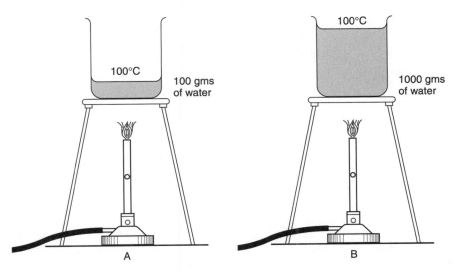

**Figure 7-7.** Both beakers of water have been heated to the same temperature, but the water in beaker B contains more heat energy than does the water in beaker A.

## SKILLS ACTIVITY **1**

## CALCULATING HEAT GAIN AND HEAT LOSS

The amount of heat energy contained in a substance is determined by its temperature and by its quantity, or mass. If two identical quantities of water have different temperatures, the quantity with the higher temperature would contain more heat energy. Or, if two different quantities of water have the same temperature, the larger quantity of water would contain more heat energy.

When water gains heat, its surroundings lose heat; and when water loses heat, its surroundings gain heat. For example, when you place an ice cube in a warm glass of soda, the soda and glass lose heat, which is gained by the ice cube, causing it to melt. When you place hot coffee in a cool cup, the coffee loses heat while the cup gains heat. Water gains heat energy during the following: (1) when ice melts; (2) when liquid water increases in temperature; and (3) when water evaporates. Water loses heat energy during the following processes: (1) when water freezes; (2) when liquid water decreases in temperature; and (3) when water condenses.

Heat energy is measured using a unit called a *calorie*. A **calorie** is the amount of heat energy needed to raise the temperature of 1 gram of water 1°C. To melt 1 gram of ice, it takes 80 calories of heat energy; and to evaporate 1 gram of water into water vapor, it takes 540 calories of heat energy. The diagram below shows (a) the gain of heat to water when heat is added and (b) the loss of heat from water when heat is removed.

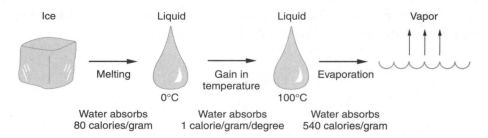

(a) Water absorbs heat and surroundings lose heat

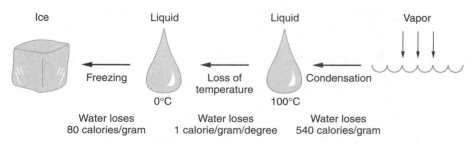

(b) Water loses heat and surroundings gain heat

**Figure 7-8.** When water absorbs heat (as it melts and evaporates), the surroundings lose heat. When water loses heat (as it condenses and freezes), the surroundings gain heat.

## Questions

1. Which beaker of water contains the greatest amount of heat energy?

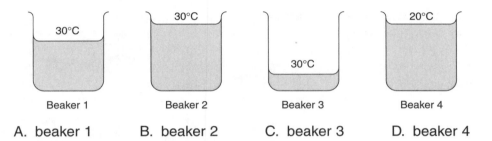

| Beaker 1 | Beaker 2 | Beaker 3 | Beaker 4 |

A. beaker 1    B. beaker 2    C. beaker 3    D. beaker 4

2. What happens to the heat energy as an ice cube melts in a dish?

    A. The ice cube gains heat and the air and dish gain heat.
    B. The ice cube loses heat and the air and dish lose heat.
    C. The ice cube gains heat and the air and dish lose heat.
    D. The ice cube loses heat and the air and dish gain heat.

3. How many calories of heat energy are gained by 10 grams of water when it (a) melts; (b) increases temperature from 20 to 90°C; and (c) evaporates?

4. How many calories of heat are needed to change 20 grams of ice into water vapor?

## Question Set 2

### Multiple Choice

1. Water differs from most other substances because it
    A. expands when heated
    B. contracts when heated
    C. expands when it freezes
    D. contracts when it freezes

**2.** Placing a metal spoon with a temperature of 20°C into a cup of water with a temperature of 90°C will cause the spoon to

A. increase in temperature

B. decrease in temperature

C. remain the same temperature

D. contract in size

**3.** A thermos bottle keeps hot liquids warm and cold liquids cool. What kind of material is used in the construction of a thermos bottle?

A. heat-conducting      C. heat-expanding

B. heat-insulating      D. heat-contracting

**4.** A thermometer works on the principle that, when heated, the substance in the thermometer will

A. contract      C. remain the same size

B. expand      D. release heat

**5.** Which graph best shows the relationship between the temperature of a substance and the motion of molecules in the substance when it is heated?

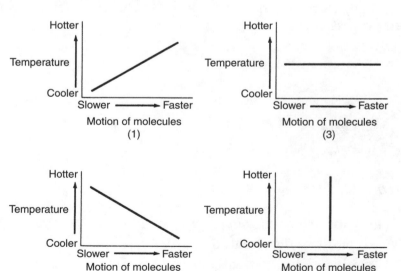

A. graph 1      B. graph 2      C. graph 3      D. graph 4

**6.** A cloud forms by the process of condensation. The gaseous water vapor changes into liquid water droplets. Heat is exchanged between the water and the surrounding air. What happens to the temperature of the surrounding air?

A. It increases.    C. It remains the same.

B. It decreases.    D. It increases, then decreases.

## *Open Ended*

**7.** The end of a metal bar is placed in a flame for 5 minutes. The temperature is measured by thermometers at four points on the bar, as shown in the diagram below.

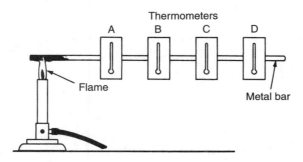

(a) What type of heat transfer does this procedure demonstrate?

(b) Predict the comparative temperature readings for each of the thermometers.

**8.** Refer to the diagram and explain (a) how you can make the colored water in the glass tube rise and (b) how you can make it fall.

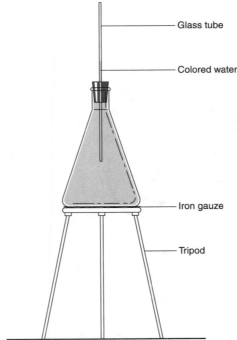

9. When warm soda is poured into a glass filled with ice, there is a heat exchange that occurs in the glass. Describe and illustrate the heat exchange that takes place in the glass of soda.

# SOUND ENERGY

 ## Sound Characteristics

***Sound*** is a form of energy produced by a vibrating object. When an object vibrates, it moves rapidly back and forth. This motion pushes and pulls the surrounding air, producing alternating layers of compressed and expanded air particles, called ***sound waves*** (see Figure 7-9). These sound waves spread outward in all directions from their source, somewhat like the circular ripples that are produced when you toss a pebble into a calm pool of water.

Objects that can produce sound include bells, radio speakers, guitar strings, or anything else that can vibrate. For instance, the sound of your voice is caused by the vibrating vocal cords in your throat. If

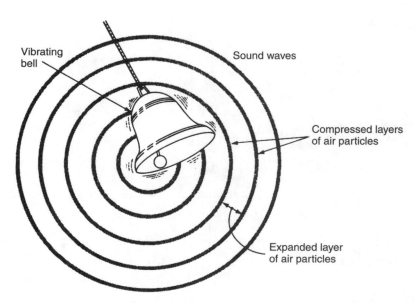

**Figure 7-9.** A vibrating object, such as a bell, produces sound waves made up of compressed and expanded layers of air particles.

you place your hand on your throat while you speak, you can feel the vibrations that produce the sound.

To be heard, a sound must be transmitted from a source to your ear. The substance that sound travels through is called the *medium*. The medium can be a solid, a liquid, or a gas. Most sounds we hear travel through air, a gas. Sound waves cannot travel through a *vacuum* because there are no particles of matter in a vacuum to transmit the sound.

# Waves

Both sound and light are types of energy that travel in the form of *waves*. The waves produced by sound, as stated above, are similar to the waves produced by a pebble tossed into a calm pool of water.

The pebble entering the water is a source of energy; it produces a series of waves that travel outward in all directions on the surface of the water. A wavy line, as shown in Figure 7-10, can represent these waves. The top of a wave is called the *crest*, and the bottom of the wave is called the *trough*. The distance from one point in a wave to a corresponding point in the next wave is called a **wavelength**. In other words, the distance from one wave crest to the next crest is a wavelength. The height of the crest, or the depth of the trough, of the wave measured from the undisturbed surface is the **amplitude** of the wave. The number of waves that pass by a fixed point in a given amount of time is called the wave's **frequency**.

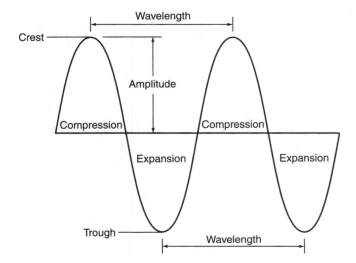

**Figure 7-10.** Characteristics of sound waves include the crest, trough, wavelength, and amplitude of the waves.

## Types of Waves

A wave that vibrates up and down at a right angle to the direction in which the wave is traveling is called a *transverse wave*. Transverse waves can be demonstrated by using a rope tied to the back of a chair and shaking the untied end of the rope up and down. Although you see the wave moving along the rope, the actual material of the rope does not move forward, but rather moves up and down with each passing crest and trough.

A wave that vibrates back and forth within its direction of travel is called a *longitudinal wave*. A longitudinal wave can be demonstrated by using a long coiled spring. Attach the spring to the back of a chair and stretch the spring out, then push it in. You will see a series of "push-and-pull" waves pass through the spring. The area where the spring coils push close together is called *compression*, and the area where the coils pull apart, or spread out, is called *rarefaction*. The wavelength is measured from compression to compression. Sound waves are longitudinal waves. Figure 7-11 illustrates the two types of waves.

## Sound Waves

Although sound waves are longitudinal waves, they can also be represented as transverse waves (see Figure 7-11). The crest of each wave

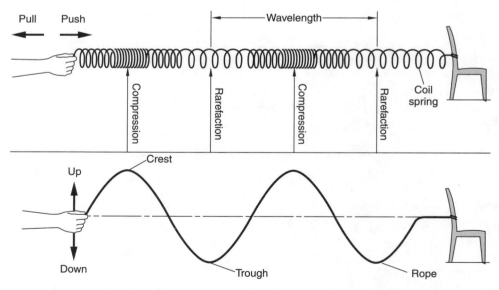

**Figure 7-11.** A coiled spring can be used to demonstrate a longitudinal wave, and a rope can be used to demonstrate a transverse wave.

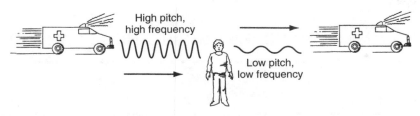

**Figure 7-12.** The Doppler effect: When the source of sound moves toward the listener, the frequency heard increases; and when the source of sound moves away from the listener, the frequency heard decreases.

represents the compressed-particle portion of the wave (the compression), and the trough represents the expanded-particle portion (the rarefaction). The larger the amplitude of the wave is, the louder the sound.

Wave frequency is commonly expressed as the number of vibrations per second. Humans can hear sounds that range from 20 to 20,000 vibrations per second. A normal speaking voice ranges between 100 to 1000 vibrations per second and has a wavelength of 0.3 to 3.5 meters. The pitch describes how high or low the sound is. A high-frequency sound has a high pitch, and a low-frequency sound has a low pitch. A violin produces a high-pitched sound, and a double bass produces a low-pitched sound.

To a motionless observer, the frequency of sound waves produced by the horn on a moving train or the siren on an ambulance increases or decreases, depending on whether the sound source is moving toward or away from the listener. This change in sound frequency, called the **_Doppler effect_**, is recognized as a change in pitch. When a blaring ambulance siren is moving toward you, the sound waves are crowded together, producing a higher frequency and a higher pitch. When the siren is moving away from you, the sound waves spread out, producing a lower frequency and a lower pitch (see Figure 7-12).

 ## The Speed of Sound

The speed of sound depends primarily on the density of the substance, or medium, through which it is passing. The denser the medium, the faster the sound waves can travel through it. Generally, sound travels fastest through solids, which have the greatest density, and slowest through gases, which have the least density. Table 7-2 gives the speed of sound through several substances. To a lesser extent, temperature also affects the speed of sound.

Although the speed of sound can vary, it is always much slower than the speed of light. During a thunderstorm, for instance, a light-

| TABLE 7-2. | SPEED OF SOUND THROUGH DIFFERENT SUBSTANCES (AT 25°C) | |
| --- | --- | --- |
| **Medium** | **State** | **Speed (m/sec)** |
| Iron | Solid | 5200 |
| Glass | Solid | 4540 |
| Water | Liquid | 1497 |
| Air | Gas | 346 |

ning bolt produces a flash of light and a clap of thunder at the same time. The speed of light is so fast that the light reaches us almost instantly. The sound of the thunder travels much more slowly, so we usually hear the thunder several seconds after we see the lightning.

## SKILLS ACTIVITY 2

### HOW DOES TEMPERATURE AFFECT THE SPEED OF SOUND IN AIR?

Sound travels at different speeds through different substances. The speed of sound is faster in solids, such as stone or metal, and slower in liquids and gases, such as water and air. The speed of sound through air is also affected by air temperature. The graph below shows the relationship between air temperature and the speed of sound. Study the graph; then answer the following questions.

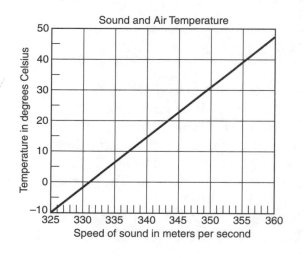

## Questions

1.  Sound travels at a speed of 340 meters per second at about which temperature?

    A. 22°C          B. 10°C          C. 6°C          D. 15°C

2.  At a temperature of 31°C, sound travels at about

    A. 345 meters per second          C. 355 meters per second
    B. 350 meters per second          D. 340 meters per second

3.  What does the graph suggest about the relationship between air temperature and the speed of sound?

    A. As air temperature decreases, the speed of sound increases.
    B. As air temperature decreases, the speed of sound remains the same.
    C. As air temperature increases, the speed of sound increases.
    D. As air temperature increases, the speed of sound remains the same.

## Question Set 3

*Multiple Choice*

1.  The bar graph below shows the average speed of sound through solids, liquids, gases, and a vacuum. Based on the graph, through which medium would sound travel fastest?

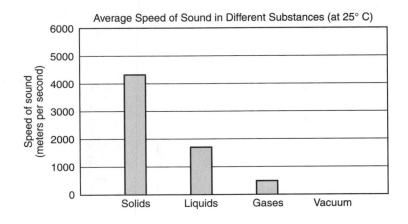

    A. air          C. liquid water
    B. rock         D. vacuum

Read the following short paragraph and study the diagram. Then answer questions 2 through 4.

Sound travels about 340 meters/second in air. Josh yelled "hello" across a canyon. The sound traveled across the canyon and returned as an echo. Josh heard the echo 2 seconds after he yelled "hello."

2.  What is the total distance the sound traveled?
    A. 340 meters
    B. 680 meters
    C. 1360 meters
    D. 170 meters

3.  What is the distance across the canyon?
    A. 340 meters
    B. 680 meters
    C. 1360 meters
    D. 170 meters

4.  If the canyon had been 1020 meters across, how long would it take for the echo to return to Josh?
    A. 5 seconds
    B. 6 seconds
    C. 3 seconds
    D. 12 seconds

5.  When using the apparatus in the diagram at right, a student could not hear the ringing bell after the air was pumped out of the bell jar. This demonstrates that sound waves

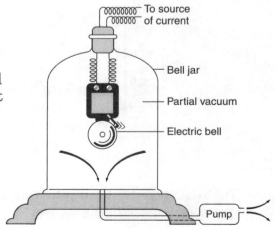

A. can travel through the glass bell jar

B. cannot travel through the glass bell jar

C. cannot travel through a vacuum

D. can travel through a vacuum

6. A passing train blows a whistle at a constant pitch as it approaches, crosses, and leaves a road crossing. A person standing by the road crossing hears the pitch of the whistle rise as the train approaches, and then get lower as the train passes by. The apparent change in pitch of the train whistle is caused by

A. its wavelength

B. the Doppler effect

C. the amplitude of its sound

D. different whistles on the train

7. Sound is produced by

A. expansions

B. contractions

C. reflections

D. vibrations

8. While visiting a historic fort during his vacation, John watched a demonstration of the firing of a cannon. When the cannon fired, the sound traveled to John and he heard the sound with his ears. What is the medium for the sound waves?

A. the cannon

B. the air

C. John's ears

D. none of the above

## Open Ended

9. What can cause sound waves to increase their speed? Explain.

10. Explain why someone can hear you calling even when he or she is in another room that is not directly in line with you.

# LIGHT ENERGY

 ## Light Characteristics

*Light* is a visible form of energy. Like sound, light travels in waves that move outward in all directions from its source. Light waves travel

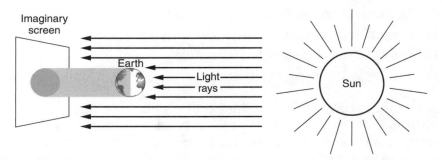

**Figure 7-13.** Light waves travel in straight paths. Shadows are produced when an object blocks their path.

in straight paths called *rays* (see Figure 7-13). Unlike sound waves, which can bend around corners and objects, light rays cannot bend around objects. That is why objects block out light rays and cast shadows. However, light can travel through a vacuum, something sound cannot do. Light from the sun travels through the vacuum of space to reach Earth. The speed of light is extremely fast, about 300,000 kilometers per second. That is almost a million times faster than the speed of sound! Light that travels over the distances we commonly encounter on Earth arrives in just a very small fraction of a second.

The sun is our main source of light energy. Fire and lightning are other sources of natural light. Light can also be produced artificially, as it is in a lightbulb.

 ## Light Can Be Reflected, Absorbed, or Transmitted

When light strikes the surface of an object, three things can happen to the light rays (see Figure 7-14). Light rays may be bounced back, or

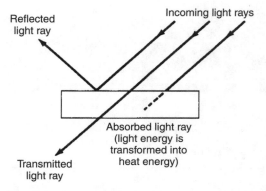

**Figure 7-14.** When light strikes a surface, the rays may be reflected from, absorbed by, and/or transmitted through the surface.

*reflected*, off the surface. Light rays may be *absorbed* as heat energy. And light rays may be *transmitted*, passing through the object. A shiny, metal surface reflects a lot of the light that strikes it. A black-topped road absorbs much of the light that strikes it as heat. And clear glass allows most light to be transmitted through it.

We see objects because they emit light or their surfaces reflect light, and the rays enter our eyes. The smoother the surface is, the more accurate the reflection. A mirror gives an accurate reflection because it has a smooth, shiny surface. A wall produces a much different kind of reflection, because its rougher surface scatters the light.

Colored objects absorb light to varying degrees. Dark-colored objects absorb more light as heat energy than do light-colored objects, which reflect more light. For this reason, people usually wear light-colored clothing to keep cool during hot, sunny weather. A blue object appears blue because it reflects blue light from the visible band of the light spectrum and absorbs all other colors of the visible band as heat energy. Likewise, a car appears green because it reflects the green light waves and absorbs all other color light waves.

Materials also differ in their ability to transmit light. Transparent materials, such as window glass, permit almost all of the incoming light to pass directly through them. Translucent materials, such as wax paper, let some light pass through them, but scatter the light rays so the images are not transmitted clearly. Opaque materials, such as wood and iron, do not allow any light to pass through them.

## Refraction

Sometimes when light passes through two media of different densities, such as from water into air, the light rays are bent, or *refracted*. That is why a pencil in a glass of water looks broken or bent where it enters the water (see Figure 7-15). The light rays being reflected from the pencil are refracted as they pass from the water into the air. This fact has been put to use in the making of lenses.

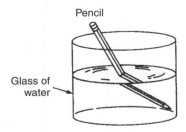

**Figure 7-15.** Refraction of light: Bending of light rays as they pass from one medium (air) to another (water, which has a different density) makes the pencil look bent or broken.

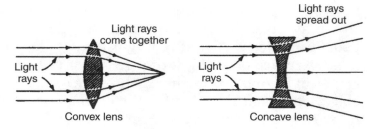

**Figure 7-16.** The shape of a lens determines how it bends rays of light.

A *lens* is a piece of transparent glass or plastic that has curved surfaces. The curved surfaces refract light rays that pass through the lens. The shape of a lens determines how it bends light, as shown in Figure 7-16. A lens with surfaces that curve outward (convex) bends light rays so that they are focused in toward a common point. A lens with surfaces that curve inward (concave) bends light rays so that they are spread out.

Images of objects seen through lenses may be larger than, the same size as, or smaller than the object itself. For instance, the lens of a camera forms smaller images of objects. A simple photocopy machine has a lens that forms images the same size as the original object. Binoculars contain lenses that magnify objects, making them appear larger.

## The Electromagnetic Spectrum

Light waves are part of a larger group of energy waves that can travel through a vacuum at the speed of light. These are called *electromagnetic waves*. They include radio waves, microwaves, infrared waves, visible light, ultraviolet rays, X rays, and gamma rays. Together, these energy waves form a continuous band of waves called the *electromagnetic spectrum* (see Figure 7-17).

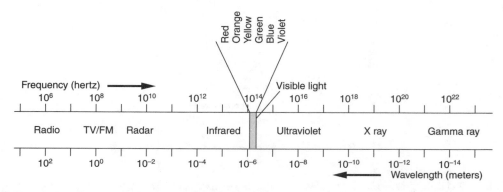

**Figure 7-17.** The electromagnetic spectrum: The frequency (hertz) increases from left to right; and the wavelength (meters) decreases from left to right.

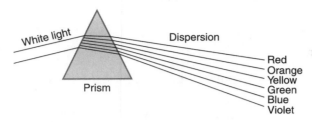

**Figure 7-18.** Illustration of dispersion of white light as it travels through a prism.

Electromagnetic waves affect our daily lives in many ways. Radio waves are used for radio and television broadcasting. Microwaves are used in communications and in microwave ovens. X rays are used to diagnose illnesses and injuries. Overexposure to some electromagnetic waves can be harmful to living things. We should be especially careful to limit our exposure to electromagnetic radiation such as X rays and ultraviolet rays, which have been linked to genetic mutations and cancer.

A narrow range of the electromagnetic spectrum is ordinary white light. If a beam of white light is passed through a glass prism, the beam is refracted and dispersed into a series of rainbow colors that are called the *color spectrum* (red, orange, yellow, green, blue, and violet). The separation occurs because each color has a different wavelength and each is refracted a different amount (see Figure 7-18). Red has the longest wavelength, and violet has the shortest wavelength. You see the color red when you look at a traffic stop sign because the red wavelength is reflected from the sign and all other wavelengths are absorbed as heat (see Figure 7-19).

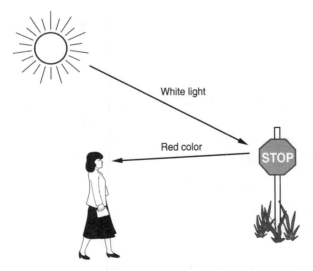

**Figure 7-19.** All visible wavelengths of white light are absorbed (as heat) by the stop sign, except for red, which is reflected (and thus seen by the person).

## The Sun's Energy

The sun is the primary source of energy on Earth. The sun produces its energy through a process called *nuclear fusion*. This process combines four atoms of hydrogen to form one atom of helium and a tremendous amount of energy. Light energy and heat energy are the major forms of energy produced by the sun. The light energy arrives on Earth with a range of wavelengths that include visible light, infrared, and ultraviolet radiation.

### SKILLS ACTIVITY 3

### COMPARING THE SPEEDS OF LIGHT AND OF SOUND

Robert made a series of observations during a thunderstorm. He recorded the time difference between each flash of lightning and the thunder that followed it. The chart below shows his findings.

| Lightning Bolt | Time Difference Between Lightning and Thunder (seconds) |
|---|---|
| *A* | 12 |
| *B* | 9 |
| *C* | 7 |
| *D* | 3 |
| *E* | 5 |
| *F* | 8 |
| *G* | 10 |
| *H* | 15 |

Robert knows that light traveling over relatively short distances arrives almost instantly, and that sound travels at about 340 meters/second in air. So, Robert estimated that for every 3-second difference in time between a flash of lightning and the thunder, the lightning bolt was about 1 kilometer (1000 meters) away. Like Robert, you can use the information in the chart to draw some conclusions and answer the following questions.

### Questions

1. The lightning bolt that was closest to Robert was

   A. *B*          B. *C*          C. *D*          D. *H*

**2.** The lightning bolt that was about 3 kilometers from Robert was

A. *A*            B. *B*            C. *C*            D. *D*

**3.** From the trend in the data, Robert concluded that the thunderstorm

A. moved away from him and then toward him

B. moved toward him and then away from him

C. was continuously moving away from him

D. was continuously moving toward him

## Question Set 4

*Multiple Choice*

**1.** A blast of dynamite set off by a roadwork crew produced a bright flash of light and a loud explosion. A person standing 2 kilometers away, with a clear view of the work site, would

A. hear the sound first, then see the flash

B. see the flash first, then hear the sound

C. see the flash and hear the sound at the same time

D. hear the sound, but not see the flash

**2.** We can see most objects because they

A. refract light                C. absorb light

B. reflect light                D. transmit light

**3.** When using the apparatus shown in the diagram below, a student could see the flame only if all three holes were lined up. What property of light does this demonstrate?

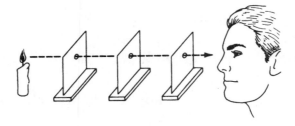

A. Light rays are reflected from smooth, shiny surfaces.

B. Light rays are absorbed as heat by dark-colored surfaces.

C. Light rays travel in straight paths and do not bend around corners.

D. Transparent objects transmit most of the light that strikes them.

**4.** The diagram below shows three ways that light can behave when striking a sheet of colored glass. The explanation for what is happening at position *C* is that the light rays are being

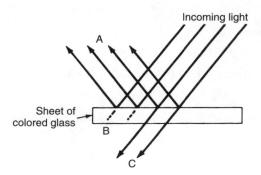

A. reflected by the glass

B. transmitted through the glass

C. absorbed by the glass

D. blocked out by the glass

**5.** Compared to the speed of light, the speed of sound is

A. much faster

B. much slower

C. nearly the same

D. hard to measure

**6.** A magnifying glass makes objects look larger. What happens when light passes through two transparent substances of different densities, such as air and a curved glass in a magnifying glass?

A. The light rays are refracted.

B. The light rays are reflected.

C. The light rays are absorbed.

D. The light rays travel in a straight line.

**7.** When white light strikes a green wall, all of the light is

A. absorbed

B. absorbed, *except* green light, which is reflected

C. reflected

D. reflected, *except* green light, which is absorbed

**8.** Which statement describes how sound waves and light waves are similar?

A. Both waves can bend around objects.

B. Both waves originate from an energy source.

C. Both waves travel at the same speed.

D. Both waves are a series of compressions and rarefactions.

*Open Ended*

9.  Each of the three diagrams represents a light ray striking a surface. Refer to the diagrams and identify (a) which diagram represents a mirror, and (b) which diagram represents a glass window. Explain your answer.

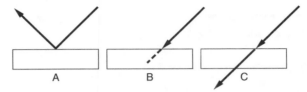

Use the diagram below, which illustrates the electromagnetic spectrum, to help you answer questions 10 and 11.

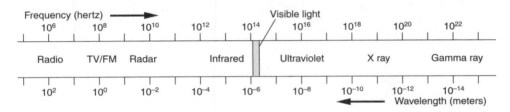

10. Referring to the spectrum, describe two differences between X rays and radio waves.

11. Which type of electromagnetic wave has a frequency of $10^{10}$ hertz and a wavelength of $10^{-2}$ meters? Is this a low-frequency wave with a long wavelength or a high-frequency wave with a short wavelength? Explain your answer.

# Chapter **8**

# Earth's Structure and Natural Processes

**Macro Statement:** Explain how Earth's crust and its surrounding "oceans" of water and air are affected by a dynamic series of interrelated natural processes that cause changes to both physical Earth features and living things.

## KNOWLEDGE STATEMENTS

**A.** Natural processes that change the features on Earth's crust include erosion, glaciation, weathering, earthquakes, and volcanoes.

**B.** The movement of water through an ecosystem is called the hydrologic cycle.

**C.** Global patterns of atmospheric movement affect local weather.

## CHAPTER OUTLINE

**External Forces Change Earth's Surface**

**Internal Forces Change Earth's Surface**

**The Hydrologic Cycle Affects Earth**

**Earth's Global Atmospheric Patterns**

# EXTERNAL FORCES CHANGE EARTH'S SURFACE

## Changes to Earth's Surface

Dynamic forces are constantly at work changing and shaping Earth's surface. Internal forces associated with earthquakes and volcanoes tend to push the land up above sea level, whereas external forces associated with weathering and erosion tend to wear the surface down to sea level. The changes to the land caused by internal forces may be noticeable within minutes or days, yet the changes caused by most external forces may take decades or centuries to become noticeable. Figure 8-1 illustrates these forces and their effects on Earth's surface.

## Weathering

External forces include the processes of *weathering* and *erosion*. Together, these processes wear down Earth's surface.

**Weathering** is the breaking down of rocks into smaller pieces, primarily by agents of weathering: rain, ice, and atmospheric gases. Both physical and chemical agents can cause weathering. In *physical weathering*, rocks are broken into smaller fragments by physical agents. For example, when water seeps into a crack in a rock and freezes, the water

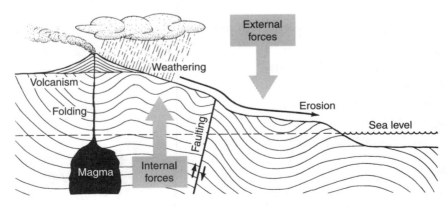

**Figure 8-1.** Earth's surface is shaped by the interaction of internal and external forces.

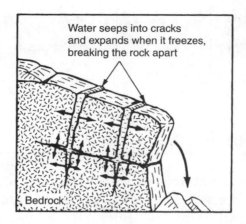

**Figure 8-2.** Physical weathering caused by water freezing in rock cracks.

expands, as shown in Figure 8-2. The roots of plants growing in cracks can also split rocks apart.

*Chemical weathering* is the breaking down of rocks through changes in their chemical makeup. These changes take place when rocks are exposed to air or water. For instance, when rainwater combines with carbon dioxide in the air, a weak acid is formed that dissolves certain minerals in rocks and causes the rocks to fall apart. Also, when oxygen and water react chemically with iron-bearing minerals in a rock, the iron is changed into rust, which crumbles away easily.

By breaking down rocks into smaller fragments, the processes of weathering assist in the formation of soil. Soil is a mixture of small rock fragments and organic matter (material produced by living things, such as decaying leaves and animal wastes). See Table 8-1.

 **Erosion**

*Erosion* is the process by which rock material at Earth's surface is removed and carried away. Erosion requires a moving force, such as flowing water, which can carry along the rock particles. This process can be seen after a heavy rain, when streams turn muddy brown from the rock material in the water.

*Gravity* and *running water* play important roles in erosion. Gravity is the main force that moves water and rock material downhill. Visible land features produced by gravity erosion are hillside scars caused by landslides, mudslides, and avalanches.

Running water carves out valleys and canyons. For example, in mountain regions, running water first cuts a steep-sided V-shaped valley. Continued running-water erosion over long periods of time cuts into the mountain's sides and produces a broad U-shaped valley. Eventually, lateral cutting action widens the valley into a flat-floor valley

| TABLE 8-1. AGENTS AND EXAMPLES OF WEATHERING ||
| --- | --- |
| **Agent of Weathering** | **Example of Weathering Caused by the Agent** |
| *Physical Weathering:* | |
| Ice wedging | Roadside rocks in a falling-rock zone after the winter thaw |
| Water abrasion | Rounded rocks in a streambed |
| Wind abrasion | Smooth-surface rocks in an arid region |
| Exfoliation | Slabs of exposed granite peeling at mountain summit |
| Plant roots | Trees growing out of the cracks in large rocks |
| Animals | Burrowing animals bringing rocks to the surface |
| *Chemical Weathering:* | |
| Carbonic acid | Caverns formed in limestone rock |
| Oxidation | Iron rust stains in rocks |
| Plant acids | Acids produced by water running over dead plants |
| Water | Water causes feldspar to decompose and produce clay |

(see Figure 8-3). The Grand Canyon in Arizona is a spectacular example of erosion caused by running water. Rivers commonly deposit the sand they carry when they enter the ocean. The Mississippi Delta has been formed by the accumulation of sand particles carried by the Mississippi River and deposited as it enters the Gulf of Mexico.

*Groundwater* forms from rain or snowmelt that filters down into the soil. Groundwater can cause the erosion of subsurface rock. As groundwater seeps through cracks in limestone, it breaks down the

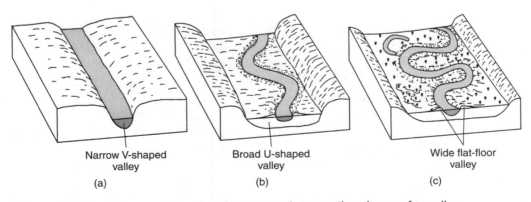

Narrow V-shaped valley
(a)

Broad U-shaped valley
(b)

Wide flat-floor valley
(c)

**Figure 8-3.** Erosion caused by running water changes the shape of a valley.

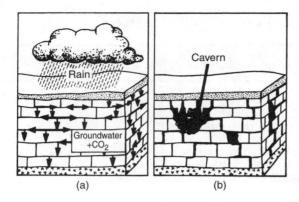

**Figure 8-4.** Groundwater containing carbon dioxide weathers and erodes limestone rock.

rock material and carries it away. Eventually, this action may create large underground caverns (see Figure 8-4).

*Glaciers* are masses of ice that form in regions where the amount of snowfall in winter is greater than the amount of snow that melts in summer, such as in a high mountain valley. The snow that does not melt piles up over the years, and its increasing weight presses the bottom layers into ice. Gravity causes the ice to flow downhill, like a river in slow motion. As a glacier creeps along, it grinds up and removes rock material from the land surface. The glaciers' cutting action produces U-shaped valleys, and their deposition of gravel as they move forms hills.

*Wind* also is an agent of erosion. In dry desert areas, sand grains blown along by the wind scrape and scour rock surfaces, slowly carving them into unusual shapes. Rock arches and bridges are features produced by wind erosion. Sand dunes are mounds of sand deposited by the wind.

Ocean *waves* breaking on a sandy beach tend to carry sand particles along the beach. Waves that wash up on a beach at an angle and carry sand back out to sea form *longshore currents*. This type of current carries sand and redeposits it along the beach, producing spits and hooks on sandy coastlines (see Figure 8-5).

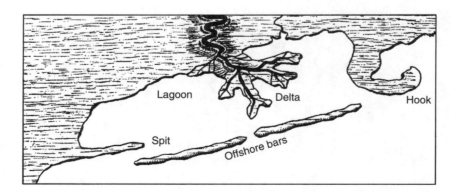

**Figure 8-5.** Some typical shoreline features are caused by erosion.

| TABLE 8-2. AGENTS AND EXAMPLES OF EROSION | |
| --- | --- |
| **Agent of Erosion** | **Example of Erosion Caused by the Agent** |
| Gravity | Landslides and mudslides carry rock and soil downhill |
| Running water | Suspended particles are carried along with the water |
| Groundwater | Rock material is removed underground to form caverns |
| Glaciers | Suspended rock material is carried along with the glacier |
| Winds | Particles are carried and rolled along with strong winds |
| Longshore currents | Sand is moved along a beach by beachfront water currents |

The forces of erosion are constantly at work, slowly moving rock material from one place to another place. See Table 8-2.

# INTERNAL FORCES CHANGE EARTH'S SURFACE

Earth's internal forces also shape its surface. These forces are usually abrupt and produce *mountains*, *earthquakes*, and *volcanoes*, which raise the land and build up Earth's surface.

## Mountains, Plains, and Plateaus

Most **mountains** are produced either by folding or faulting of Earth's surface layers of rock. **Folding** takes place when forces in Earth's crust press rocks together from the sides, bending the layers into up-folds and downfolds (see Figure 8-6). This process causes ridges and

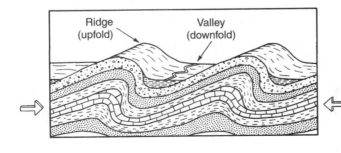

**Figure 8-6.** Folding: Forces in the crust can squeeze rock layers into folds.

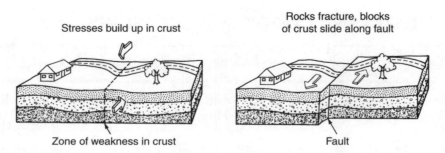

**Figure 8-7.** Faulting: When stresses in the crust reach the breaking point, the crust fractures and slips.

valleys to form on the surface. For example, folding produced the Appalachian Mountains in the eastern U.S.

***Faulting*** occurs when forces in Earth's crust squeeze or pull rock beyond its capacity to bend or stretch. The rock then breaks and slides along a crack or fracture called a *fault*, relieving the stress in the crust (see Figure 8-7). Faulting can produce mountains in a number of ways, as shown in Figure 8-8. Faulting produced the Sierra Nevada Mountains in California.

Some mountains are ***volcanoes***. *Magma*, a liquid rock solution, pushes up to Earth's surface and pours out. At the surface, the magma is called *lava*. The lava and volcanic rock tend to build upward to form a cone-shaped mountain called a volcanic cone (see Figure 8-9). The Hawaiian Islands are a series of volcanic mountains that extend up from the ocean floor.

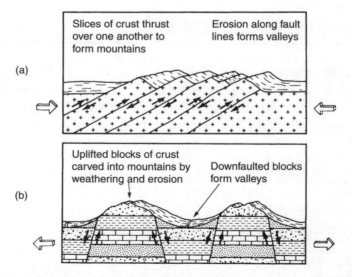

**Figure 8-8.** Mountains can be formed by thrust faulting (a) and by block faulting (b).

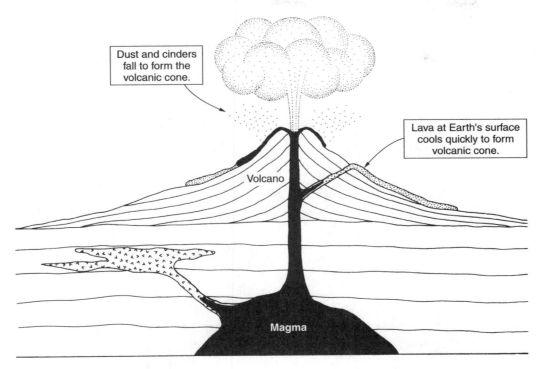

Dust and cinders
fall to form the
volcanic cone.

Lava at Earth's surface
cools quickly to form
volcanic cone.

Volcano

Magma

**Figure 8-9.** Volcanic mountains are built from an accumulation of cinders, dust, and lava.

Besides mountains, other landforms that may result from uplift include plains and plateaus. *Plains* are broad, flat regions found at low elevations. They are often made up of sedimentary rock layers that were formed underwater and slowly raised above sea level. *Plateaus* are large areas of horizontally layered rocks with higher elevations than plains. They can form in several ways. A large block of crust may rise up along faults to create a plateau, or a plateau may be gradually uplifted without faulting. Plateaus can also be produced by lava flows that spread outward rather than build upward.

## Earthquakes

Sudden movements of rocks sliding along faults in the crust are called *earthquakes*. Many earthquakes are associated with land uplift and mountain building. When an earthquake occurs, it produces strong vibrations that travel through Earth.

Earthquakes produce three types of vibration waves. *Primary waves* (P-waves) and *secondary waves* (S-waves) travel through Earth, while *longitudinal waves* (L-waves) travel only along Earth's

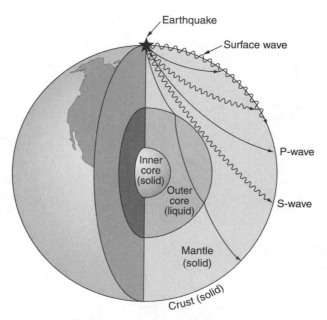

**Figure 8-10.** Paths of seismic waves are shown traveling on the surface of Earth (surface waves) and through Earth (P-waves and S-waves).

surface. P-waves can travel through liquids and solids; however, S-waves can travel only through solids. Analysis of how the three waves travel through Earth provides clues as to Earth's structure (see Figure 8-10).

## The Structure of Earth

The outer layer of Earth is called the ***crust***. It is composed of solid rock material and forms a layer that covers Earth. Under the oceans, the crust is about 5 kilometers thick and contains mostly basalt-like igneous rock. Under the continents, the crust is about 50 kilometers thick and contains mostly granite-like igneous rock (see Figure 8-11).

Below Earth's crust is a layer called the ***mantle***. The mantle is about 2900 kilometers thick and is thought to consist of dense iron-rich and magnesium-rich rock material. It is known to be solid because S-waves can travel through it, yet it flows very slowly and causes sections of Earth's crust to move.

At Earth's center is the ***core***, which is made up of an outer zone and an inner zone. The *outer core* is about 2300 kilometers thick. It is thought to be liquid because S-waves cannot travel through it. The *inner core* has a radius of 1200 kilometers, and it is thought to be solid because P-waves travel faster through it. The core is believed to be an iron and nickel mixture.

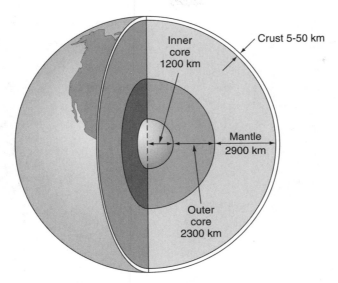

**Figure 8-11.** Cross-sectional diagram of Earth shows its internal structure.

## Plate Tectonics

There is much evidence that forces at work inside Earth have raised the level of the land. For example, many mountaintops are made of sedimentary rock that was formed originally on the ocean floor. Folds and faults seen in many rock outcrops are also signs of crustal movements caused by internal forces. Scientists explain these forces and the movements they produce by the theory of ***plate tectonics***.

According to this theory, Earth's crust is broken up into a number of large pieces, or *plates*, that slowly move and interact in various ways. Some plates are spreading apart, some are sliding past each other, and some are colliding. These movements cause mountain building, volcanic activity, and earthquakes along the plate edges. Figure 8-12 shows Earth's major crustal plates.

Scientists think that plate motions are caused by heat circulating in Earth's mantle, the thick zone of rock beneath the crust. The heat softens mantle rock so that it flows very slowly, following the heat currents and carrying along overlying pieces of crust (see Figure 8-13).

The processes of plate tectonics create many of Earth's surface features. The collision of two plates carrying continents produces great mountain ranges. The Himalayas in Asia were formed in this way.

When one plate slides sideways past another plate, a major fault and earthquake zone is produced. In California, the Pacific Plate is sliding past the North American Plate along the San Andreas Fault, sometimes causing severe earthquakes (see Figure 8-14).

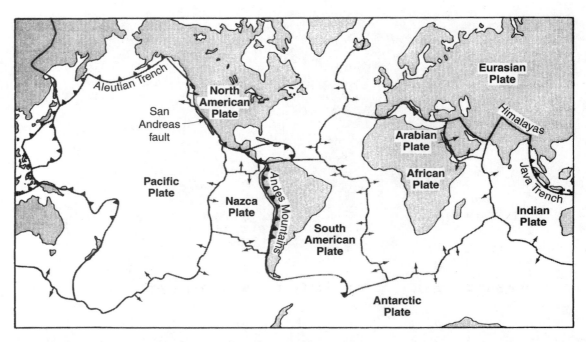

**Figure 8-12.** Earth's major crustal plates: Arrows show where plates are spreading apart; triangular "teeth" show where one plate is sliding beneath another plate.

Where plates are spreading apart, ocean basins are formed. Large continents are broken into smaller landmasses that move away from each other in a process called *continental drift*. This is taking place today, for example, where the Arabian Plate is splitting away from the African Plate, opening up the Red Sea.

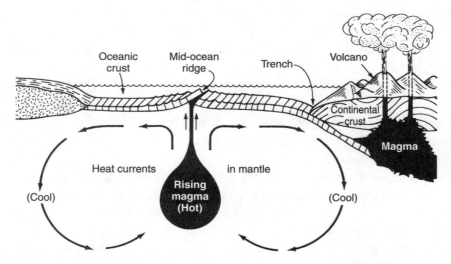

**Figure 8-13.** Plate tectonics: Heat currents in the mantle cause movements of Earth's crustal plates, producing many features on the seafloor and on the continents.

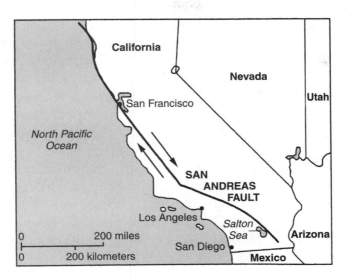

**Figure 8-14.** The San Andreas Fault in California: Activity along the fault produces earthquakes.

 ## Geologic Forces Affect People

Both internal and external Earth forces can have devastating effects on people. When these geologic forces act suddenly in a populated area, they destroy buildings, cause many deaths, and the region may take years to recover. It is not uncommon to read newspaper headlines describing a major earthquake, volcanic eruption, flood, or mudslide.

Sudden geologic forces are thought of as destructive because they kill people and destroy property. However, sometimes they can have a positive effect. Volcanoes and earthquakes can produce new land, and floods can revitalize the land adjacent to a river by enriching the soil with nutrients and making farmland productive. The following historic and recent events demonstrate how people can be affected by sudden geologic activity.

- *Volcanic Eruption:* In A.D. 79, Mt. Vesuvius, a 1280-meter volcanic mountain, unexpectedly erupted in southern Italy. The eruption produced a sudden flow of heated mud and ash that slid down the mountain and quickly engulfed the city of Pompeii and two nearby towns. About 16,000 people were killed by the eruption.

- *Earthquake:* A sudden movement along the San Andreas Fault in 1906 caused an earthquake that (temporarily) destroyed the city of San Francisco, California. The city burned to the ground and more than 500 people were killed.

- *Soil Erosion:* During the 1930s, a large area of the Great Plains, in America's Midwest, was subjected to severe weather conditions. Blizzards, floods, extreme hot and cold temperatures, and widespread drought conditions made the soil susceptible to wind erosion. Strong dirt storms blew for extended periods of time and stripped the land of its valuable topsoil. Large numbers of farms became unproductive, leading to economic hardship for many people.

- *Flood:* In 1993, a long period of heavy rain caused the "flood of the century" along the Mississippi River. About eight million acres in nine states were underwater while the river was above flood stage, from April to September. It is estimated that 50 people died, 25,000 people were evacuated, and more than 50,000 homes were damaged. The estimated economic loss was more than $10 billion.

- *Mudslide:* In 1999, torrential rains in a mountainous region of Caracas, Venezuela, caused mud and boulders to slide downhill, destroying everything in their path. More than 15,000 people were killed by the mudslide, and an estimated 100,000 became homeless.

 **Fossils**

*Fossils* are the remains or traces of organisms that lived long ago (see Figure 8-15). Fossils are formed when a dead plant or animal (or trace of it, such as a footprint) is covered by sediment that later hardens into rock. Almost all fossils are found in sedimentary rock.

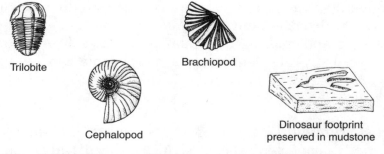

Trilobite

Brachiopod

Cephalopod

Dinosaur footprint preserved in mudstone

**Figure 8-15.** Illustration of some fossil types, including shells and a footprint.

Scientists have learned much about Earth's past by studying fossils. Fossil evidence has helped scientists trace the evolution of life from tiny ancient organisms to the complex life-forms of today. Fossils also provide important clues to ancient environments. For example, corals are known to live only in warm, sunlit ocean waters. When scientists find fossil corals in sedimentary rocks, they know that a warm, shallow sea once covered the area.

## SKILLS ACTIVITY **1**

## PREDICTING AN EXPERIMENTAL RESULT

Rocks in a stream constantly knock and scrape against each other and against the streambed as the flowing water carries them along. The longer the rocks are in the stream, the more they tumble about and strike one another. To simulate this action and study its effects on the rocks, a student carried out the following experiment.

Twenty-five marble chips and a liter of water were placed in a large coffee can marked *A*. The can was then covered with a lid and shaken for 30 minutes. Then 25 marble chips and a liter of water were placed in a second can, marked *B*, and covered. This can was shaken for 120 minutes. The illustration below shows the materials used in the experiment. Keep in mind what you have learned about weathering to help you answer the following questions.

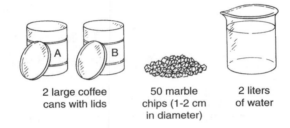

|  2 large coffee | 50 marble | 2 liters |
| cans with lids | chips (1-2 cm | of water |
| | in diameter) | |

## Questions

1.  Which is the best prediction of the experiment's result?

    A.  The marble chips in can *A* will be smaller and rounder than the chips in can *B*.

    B.  The marble chips in can *B* will be smaller and rounder than the chips in can *A*.

    C.  There will be no difference between the marble chips in cans *A* and *B*.

2.  Which graph best predicts what would happen to rocks in a fast-moving stream over time?

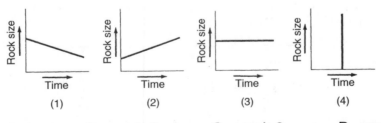

A.  graph 1          B.  graph 2          C.  graph 3          D.  graph 4

## Question Set 1

*Multiple Choice*

1. The diagram below shows a tree growing out of a cracked rock. This is an example of
   A. water erosion
   B. physical weathering
   C. chemical weathering
   D. an internal geologic force

2. The diagram below shows the mineral magnetite, which contains iron, changing into rust particles. This is an example of

Magnetite

Black, metallic, and magnetic     Black and rusty red, and less magnetic     Rusty red and nonmagnetic

   A. physical weathering
   B. chemical weathering
   C. erosion by running water
   D. the role of gravity in erosion

3. The sedimentary rock layers in the diagram were originally formed in horizontal layers. What force is responsible for changing them?

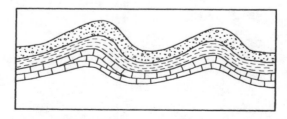

   A. volcanoes      C. groundwater erosion
   B. faulting       D. folding

4.  The theory that Earth's crust is broken up into large pieces that move and interact is called
    A.  evolution of life            C.  the rock cycle
    B.  mountain building            D.  plate tectonics

5.  Major mountain ranges are formed when crustal plates
    A.  push into each other         C.  move away from each other
    B.  slide past each other        D.  break into smaller plates

6.  If crustal block *A*, to the left of the fault in the diagram, suddenly shifted downward several feet, what would most likely occur at location *C*?

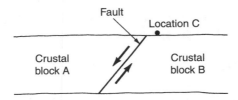

    A.  An earthquake would occur.
    B.  A volcanic eruption would occur.
    C.  A mountain would form.
    D.  An ocean would form.

7.  Earth is made up of a crust, mantle, outer core, and inner core. The crust is solid and broken into plates that seem to float on the mantle. The mantle is solid, but flows like heated plastic. The outer core is liquid, and the inner core is solid. Much of this knowledge about the internal structure and composition of Earth comes from
    A.  deep mining operations
    B.  earthquake vibration waves
    C.  underwater drilling operations
    D.  the rock structure of mountains

8.  Weathering is responsible for
    A.  creating wide valleys
    B.  forming mountain ranges
    C.  changing rocks into soil
    D.  changing sediments into rock

9.  Earthquakes and volcanoes are usually considered to be destructive forces because they kill people and damage buildings and other structures. Why are they sometimes considered to be beneficial geologic forces?
    A.  They rarely occur anymore.
    B.  They build up Earth's surface.

      C. They occur only in remote regions.

      D. They support unique life-forms.

**10.** Which event describes a force that builds up Earth's land surface?

      A. a volcano erupting in the Hawaiian Islands

      B. the flow of water in the Mississippi River

      C. waves striking the beaches of New Jersey

      D. a glacier forming on the top of a mountain

## Open Ended

**11.** What changed the land surface in the series of diagrams shown below? Explain the process for each diagram.

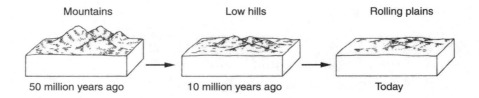

Mountains             Low hills             Rolling plains

50 million years ago      10 million years ago      Today

**12.** Why is a big earthquake more likely to occur in California than in New Jersey?

**13.** Describe an abrupt geologic event that affects people. Explain how this event can be both destructive and beneficial to people.

# THE HYDROLOGIC CYCLE AFFECTS EARTH

## Distribution of Earth's Water

Earth is unique among the known planets in that it harbors life and, also, in that it has large quantities of liquid water needed to sustain that life. At normal Earth temperatures, water can be found in all three states of matter—solid, liquid, and gas. About 75 percent of Earth's surface is covered by water, with by far the largest amount found in the oceans. Lesser amounts of liquid water can be found in lakes, rivers, streams, and underground aquifers; these are sources of freshwater. Glacial ice in the polar regions and on high mountaintops

| TABLE 8-3. | DISTRIBUTION OF EARTH'S WATER | |
|---|---|
| **Source** | **Percent** |
| Oceans | 97.24 |
| Glaciers and icecaps | 2.13 |
| Groundwater | 0.60 |
| Freshwater lakes | 0.01 |
| Inland seas | 0.01 |
| Soil/Atmosphere/Rivers | 0.01 |

contains large amounts of frozen freshwater. Gaseous water vapor, or humidity, is found throughout the atmosphere. Table 8-3 shows how Earth's water is distributed.

## The Water Cycle

The **water cycle** is the continuous movement of water entering and leaving the atmosphere (see Figure 8-16). Heat from the sun changes liquid water into water vapor. This is called **evaporation**. Evaporation takes place when a puddle of rainwater shrinks and dries up on a hot, sunny day. Water enters the atmosphere by evaporation from oceans, lakes, and rivers, and by plants releasing water vapor from their leaves. The movement of water through the living and nonliving parts of an ecosystem is called the water cycle, or *hydrologic cycle*.

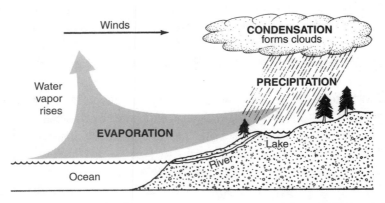

**Figure 8-16.** The water cycle is the continuous movement of water through Earth's atmosphere.

Warm air can hold more water vapor than cool air can. When warm, moist air rises, it expands and cools, and the cool air cannot hold as much water vapor. Some of water vapor changes back into droplets of liquid water. The process of water vapor changing back into liquid water is called **condensation**.

Condensation that takes place near the ground is called *fog*. When moist air rises high into the atmosphere and cools, condensation forms *clouds*. If enough water vapor condenses, the tiny water droplets may join together into larger, heavier drops that fall to Earth as *precipitation*. Rain is a liquid form of precipitation; snow, sleet, and hail are solid (frozen) forms of precipitation.

When rain strikes Earth's surface, some of it flows from the land down toward sea level. The flowing of water on Earth's surface is called *runoff*. Rivers and streams are forms of surface runoff. Eventually, much of the liquid water is heated again by the sun and evaporates back into the atmosphere. Then the cycle of evaporation, condensation, precipitation, and runoff continues.

Within the water cycle, living organisms remove, use, and return water to the atmosphere. Plants absorb water through their roots and then release water to the atmosphere through their leaves, in a process called transpiration. Animals ingest water and then release water to the atmosphere in the processes of respiration, perspiration, and excretion (of wastes).

## Water as a Solvent

Water is an excellent solvent. That means water dissolves most naturally occurring elements. As rainwater seeps into the ground, runs across the land, or accumulates in lakes, it dissolves organic and inorganic substances that come in contact with it. Even carbon dioxide, a gas, dissolves in rainwater as it falls. The water eventually makes its way to the ocean where it may evaporate back into the atmosphere, leaving minerals behind in the ocean. The most abundant salt ions found in seawater are chlorine, sodium, sulfate, magnesium, calcium, and potassium (see Figure 8-17). Sodium and chlorine combine to form ordinary table salt, which is by far the most abundant substance in seawater.

Salinity refers to the amount of dissolved salts in seawater. The constant churning caused by waves and currents maintains a fairly uniform salinity throughout the ocean, usually about 35 parts per thousand. However, under certain conditions, salinity will vary within a range of 33 to 38 parts per thousand. Warmer areas with a restricted circulation have a higher evaporation rate and, therefore, a greater concentration of salts and a higher salinity. The Mediterranean Sea and the Red Sea are examples of bodies of water with higher-than-average salinity. Areas where rivers empty into the ocean have a lower

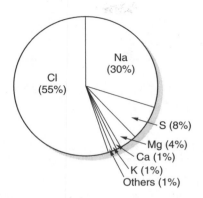

**Figure 8-17.** Every 1000 grams of seawater contain about 35 grams of salt. The most abundant salt elements are sodium and chlorine, in the form of sodium chloride (NaCl).

salinity, because the fresher river water dilutes the salty seawater. The Baltic Sea has a lower-than-average salinity because it receives a large amount of freshwater runoff from the land.

## Uses of Water

Less than 1 percent of Earth's water is usable by humans. Besides using water for drinking, bathing, cooking, and cleaning, people use large amounts of water for industrial processes, irrigation, mining, and livestock. Freshwater is a critical resource for all humans on Earth.

About 80 percent of the water that people use comes from surface freshwater sources such as rivers, lakes, and reservoirs (see Figure 8-18). The other 20 percent comes from groundwater, which is obtained from wells and springs. Water in the oceans, glaciers, and atmosphere is either not easily available or not acceptable for use by people.

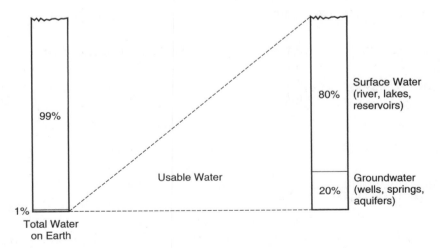

**Figure 8-18.** Only 1 percent of all Earth's water is usable by humans. Of the usable water, about 80 percent is surface water and 20 percent is groundwater.

## Water Pollution

A serious problem affecting the freshwater supply is *pollution*. Polluted water contains substances that cause it to be harmful to people, animals, and plants.

Pollution can seriously affect our supplies of surface water and groundwater. ***Pollutants*** can come from a variety of sources (see Figure 8-19). Historically, communities have dumped wastes and sewage into local rivers and lakes. Industries have emptied waste chemicals into streams and buried barrels of used chemicals in the ground. Over time, the barrels disintegrate, releasing their contents into the groundwater and polluting it. Pesticides protect our crops from insects, but are harmful when they wash off farmlands and enter our groundwater supply. Naturally occurring pollutants, such as salts and chemicals in some rocks, can also affect the freshwater supply.

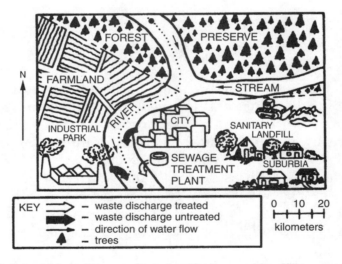

**Figure 8-19.** Pollutants from homes, factories, farms, and landfills are sometimes released into local waterways, such as rivers.

Populous regions are more prone to water pollution problems than are less-populated areas. Densely populated areas produce greater amounts of sewage, garbage, and industrial wastes, and are therefore more likely to have polluted water supplies. Constant monitoring of water quality is necessary to maintain clean and safe freshwater resources.

## Purification of Water

Although water pollution is a serious problem, there are natural processes that help purify water. Polluted water that is exposed to the air evaporates into the atmosphere. Evaporation changes liquid water into a gas, or vapor. During this process, only the water is transformed from liquid to gas, and all other chemicals and pollutants are left behind. This can be observed by boiling a pan of salty water. After all the water has boiled away (that is, evaporated), you can see a layer of tiny salt crystals left in the bottom of the pan.

When water vapor condenses and falls back to Earth as rain or snow, it is pure freshwater again. In this way, much of Earth's water supply is constantly being purified and once again made usable by people.

However, this purification process may take a long time to undo the damage of pollution. To make surface water supplies safe again for human use, it takes effort by people to eliminate sources of pollution and a long time for nature to refresh bodies of water with clean rainwater. Groundwater supplies take even longer to refresh, and are more difficult to monitor for pollution.

## SKILLS ACTIVITY 2

### INTERPRETING DATA IN A CHART

As surface water and groundwater flow toward the ocean, they come into contact with rocks, minerals, and soils. Some minerals may dissolve in the water and become part of it. Water that contains a lot of dissolved minerals is called *hard water*, and water with a low mineral content is called *soft water*.

When a river reaches the ocean, the river water and seawater mix. When seawater at the ocean's surface evaporates, the dissolved minerals are left behind to accumulate in the ocean. The most abundant mineral in seawater is sodium chloride, or common table salt. As any beachgoer knows, the sodium chloride gives seawater a salty taste. Some minerals are extracted from the seawater by small marine organisms to make their shells and skeletons; the percentage of such minerals in seawater is much lower than it is in the river water that empties into the ocean.

Study the data in the following chart and then answer the questions below.

**Percentages of Dissolved Minerals in River Water and Seawater**

| Mineral | River Water | Seawater |
|---------|-------------|----------|
| Carbonate | 35.2 | 0.4 |
| Calcium | 20.4 | 1.2 |
| Silicate | 11.7 | Trace |
| Chloride | 5.7 | 55.0 |
| Sodium | 5.8 | 31.0 |
| Magnesium | 3.4 | 3.7 |
| Potassium | 2.1 | 1.1 |
| Sulfate | 12.1 | 7.7 |

## Questions

1. The two minerals that have accumulated the most in seawater are

   A. potassium and sulfate

   B. calcium and carbonate

   C. sodium and chloride

   D. sodium and potassium

2. Some sea animals make their shells and skeletons from minerals in seawater, thereby reducing the amount of these minerals in the water. The three minerals that these marine animals utilize the most to produce their shells and skeletons are

   A. magnesium, potassium, and sulfate

   B. calcium, silicate, and sodium

   C. carbonate, calcium, and silicate

   D. sodium, magnesium, and potassium

3. The mineral content of rivers can vary greatly from the data given in the chart above. Which of the following is the most likely cause of mineral content variation?

   A. The amount of water in different rivers varies greatly.

   B. Rivers flow over different types of rocks, minerals, and soils.

   C. Rivers have different lengths and widths.

   D. Some rivers flow into a lake and some rivers flow into the ocean.

## Question Set 2

*Multiple Choice*

Refer to the following diagram, which represents the water cycle, to answer questions 1 and 2.

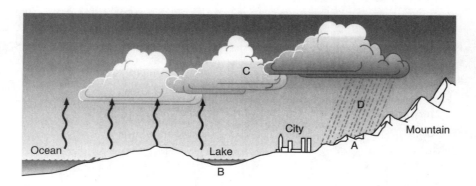

1.  Where in the diagram is the most likely location of polluted water?

    A. *A*          B. *B*          C. *C*          D. *D*

2.  Where in the diagram is the process of condensation taking place?

    A. *A*          B. *B*          C. *C*          D. *D*

3.  Purification of water is essential to maintain freshwater supplies for human usage. What natural processes can purify seawater and polluted water into freshwater that people could use?

    A. water seeping into the ground and filtering through the soil

    B. water freezing and thawing repeatedly

    C. evaporation and condensation of water

    D. water running over the ground and settling in a reservoir

4.  The diagram shows the location of an industrial city near a river and some lakes formed by dams on the river. Where is the best location to get clean water for the people of the city?

    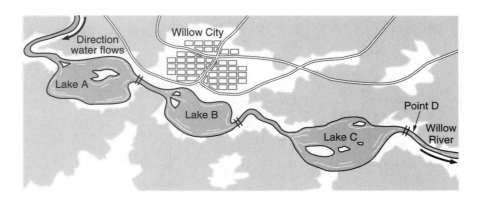

    A. lake *A*

    B. lake *B*

    C. lake *C*

    D. downstream at point *D*

5.  Mr. Collins purchased a house on a secluded lake in northwest New Jersey in 1975. At the time, there were only six houses on the lake. Today, there are 52 houses on the lake. Between 1975 and today, the water in the lake most likely

    A. became more polluted

    B. became less polluted

    C. remained the same

    D. was drained out

Use the following information to answer question 6.

In 1960, the river water upstream from a city showed few signs of pollution, while the water downstream showed a dangerously high level of pollution. The following graph shows the distribution of pollution in the river at that time.

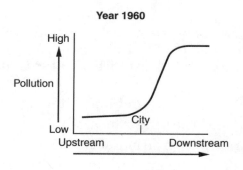

6. Which graph indicates the most successful correction of the pollution problem for the city?

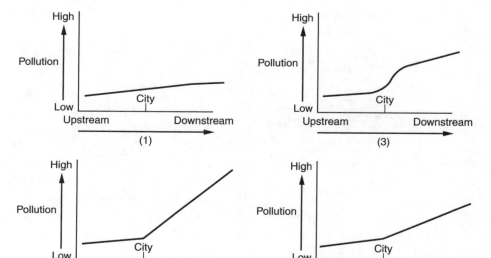

    A. graph 1     C. graph 3
    B. graph 2     D. graph 4

7. Most of the water used by people for drinking, bathing, and other purposes comes from
    A. the oceans
    B. groundwater
    C. mountaintop glaciers
    D. rivers, lakes, and reservoirs

Use the information in the following chart to answer question 8.

### THE DISTRIBUTION OF EARTH'S WATER

| Source | Percent | Source | Percent |
|---|---|---|---|
| Oceans | 97.24 | Freshwater lakes | 0.01 |
| Glaciers and icecaps | 2.13 | Inland seas | 0.01 |
| Groundwater | 0.60 | Soil/Atmosphere/Rivers | 0.01 |

8. Clean, available freshwater is an important resource that humans need to survive. Based on the chart, what can be correctly stated about Earth's freshwater supply?
   A. Most of the water on Earth is part of our freshwater supply.
   B. The freshwater supply consists of less than 3 percent of all the water on Earth.
   C. The freshwater supply consists of more than 97 percent of all the water on Earth.
   D. Most of the freshwater on Earth is available for use by humans.

### Open Ended

9. Animals ingest water in order to carry out their life processes. By what means do animals release water back into the atmosphere?

10. Plants use water as part of the process of photosynthesis. Describe how plants get water from their environment and how they release water back into the atmosphere.

# EARTH'S GLOBAL ATMOSPHERIC PATTERNS

## The Sun's Energy

The sun is the main source of the energy in Earth's *atmosphere*. As the sun heats Earth's surface, the surface radiates this heat energy back into the atmosphere. However, the sun does not heat Earth's surface evenly; consequently, the atmosphere is not heated evenly either. This uneven distribution of heat energy in the atmosphere is the cause of **weather**.

The heating of Earth's surface depends to some extent on the nature of the surface, since some kinds of surfaces get hotter than others do. For instance, pavement and sand get much hotter than do grass and water. On a larger scale, ocean, forest, and desert surfaces are all affected in different ways by the sun. These surfaces, in turn, heat the air above them differently, producing variations in air temperature.

When air is heated, it becomes lighter (less dense) than the surrounding air. Therefore, warm air rises. Cool air is heavier (more dense), so it tends to sink. As air rises or falls, the surrounding air rushes in to replace it, causing air to circulate, as shown in Figure 8-20. This air circulation, which can take place over a few kilometers or over thousands of kilometers, brings about changes in the weather.

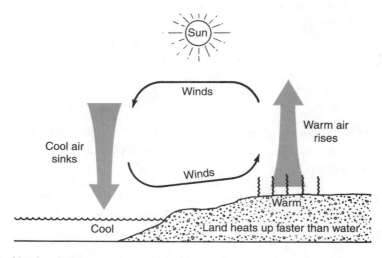

**Figure 8-20.** Air circulation patterns bring about changes in the weather.

The heating of Earth's surface also depends on the angle at which the sun's rays strike the planet's surface (see Figure 8-21). Near the equator, the sun's rays strike Earth vertically or nearly vertically (see area A in Figure 8-21). This concentrates the sun's energy within a small area, heating the surface very effectively. However, since Earth's surface is curved, the sun's rays strike areas away from the equator at a slanting angle (see areas B and C in Figure 8-21). This spreads energy over a wider area, heating Earth's surface less effectively. The farther from the equator, the more slanted the sun's rays are, and the less effectively they heat the surface.

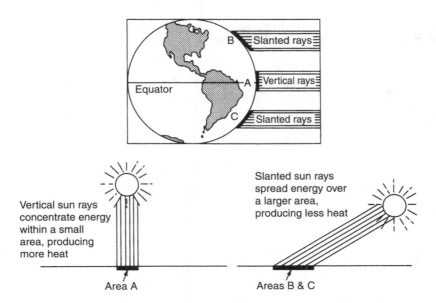

**Figure 8-21.** The angle of the sun's rays affects the heating of Earth's surface.

 ## Sea Breezes and Land Breezes

Sea breezes and land breezes commonly form along coastlines, such as the New Jersey shore, due to uneven heating of Earth's surface. On warm, cloudless summer days, the sun heats the land and water at the beach. The land heats more efficiently (and more rapidly) than the water does, which causes the air above the land to get warmer and rise. The air over the water becomes an area of cooler, sinking air. By midday, a cool breeze is formed that blows in from the water. Figure 8-22a illustrates the complete circulation of air forming a sea breeze.

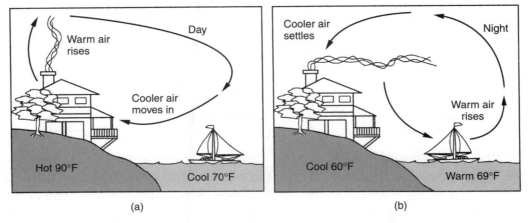

**Figure 8-22.** Sea breeze (a): During the day, cool air moves in from the water to the land. Land breeze (b): During the evening, cool air moves out from the land to the sea.

At night, a land breeze may form because the land cools faster than the water does, while the water and air above it remains warm. The warm air over the water rises, and the cooler air over the land sinks. This produces a movement of air from the land to the sea. Land breezes usually do not form as well as sea breezes. Figure 8-22b illustrates the complete circulation of air forming a land breeze.

Perhaps on a cloudless summer day you will recognize the formation of a sea breeze along the New Jersey shore. In the late morning, after the sun has had time to heat the land and cause the warm air to rise, you will feel a cool breeze blowing in from the ocean.

## Air Masses

A large body of air that has uniform temperature and moisture conditions throughout it is called an **air mass**. Much of our weather is determined by air masses.

An air mass forms when air stays over a large area of Earth's surface and takes on the temperature and moisture characteristics of that area. An air mass that forms over a warm body of water, like the Gulf of Mexico, will be warm and moist. Air masses that enter the United States from Canada are usually cold and dry because they formed over a cool land surface. An air mass builds up over an area for a few days and then begins to drift across Earth's surface.

There are four different surface conditions that affect the formation of air masses. Air masses that originate over *land* are dry. Those that form over *water* are moist. Cold air masses originate near the *poles*, and warm air masses form near the *equator*.

The major air masses that affect the continental United States enter the country from the north, west, and south (see Figure 8-23). They are then blown from west to east by the prevailing winds. As an air mass moves, it changes the local weather conditions at the surface below. The weather may become warmer, cooler, wetter, or drier, depending on the type of air mass passing by the area.

## High- and Low-Pressure Systems

Surface air pressures are usually highest in the centers of air masses, so these areas are called **high-pressure systems**, or simply *highs*. The air in a high tends to sink, and winds blow outward from the center, turning in a clockwise direction in the Northern Hemisphere (see Figure 8-24a). High-pressure systems usually bring clear skies, dry weather, and gentle **winds**.

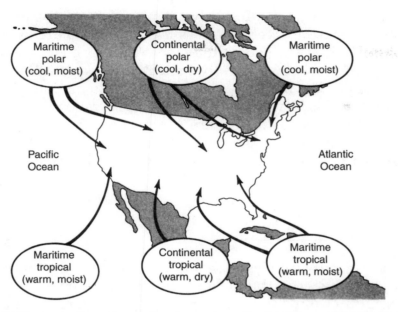

**Figure 8-23.** The map shows the major air masses affecting the continental United States.

Surface air pressures are lower toward the edges of air masses, so these areas form ***low-pressure systems***, or *lows*. The air in a low tends to rise, and winds spiral in toward the center in a counterclockwise direction in the Northern Hemisphere (see Figure 8-24b). (*Note:*

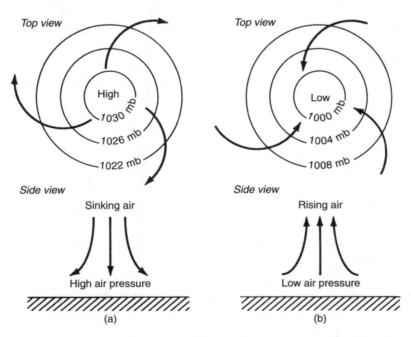

**Figure 8-24.** The diagrams show movement of air currents in a high-pressure system (a) and in a low-pressure system (b). (*Note:* The *mb* stands for millibars.)

In both highs and lows, winds always blow from areas of higher air pressure to areas of lower air pressure.) Low-pressure systems usually bring cloudy, wet weather, often with strong, gusty winds.

Highs and lows are generally indicated on weather maps by the letters *H* and *L*. The highs on weather maps usually indicate the centers of air masses. A low forms between highs, much like a valley between two mountains. Highs are large and tend to move slowly; therefore, weather changes are usually gradual, rather than sudden. Changes in air pressure readings signal the passing of highs and lows.

## Fronts

When one air mass collides with another air mass, a boundary called a *front* forms between them. Weather conditions on each side of the front often differ in temperature, humidity, and density. These differences prevent the air masses from mixing. The cooler, drier air is heavier and remains close to the ground, while the warmer, moister air is lighter and rises upward. This causes a low-pressure system to develop along the front, often producing clouds, strong winds, and precipitation. These lows produce the most common storm systems of our latitudes.

Different kinds of fronts are formed depending on which air mass pushes into the other.

- *Cold Front*. If a cold air mass pushes into and under a warm air mass, a *cold front* is formed (see Figure 8-25). Cold fronts usually bring brief, heavy downpours, gusty winds, and cooler temperatures. On hot, humid summer days, the passing of a cold front typically causes thunderstorms, followed by a decrease in temperature and humidity.

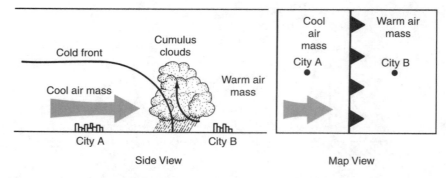

**Figure 8-25.** In a cold front, cold air pushes into and under a warm air mass.

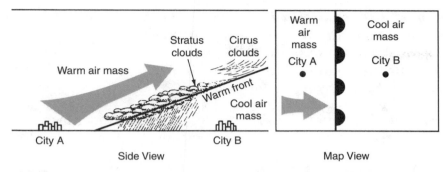

**Figure 8-26.** In a warm front, warm air pushes into and over a cool air mass.

- *Warm Front.* When a warm air mass pushes into and over a cold air mass, a ***warm front*** is created. The warm air slides up and over the cooler air (see Figure 8-26). Warm fronts bring light precipitation lasting a day or two and warmer temperatures. When the sky is overcast all day with light rain falling, a warm front is most likely present.

Clouds are produced when warm air is forced to rise. This can occur along a front, when air crosses a mountain, or when differential heating causes some areas on Earth's surface to heat faster than other areas. Strong vertical updrafts, as produced along a cold front, can develop puffy *cumulus* clouds. When air rises at a low angle, as it does along a warm front, flat layers of *stratus* clouds are formed. Wispy, feathery-looking *cirrus* clouds, which are composed of ice crystals, form high in the atmosphere. An increase of cirrus clouds, which eventually lower and become thick stratus clouds, may indicate that a warm front is approaching. (See Figures 8-25 and 8-26.)

## Climate

The ***climate*** is the general character of the weather that prevails in an area from season to season and from year to year. It can be thought of as the average weather of an area over a long period of time.

Some of the factors that combine to produce different climates are described below.

- One factor is ***latitude***, which is the distance north or south of the equator. Places at high latitudes, far from the equator, tend to have colder climates than places at lower latitudes. For instance, Canada is at higher latitude than Mexico, so it has a colder climate.

- Another factor is **altitude**, which is the height (elevation) above sea level of a place. Higher elevations are cooler than lower elevations. Just as a mountaintop is colder than its base, a city at a higher altitude will have a cooler climate than a city at a lower altitude (that has the same latitude).

- *Large bodies of water* can affect climate. Land areas close to oceans or large lakes generally have more moderate climates (cooler summers and warmer winters) than areas far from water. Water absorbs and gives off heat more slowly than land does. Therefore, as the land heats up during summer, the water stays relatively cool, keeping coastal areas cooler in summer than places farther inland. In winter, the situation is the opposite. The water loses heat absorbed during summer more slowly than the land does, keeping coastal areas warmer in winter than areas farther inland.

- *Topography* can also influence climate. The side of a mountain range facing the **prevailing winds** tends to have a cool, moist climate, while the opposite side of the mountains has a warmer, drier climate. This is illustrated in Figure 8-27.

- *Ocean currents* carry warm water northward and cool water southward. Many coastal areas have their temperature modified by ocean currents. Great Britain and Labrador (in Canada) are both at approximately the same latitude and same altitude. However, due to the warm ocean current that flows past Great Britain, the winters there are much milder than those in Labrador.

 Both temperature and moisture patterns affect the climate of a region. The climatic temperature patterns of a region usually refer to the average monthly and average yearly temperature. The range between the high-temperature month and low-temperature month also

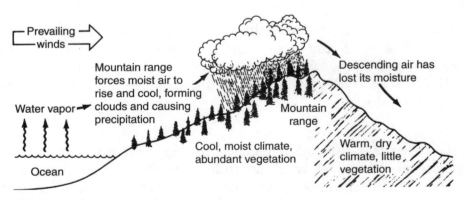

**Figure 8-27.** A mountain range can affect the climate.

can be used to describe the climate of a region. You can see how each of the climate factors listed above affects the temperature of a region.

The cycling of water in and out of the atmosphere also plays a role in affecting a region's climate. The interaction of the hydrosphere and the atmosphere distributes water around Earth. Atmospheric winds and weather systems carry water great distances over Earth's surface. Regions in which a large amount of water is in the atmosphere have a moist and humid climate; and regions in which a small amount of water is in the atmosphere have a dry and arid climate.

## Wind Belts

The uneven heating of Earth's surface causes hotter air at the equator to rise and spread to the north and south, while cooler air near Earth's poles moves toward the equator to replace the rising air. Earth's rotation breaks this simple circulation into global *wind belts*, in which winds blow in different directions at different latitudes (see Figure 8-28). Winds commonly blow in the same direction within each of the belts of latitude.

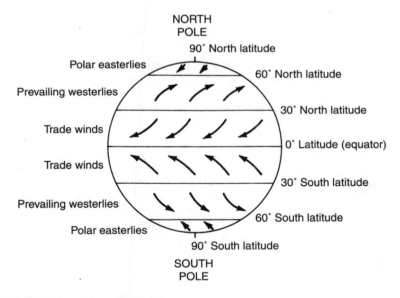

**Figure 8-28.** Earth's major wind belts.

The wind belts are named for their ***wind direction***—the direction from which they blow. Most of the United States lies in the Northern Hemisphere between 30°N and 60°N latitude, within the area of the *prevailing westerlies*. These winds cause most weather systems to move from west to east in the United States. In the Northern

Hemisphere above 60°N latitude, the winds are the polar easterlies; and between 0°N and 30°N latitude there are the trade winds, which are also easterlies.

## Motions of Ocean Water

The waters of the ocean are in constant motion. The exchange of energy between the ocean and the atmosphere plays a major role in the motion of ocean water. On a local scale, this exchange of energy can be seen as waves caused by the wind. Globally, the constant movement of air within the wind belts produces water currents that are driven great distances across the ocean.

The surface ocean currents in the North Atlantic Ocean flow in a "figure-8" pattern. Above and below the equator, the trade winds drive the currents westward; in the middle latitudes, the prevailing westerlies drive the currents eastward; and in the polar regions, the polar easterlies drive the currents westward again. The rotation of Earth and the ocean's contact with landmasses cause the currents to deflect north and south (see Figure 8-29).

The North Atlantic Drift is an ocean current that flows northeast from the middle Atlantic coast of North America to Great Britain. Its driving force is the prevailing westerlies. Because it moves northward away from the equator, the current brings warmer water into a cooler region. As a result, this slow, warm current moderates the climate of Great Britain. In fact, although Great Britain and Labrador are both

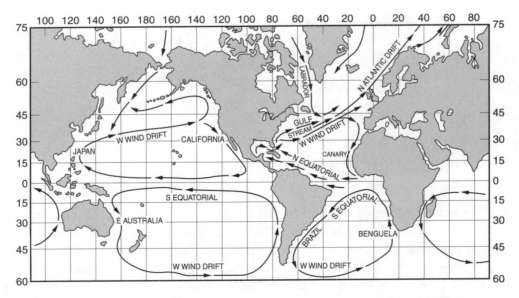

**Figure 8-29.** Major world ocean (surface) currents are driven by the wind belts.

at approximately the same latitude and same altitude (as stated on page 218), because of the North Atlantic Drift, Great Britain's winters are much milder than Labrador's.

## Weather Forecasting

**Weather forecasting** is an attempt to make accurate predictions of future weather. The accuracy of weather forecasting is improving as technology advances. In addition to weather balloons, thermometers, and barometers, weather forecasters now have a wide array of weather satellites, radar devices, and computer systems at their disposal.

Short-range local forecasts are comparatively easy. They are based mostly on *air pressure* readings and observations of *cloudiness* and *wind direction*. Changes in these weather elements are usually good indications of the weather for the next 24 hours.

Today, weather forecasters also use information from weather satellites and radar to improve their forecasts. This information is used to produce up-to-date weather maps, such as the one shown in Figure 8-30. The data plotted on weather maps allow scientists to see large-scale weather systems and their possible motion. Weather systems generally move from west to east across the United States. Therefore, if a weather map shows a high-pressure system immediately to our west, we can forecast fair weather for the next day. Conversely, if the map shows a low-pressure system to our west, we can expect stormy weather. Weather maps can also help predict upcoming temperature and precipitation changes for the next several days.

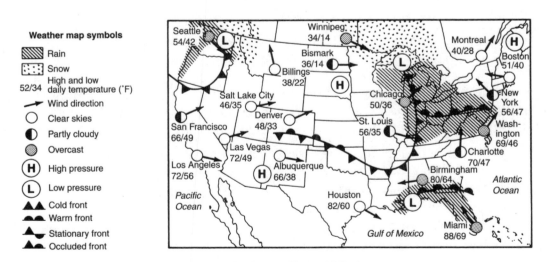

**Figure 8-30.** A weather map is useful for making predictions.

## SKILLS ACTIVITY **3**

### DESIGNING AN EXPERIMENT; PREDICTING RESULTS

Cold air is heavier and denser than warm air is. Therefore, cold air tends to sink and warm air tends to rise. To design an experiment that can demonstrate this, you would need cool air and warm air, a way to control the flow of air, and several thermometers.

For instance, a small room with a window provides a means of controlling airflow (see the diagram). On a day when the temperature outside is lower than the indoor temperature by at least 10°C, you could open the window to let in cold air and measure temperature changes in the room with thermometers. If it is true that cold air sinks and warm air rises, the lower levels of the room will get colder more quickly than the higher levels will. Study the diagrams below and answer the following questions.

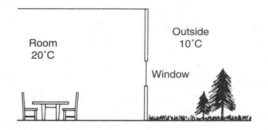

## Questions

1. How should the thermometers be arranged in the room to show that cold air sinks and warm air rises?

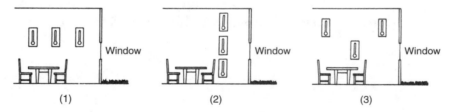

A. arrangement 1

B. arrangement 2

C. arrangement 3

D. none of these

2. If this experiment were performed on a summer day, when the outdoor temperature was 10°C higher than the indoor temperature, what would probably happen in the room after opening the window?

A. The temperature near the ceiling would increase faster than the temperature near the floor.

B. The temperature near the floor would increase faster than the temperature near the ceiling.

C. The temperature at all levels of the room would increase at the same rate.

D. There would be no change in temperature anywhere in the room.

## Question Set 3

*Multiple Choice*

1. In the diagram, the most likely reason for City *B* to be cooler than City *A* is that
   A. City *B* is at a different latitude
   B. City *B* is at a higher altitude
   C. City *B* is closer to the ocean
   D. City *B* is closer to the sun

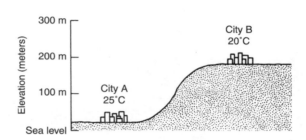

2. The diagram below shows two cities, *A* and *B*, and their positions on a continent. How will the climates of the cities compare?

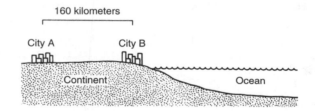

   A. City *B* will have warmer summers and cooler winters than City *A*.
   B. City *B* will have cooler summers and warmer winters than City *A*.
   C. City *B* will have cooler summers and cooler winters than City *A*.
   D. Both cities will have the same climate in summer and in winter.

3. The most likely reason that Newark has a cooler climate than Miami is their difference in
   A. distance from the ocean
   B. altitude
   C. air pressure
   D. latitude

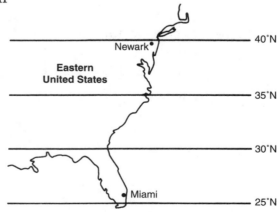

4. The main source of energy that sets Earth's atmosphere in motion and causes weather is

A. volcanism    B. gravity    C. the ocean    D. the sun

Questions 5 and 6 refer to the data and diagram below, which represents a New Jersey beach on a hot summer day at about 2:00 P.M.

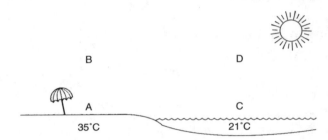

*Diagram Key:*
A—the air at 1 meter above the beach sand
B—the air at 1500 meters above the beach sand
C—the air at 1 meter above the ocean water
D—the air at 1500 meters above the ocean water

5. The uneven heating of the region causes a cool breeze to form by midday. In which direction is the air moving to form a cool breeze on the beach?

A. from *B* to *A*         C. from *D* to *C*
B. from *C* to *A*         D. from *A* to *C*

6. Clouds form when warm air rises. The water vapor in the air condenses into water droplets, thus forming a cloud. At which location might clouds be forming?

A. at *A*      B. at *B*      C. at *C*      D. at *D*

7. During winter, air masses that form over northern Canada often move south and affect the weather in New Jersey. Such an air mass would be

A. dry and warm         C. moist and warm
B. dry and cold         D. moist and cold

8. In the diagram, the air mass most likely to affect New Jersey the next day would be

A. air mass *A*
B. air mass *B*
C. air mass *C*
D. air mass *D*

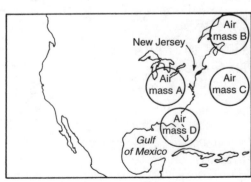

Questions 9 and 10 refer to the following diagram.

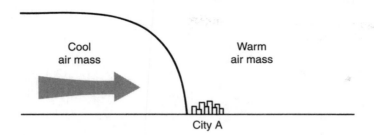

9. The line separating the cold air mass from the warm air mass represents a
   A. warm front
   B. cold front
   C. line of latitude
   D. high-pressure system

10. City *A* is most likely about to experience
    A. a light rain, followed by warmer temperatures
    B. heavy rains lasting several days
    C. no change in its weather conditions
    D. brief downpours, followed by cooler temperatures

## Open Ended

11. On a sunny summer day, a thermometer was placed above each of the surfaces shown in the diagram below. Describe the differences expected in each of the thermometer readings.

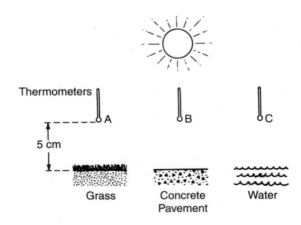

12. What atmospheric condition explains why some people might spend their summer vacation near an ocean or a lake?

Use the August weather map of New Jersey and the table below to answer questions 13 and 14.

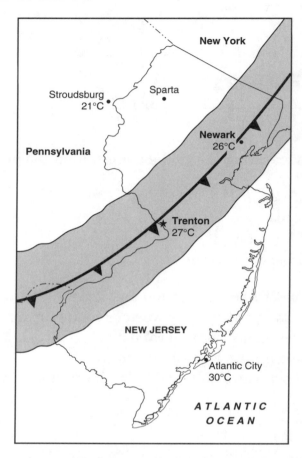

| City | Present Weather Conditions |
| --- | --- |
| Stroudsburg, PA | clear skies, cool temperatures |
| Newark, NJ | windy, with thunderstorms |
| Trenton, NJ | windy, with thunderstorms |
| Atlantic City, NJ | clear skies, hot and humid |

13. Describe what the weather is most likely to be in Sparta.

14. Predict the weather most likely to occur in Atlantic City within the next 6 hours.

15. Describe the main difference between weather and climate.

16. What does the letter "H" indicate on a weather map?

17. What type of weather would be in the area marked by an "H"?

# Chapter 9

# The Solar System

**Macro Statements:** Identify and compare the components of the solar system and explain how the position of the sun and moon affect events on Earth.

## KNOWLEDGE STATEMENTS

**A.** Planets of varying size, composition, temperature, gravity, and surface features move around the sun in elliptical orbits.

**B.** Phases of the moon, eclipses, and tides are caused by the relative positions of the Earth, sun, and moon.

## CHAPTER OUTLINE

**Origin and Structure of the Solar System**

**The Moon and Its Relationship to Earth**

# ORIGIN AND STRUCTURE OF THE SOLAR SYSTEM

## The Solar System

The **solar system** consists of our sun and all the celestial bodies that revolve around it. The major members of the solar system are the sun and the nine *planets* (see Figure 9-1). A number of other objects also come under the influence of the sun's gravity, and so belong to the solar system. These include natural satellites, or moons (objects that revolve around planets), asteroids, comets, and meteoroids. Most celestial bodies in the solar system have regular and predictable motions.

Before 1957, all of our knowledge about the solar system came from sky observations made from Earth and the examination of meteorites, fragments of the solar system that landed on Earth. Since then, the uses of spacecraft and space probes have extended our ability to gather information about objects in the solar system.

## Formation of the Solar System

Although astronomers have some evidence to support a theory for the origin of the universe and our solar system, many questions still remain. Scientists hypothesize that about 15 billion years ago, a violent explosion created the *universe*, producing energy and all the material from which the stars, planets, satellites, and all other objects formed. This idea is called the *big bang theory*. If such an explosion did occur,

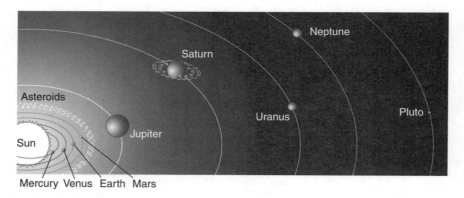

**Figure 9-1.** The solar system.

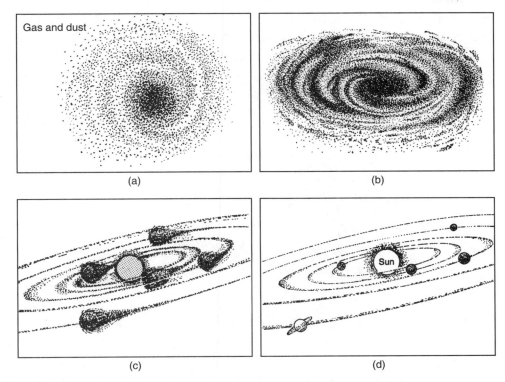

**Figure 9-2.** Origin of the solar system: Cloud of gas and dust in space (a); condensation of cloud (b); early sun and planet formation (c); and present-day solar system (d).

one would expect to find all the *galaxies* (large groups of stars) moving outward and away from one another, and this is exactly what astronomers have found.

Scientists further think that the expanding gases and dust particles condensed into local systems to form galaxies filled with stars. About 5 billion years ago, a dense area in the center of our local cloud of rotating gases and dust became our star, the sun (see Figure 9-2). The sun originally contained about 99 percent of the original cloud material in our solar system. Soon afterward, the remaining material condensed into the planets, satellites, comets, meteoroids, and asteroids. The age of the oldest rocks from Earth, the moon, and meteorites is 4.5 billion years old. This is evidence that they all formed at about the same time.

## The Sun

The sun is a hot, bright ball of gases. Nuclear reactions in the sun's interior release enormous amounts of energy, mostly as light and heat.

The sun is by far the largest object in our solar system. It is many times larger than Earth. In fact, if the sun were hollow, about one million Earths could fit inside it (see Figure 9-3).

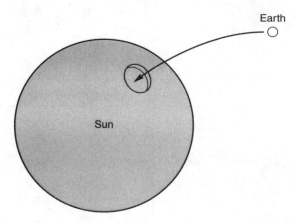

**Figure 9-3.** If the sun were hollow, more than one million Earths could fit inside it.

The sun is a *star*, like the stars we see at night. Although the sun is an average size star, it seems much larger than other stars because it is much closer to Earth. Light from the sun takes 8 minutes and 20 seconds to reach Earth. In contrast, light from the nearest star (other than the sun) takes more than 4 years to reach Earth! The sun is Earth's main source of energy, providing the heat and light necessary for the existence of life.

 **Planetary Motions**

Planets, asteroids, and comets move around the sun in a motion called **revolution**. The path of these objects is called an **orbit**. The shape of the orbits for objects in the solar system is slightly oval, or *elliptical*. Whereas a circle has one central point, an ellipse has two points, called *foci* (see Figure 9-4). The sun is located at one of the foci points, near the center of our solar system. It takes Earth 365¼ days (one Earth year) to revolve once around the sun (see Figure 9-5). Most of the orbits of planets are slightly elliptical (that is, almost circular). The orbits of comets are highly elliptical.

Each of the planets also spins on its axis. This motion is called **rotation**. It takes Earth 24 hours (one Earth day) to rotate once on its axis (see Figure 9-6). Most of the planets rotate from west to east; however, Venus rotates backward from east to west, and Uranus rotates on its side because its axis is tilted 98°.

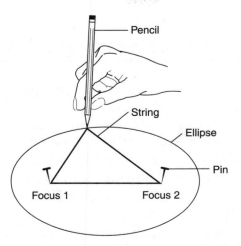

**Figure 9-4.** The orbital shape for objects in the solar system is elliptical. By wrapping a loop of string around two pins (foci points) and extending the loop with a pencil, you can draw an ellipse.

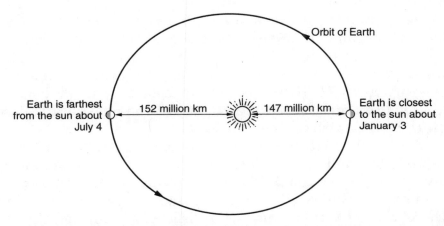

**Figure 9-5.** Earth travels in an elliptical orbit around the sun, which is at a focus point.

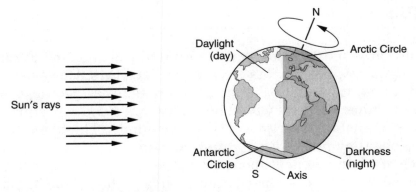

**Figure 9-6.** Earth's rotation causes the change from day to night.

## Earth's Position in the Solar System

Over the past 2000 years, advances in technology and ongoing scientific inquiry have helped determine Earth's position in the solar system and in the universe. In about A.D. 140, the Greek astronomer Ptolemy utilized inquiry and observation skills to develop an Earth-centered, or *geocentric*, model of the solar system. His geocentric solar system had the moon, sun, and five other known planets revolving around Earth. This theory was accepted by most until the Polish astronomer Nicolaus Copernicus (1473–1543) proposed a *heliocentric*, or sun-centered, model of the solar system. Using mathematical calculations and scientific inquiry, he determined that the sun was at the center of the solar system and that each of the six known planets—including Earth—revolved around it. Although his model more accurately explained and predicted the motions of the planets, it did not offer definitive proof that Earth rotated on its axis and revolved around the sun.

In the second half of the 1500s, Danish astronomer Tycho Brahe (1546–1601) built an observatory that had the most advanced astronomical instruments of the day. Using these instruments, Tycho made many accurate observations and measurements of the planets, stars, and other astronomical objects. In 1600, German astronomer Johannes Kepler (1571–1630) became an assistant to Tycho and, by studying his recorded observations, was able to explain and describe planetary motion with mathematical laws.

In 1609, Italian astronomer/physicist Galileo Galilei (1564–1642) built a telescope and became the first scientist to use this new device to study the night sky. In addition to observing and learning about the moon and stars, Galileo discovered sunspots, moons around Jupiter, and the phases of Venus. This latter discovery confirmed that Venus traveled around the sun, as suggested by Copernicus's model of the solar system.

## The Planets

There are nine *planets* that revolve around the sun (see Figure 9-7). In the night sky, the planets look much like stars. However, as days and weeks go by, planets change position against the background of motionless stars. Also, they tend not to "twinkle" the way stars do. Unlike stars, planets do not give off their own light. The planets are visible because they reflect the light of the sun.

Much of what we know about the planets has been discovered with the help of space probes. Space probes have gathered much planetary information by transmitting pictures, collecting samples, and measuring physical features. Table 9-1 lists some of the physical traits

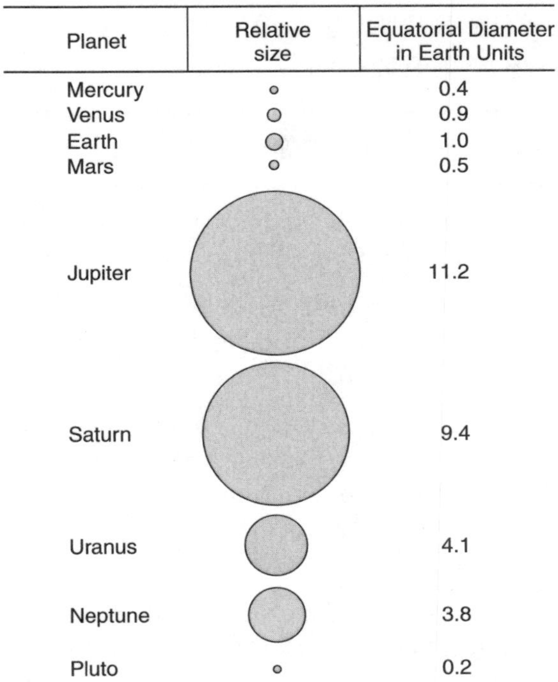

| Planet | Relative size | Equatorial Diameter in Earth Units |
|---|---|---|
| Mercury | ○ | 0.4 |
| Venus | ○ | 0.9 |
| Earth | ○ | 1.0 |
| Mars | ○ | 0.5 |
| Jupiter | ● | 11.2 |
| Saturn | ● | 9.4 |
| Uranus | ● | 4.1 |
| Neptune | ● | 3.8 |
| Pluto | ○ | 0.2 |

**Figure 9-7.** Relative sizes of the other planets in our solar system compared to Earth.

**TABLE 9-1.   PHYSICAL CHARACTERISTICS OF THE PLANETS IN OUR SOLAR SYSTEM**

| Planet (in order from the sun) | Distance from sun (Earth-sun units*) | Size (width in km) | Time to revolve once around sun | Time to rotate once on axis | Number of satellites | Density (Earth = 1) | Surface temp. (°C) | Surface gravity (Earth = 1) |
|---|---|---|---|---|---|---|---|---|
| Mercury | 0.4 | 4,878 | 88 days | 59 days | 0 | 0.98 | 180–430 | 0.38 |
| *Inner Planets:* | | | | | | | | |
| Venus | 0.7 | 12,104 | 225 days | 243 days | 0 | 0.95 | 465 | 0.91 |
| Earth | 1.0 | 12,756 | 365.25 days | 24 hrs | 1 | 1.00 | −89–58 | 1.00 |
| Mars | 1.5 | 6,787 | 1.88 yrs | 24.6 hrs | 2 | 0.71 | −82–0 | 0.38 |
| *Outer Planets:* | | | | | | | | |
| Jupiter | 5.2 | 142,800 | 11.86 yrs | 9.9 hrs | 28† | 0.24 | −150 | 2.64 |
| Saturn | 9.5 | 120,660 | 29.63 yrs | 10.6 hrs | 30† | 0.12 | −170 | 0.93 |
| Uranus | 19.2 | 51,118 | 83.97 yrs | 17 hrs | 21† | 0.23 | −200 | 0.89 |
| Neptune | 30.1 | 49,528 | 165 yrs | 16 hrs | 8† | 0.30 | −210 | 1.12 |
| Pluto | 39.5 | 2,300 | 248 yrs | 6.4 days | 1 | 0.32 | −220 | 0.06 |

*An Earth-sun (or astronomical) unit is the average distance from Earth to the sun (149,600,000 kilometers).
†Number of known natural satellites; the actual number may be higher.

### TABLE 9-2. PLANETARY ATMOSPHERES AND OUTSTANDING FEATURES

| Planet | Atmosphere | Outstanding Features |
| --- | --- | --- |
| Mercury | Trace hydrogen and helium | Craters and plains like our moon; fastest revolving planet |
| Venus | 96.5% carbon dioxide; 3.5% nitrogen; sulfuric acid clouds | Thick clouds hide surface; mountains, plains, and highlands; volcanoes and lava flows; third brightest object in our sky |
| Earth | 78% nitrogen; 21% oxygen; water-droplet clouds | 71% covered with water; crustal plates that move; contains living organisms; presence of water as a liquid, solid, and gas |
| Mars | 95.3% carbon dioxide; 2.7% nitrogen; 1.6% argon | Polar ice caps of frozen carbon dioxide; Olympus Mons—giant volcano; Valles Marineris—giant canyon system; appears red in our night sky |
| Jupiter | 90% hydrogen; 10% helium | Largest planet in our solar system; gas planet, surface not visible; bright, circulating cloud bands; 56,000-km-deep hydrogen ocean; Giant Red Spot has stormlike feature |
| Saturn | 75% hydrogen; 25% helium | Gas planet, surface not visible; faint, circulating cloud bands; magnificent ring structure; less dense than water —it would float in water! |
| Uranus | 83% hydrogen; 15% helium; 2% methane | Gas planet, surface not visible; planet appears blue; is made of rock and ice; faint, circulating cloud bands; axis is tilted 98°—appears to be rolling on side |
| Neptune | 80% hydrogen; 19% helium; 1% methane | Gas planet, surface not visible; planet appears blue; is made of rock and ice; faint, circulating cloud bands; Neptune and Pluto cross orbits; mysterious Great Dark Spots visible |
| Pluto | Thought to contain nitrogen, carbon dioxide, and methane | Smallest planet in our solar system; dark and light areas—perhaps ice caps; from January 1979 to February 1999, it was the eighth planet in solar system (in distance from sun); Pluto and Charon rotate around each other |

of each planet in our solar system. Table 9-2 compares the atmospheres and outstanding features of each planet.

## Satellites

Natural **satellites** are solid objects in the solar system that revolve around planets. There are several explanations for the development of a satellite. Some satellites appear to have formed at the same time as the planet, others appear to be smaller planets that were captured, and still others appear to be captured asteroids. The larger planets also contain ring structures similar to what is commonly seen around Saturn. The rings are composed of rock fragments and/or ice crystals that range in size from that of dust particles to large boulders.

Larger satellites are visible from Earth and have been observed for many years. Smaller satellites are being identified and named regularly as space exploration technology improves. Jupiter, Saturn, Uranus, and Neptune appear to have more satellites than presently identified.

Mercury and Venus are the only planets that do not have any satellites. The moon is the only natural satellite that revolves around Earth.

Mars has two irregularly shaped satellites, Phobos and Deimos. These rocklike bodies are relatively close to Mars and revolve rapidly around it. Phobos revolves in about 7 hours and Deimos revolves in about 31 hours.

Jupiter has 17 named satellites and at least 11 other rocky objects that have been identified. The four largest satellites, Ganymede, Callisto, Io, and Europa, can be viewed with a small telescope from Earth (see Figure 9-8). Io has active volcanoes. Jupiter also has a faint ring structure composed of small grains of rock material.

Saturn has 18 named satellites and at least 12 smaller rocky objects that have been identified. Titan is the largest of the 30 satellites; it con-

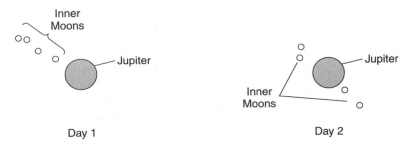

**Figure 9-8.** The changing positions of Jupiter's four inner satellites. (You can use a small telescope to observe these satellites.)

**Figure 9-9.** Saturn is the planet with the most prominent ring structure. The rings are composed of rock fragments and/or ice crystals of many sizes.

tains a thick atmosphere that hides its surface. A well-defined ring structure also revolves around Saturn (see Figure 9-9). The whole ring structure is less than 1 kilometer in width.

Uranus has 21 identified satellites; it is likely that more exist, which have not yet been located. Some of the unique features found on this planet's largest satellites are: Miranda has ridges and valleys on its surface; Ariel has rifts and fault scarps on its surface; Umbriel has an extremely dark surface; Titania has many craters and faults related to tectonic activity; and Oberon contains abundant craters. A faint ring structure exists around Uranus. The whole ring structure is up to 10 meters in width.

Neptune has eight satellites. The largest satellite is Triton; its surface contains craters and a strange area with a texture that resembles cantaloupe skin. Pluto has one satellite, named Charon. Pluto's diameter is only 2260 kilometers, while Charon's diameter is 1200 kilometers. The two bodies are 19,200 kilometers apart and they revolve around a common, central point as if they were tumbling together through space.

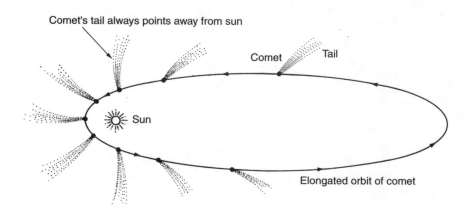

**Figure 9-10.** The typical orbit of a comet around the sun is highly elliptical.

## Asteroids, Comets, and Meteoroids

*Asteroids* are rock fragments of various shapes and sizes that revolve around the sun. Many are found in a region called the asteroid belt, between the orbits of Mars and Jupiter (refer to Figure 9-1). Some scientists think that the asteroids are materials left over from the birth of our solar system that never combined to form a planet.

A *comet* is a loose mass of rock, ice, dust, and gases that moves through space as a unit. Comets travel in stretched-out elliptical orbits. As a comet approaches the sun, energy from the sun makes the comet glow and produce a "tail." The comet's tail always points away from the sun, regardless of the direction in which the comet is moving (see Figure 9-10).

A *meteoroid* is a rock fragment that orbits the sun in association with asteroids and comets. Sometimes these fragments enter Earth's atmosphere at high speed. Contact with the atmosphere creates friction, which causes the meteoroid to heat up and burn. This produces a bright streak across the night sky, called a **meteor** or a "shooting star." Occasionally, a large meteoroid does not burn up completely and a chunk of rock, called a *meteorite*, reaches Earth's surface.

A large group of meteoroids traveling together in an orbit around the sun is referred to as a *swarm*. Swarms are usually associated with comets and, over a period of time, they disperse their particles throughout their orbital path. If Earth's orbit intersects the path of a meteoroid swarm each year, a predictable meteor shower will occur (see Figure 9-11). On these nights, many meteors will occur in a specific area of the night sky. The Perseid meteor shower occurs around August 11 each year, when Earth passes through the orbit of a large swarm of meteoroids.

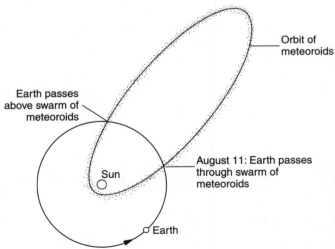

**Figure 9-11.** A swarm of meteoroids scatters particles throughout its orbit. If Earth passes through the particles, the planet experiences a meteor shower.

## SKILLS ACTIVITY **1**

### ANALYZING A CONNECTION BETWEEN TECHNOLOGY AND SCIENCE KNOWLEDGE

In 1610, Galileo discovered moons, or satellites, revolving around planets in the solar system. Using a telescope to observe the night sky, he saw four moons revolving around Jupiter. Since that time, discoveries made by other astronomers include three previously unknown planets and many more satellites.

In the early 1600s, Kepler formulated laws on the motion of objects in space. When objects were observed to move differently than predicted by these laws, curious astronomers investigated the cause. They found that the gravitational force exerted by an as-yet-unknown object could explain the unpredictable motions. Using mathematical calculations, they could determine the approximate size and location of the object. Searching for these objects led to the discovery of the three outermost planets and some of the satellites in the solar system.

The use of space probes and telescopes has aided in the discovery of distant satellites. The telescope was first used for astronomy in 1609, when Galileo made some initial discoveries with it. Today, after many technological improvements, different types of telescopes continue to look farther into space. Over the past 30 years, space probes sent to the outer reaches of the solar system have helped scientists discover many additional satellites.

The table below lists the known planets and the number of known satellites at different dates. Use the information presented above and in the table to answer the following questions.

**Number of Known Satellites and Their Discovery Dates**

| Planet | 1609 | 1892 | 1962 | 1982 | 2002 |
| --- | --- | --- | --- | --- | --- |
| Mercury | 0 | 0 | 0 | 0 | 0 |
| Venus | 0 | 0 | 0 | 0 | 0 |
| Earth | 1 | 1 | 1 | 1 | 1 |
| Mars | 0 | 2 | 2 | 2 | 2 |
| Jupiter | 3 | 4 | 12 | 16 | 28 |
| Saturn | 0 | 8 | 9 | 16 | 30 |
| Uranus | ND* | 4 | 5 | 5 | 21 |
| Neptune | ND* | 1 | 2 | 2 | 8 |
| Pluto | ND* | ND* | 0 | 1 | 1 |

*ND: Planet not yet discovered.

## Questions

1. The discoveries of additional planets and satellites over the past 400 years were made possible by

   A. curious scientists and improved technology

   B. Kepler's laws of planetary motion

C. the use of mathematical calculations

D. all of the above

2. Astronomers will most likely continue to find additional satellites around the outer planets because

A. space technology keeps improving

B. mathematical skills are improving

C. their predictions are improving

D. the laws of motion are changing

3. Why has the number of known satellites for the inner planets (Mercury, Venus, Earth, and Mars) remained almost constant, while the number of known satellites for the outer planets has increased during the past 400 years?

## SKILLS ACTIVITY 2
### DETERMINING A QUANTITATIVE RELATIONSHIP

For a planet to remain in orbit around the sun, the gravitational pull of the sun on the planet must be in balance with the planet's speed and distance from the sun. Without this balance, the planet would not stay in orbit.

Since the effect of the sun's gravity becomes stronger the closer an object gets to it, planets near the sun have to move faster than planets farther away to avoid being pulled into the sun. This suggests that there is a relationship between a planet's orbital speed and its distance from the sun.

**Planet's Average Orbital Speed and Average Distance From the Sun**

| Planet | Average Orbital Speed (kilometers/second) | Average Distance from the Sun (kilometers) |
|---|---|---|
| Mercury | 47.60 | 57,900,000 |
| Venus | 34.82 | 108,200,000 |
| Earth | 29.62 | 149,600,000 |
| Mars | 23.98 | 227,900,000 |
| Jupiter | 12.99 | 778,000,000 |
| Saturn | 9.58 | 1,427,000,000 |
| Uranus | 6.77 | 2,871,000,000 |
| Neptune | 5.41 | 4,497,000,000 |
| Pluto | 4.72 | 5,913,000,000 |

The table reveals that as a planet's distance from the sun increases, its orbital speed decreases. This is called an *inverse relationship*, because as one quantity increases (distance from the sun), the other quantity decreases (orbital speed). Use information presented above and in the table to answer the following questions.

## Questions

1. If Earth moved closer to the sun, to remain in orbit its orbital speed would have to

   A. increase
   B. decrease

   C. increase, then decrease
   D. remain the same

2. If a planet farther from the sun than Pluto were to be discovered, its orbital speed would probably be

   A. faster than Pluto's
   B. slower than Pluto's

   C. the same as Pluto's
   D. impossible to determine

3. If the orbital speed of a newly discovered asteroid was found to be 18.61 kilometers per second, between which two planets would the asteroid's orbit be located?

## Question Set 1

*Multiple Choice*

1. Carol saw a "shooting star" in the night sky. What she actually saw was a
   A. comet
   B. meteor
   C. planet
   D. moving star

2. Which series represents solar system objects from largest to smallest?
   A. sun, moon, Earth, asteroid
   B. sun, Earth, Mars, asteroid
   C. sun, Mars, Jupiter, asteroid
   D. Jupiter, Earth, asteroid, Mars

3.  Jesse saw a group of starlike objects in the night sky on April
    7. A month later, he noticed that one of the objects had moved
    to a different position (see diagram). The object that moved was
    most likely a

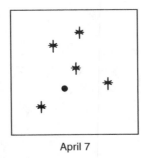
April 7

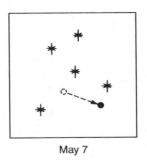
May 7

A.  star
B.  planet

C.  meteoroid
D.  weather balloon

4.  The major members of the solar system are the
    A.  comets and meteoroids
    B.  asteroids and satellites
    C.  sun and the moon
    D.  sun and the planets

5.  Earth is apparently the only planet in our solar system that
    A.  has a natural satellite
    B.  revolves around the sun
    C.  supports living organisms
    D.  has a day side and a night side

## Open Ended

6.  The table below lists the length of rotation for five of the
    planets. Which planet is spinning most rapidly on its axis?

| Planet | Length of One Rotation |
| --- | --- |
| Mercury | 59 days |
| Venus | 243 days |
| Earth | 24 hrs |
| Mars | 24.6 hrs |
| Jupiter | 9.9 hrs |

7. The diagram shows the four inner planets at various positions in their orbits. Which planet would be visible from Earth in the night sky? Why?

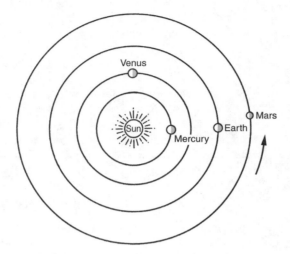

8. To revolve completely around the sun, Earth takes 365¼ days and Mars takes 687 days. At the end of one Earth year, about how far along will Mars be in its orbital path?

9. Contrast the planets Earth and Mars by stating three differences between them.

10. The table below lists some data about the nine planets. Review the data carefully and determine one way you can divide the planets into two groups. Explain what criteria you used to group the planets.

| Planet (in order from the sun) | Distance from the sun* | Size (width in km) | Time to revolve once around sun | Time to rotate once on axis | Number of natural satellites |
|---|---|---|---|---|---|
| Mercury | 0.4 | 4,878 | 88 days | 59 days | 0 |
| Venus | 0.7 | 12,104 | 225 days | 243 days | 0 |
| Earth | 1.0 | 12,756 | 365.25 days | 24 hrs | 1 |
| Mars | 1.5 | 6,787 | 1.88 yrs | 24.6 hrs | 2 |
| Jupiter | 5.2 | 142,800 | 11.86 yrs | 9.9 hrs | 17 |
| Saturn | 9.5 | 120,660 | 29.63 yrs | 10.6 hrs | 18 |
| Uranus | 19.2 | 51,118 | 83.97 yrs | 17 hrs | 21 |
| Neptune | 30.1 | 49,528 | 165 yrs | 16 hrs | 8 |
| Pluto | 39.5 | 2,300 | 248 yrs | 6.4 days | 1 |

*In Earth-sun units, i.e., the average distance from Earth to the sun (149,600,000 kilometers).

# THE MOON AND ITS RELATIONSHIP TO EARTH

## The Moon

The moon is a sphere of rock that revolves around Earth as Earth revolves around the sun. It is Earth's only natural satellite and our nearest neighbor in space. There is no water or air on the moon, so it cannot support life. Because the moon is so small, its gravity is too weak to hold moisture or an atmosphere at its surface.

The moon has a variety of surface features. The dark areas of the moon are low, flat plains. The light areas are mountainous highlands. As shown in Figure 9-12, the moon's surface is pockmarked by numerous *craters*, which are circular pits ringed by walls, or rims. Rock fragments that struck the moon's surface formed most of its craters.

**Figure 9-12.** The moon has darker and lighter areas and is pockmarked by numerous craters, which formed when rocks struck its surface. (Photograph courtesy of NASA.)

Moon phases, eclipses, and tides are produced by the relative positions of the Earth, moon, and sun. These events are predictable because the motion of these objects is known with great accuracy.

## Motions and Phases of the Moon

The moon takes 29½ days, about one month, to revolve around Earth. This is the period of time from one full moon to the next full moon (see Figure 9-13). As the moon orbits Earth, it also rotates on its axis. Because the moon completes one rotation in the same amount of time it takes to orbit Earth once, the same side of the moon always faces Earth (see position *A* in Figure 9-13). Not until 1966, when a spacecraft circled the moon and took photographs, did we learn what the moon's far side looks like.

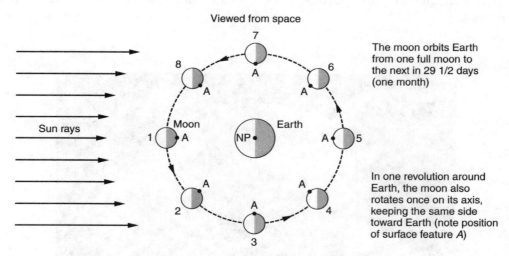

**Figure 9-13.** The moon takes 29½ days to complete its orbit of Earth. As the moon rotates on its axis, it keeps the same side facing Earth.

The moon does not give off its own light, but reflects light from the sun. The sun illuminates half of the moon's surface at all times, just as it always illuminates half of Earth. As the moon revolves around Earth, we see varying amounts of its lighted side, so the shape of the moon appears to change. These apparent changes in shape are called the **phases** of the moon.

At the phase called **new moon**, the moon is between Earth and the sun. The side facing Earth is dark, so the moon cannot be seen. At **full moon** phase, the moon is on the opposite side of Earth from the sun,

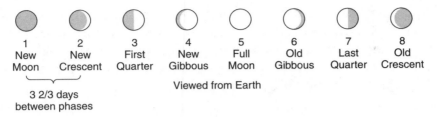

| 1 | 2 | 3 | 4 | 5 | 6 | 7 | 8 |
|---|---|---|---|---|---|---|---|
| New Moon | New Crescent | First Quarter | New Gibbous | Full Moon | Old Gibbous | Last Quarter | Old Crescent |

3 2/3 days between phases

Viewed from Earth

**Figure 9-14.** The phases of the moon: It takes 29½ days from one full moon to the next.

and the side facing Earth is completely illuminated. Figure 9-14 shows the main phases of the moon, as viewed from our planet.

## Eclipses

When the sun, Earth, and moon are in a straight line, an event called an *eclipse* occurs. Either the moon passes between the Earth and sun, or the Earth passes between the moon and sun.

A *lunar eclipse* takes place when Earth is positioned between the sun and the moon, which causes Earth's shadow to fall on the moon. This can happen only when the moon is full, as shown in Figure 9-15(a). A lunar eclipse is visible from many places on Earth and takes a few hours from start to finish.

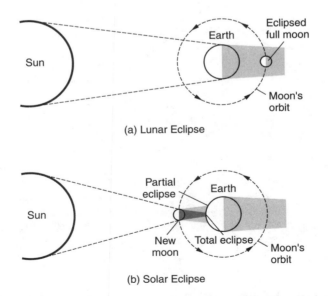

(a) Lunar Eclipse

(b) Solar Eclipse

**Figure 9-15.** Eclipses: A lunar eclipse occurs when the moon passes into Earth's shadow (a); a solar eclipse occurs when the moon casts its shadow on Earth, thereby blocking the rays of the sun (b).

A *solar eclipse* takes place when the moon is positioned between the sun and Earth, and casts its shadow on Earth. This can occur only during new moon phase, as shown in Figure 9-15(b). A solar eclipse is visible only over a small area on Earth. A *total eclipse*, in which the sun is completely blocked by the moon, lasts only a few minutes.

## The Moon and Earth's Tides

The tides are the regular rise and fall in the level of ocean waters that take place twice each day. These changes in sea level are caused by the gravitational pull of the moon and, to a lesser extent, the sun. The moon is much closer to Earth than the sun is, so the moon's gravity affects Earth's tides more strongly than does the sun's gravity.

The pull of the moon's gravity draws the ocean waters into two large bulges, one on the side of Earth facing the moon and one on the opposite side of Earth. High tides occur at each of these two positions (see Figure 9-16). Halfway between the tidal bulges, and one-quarter of the way around Earth, the ocean level falls, producing low tides. As Earth rotates, locations on Earth experience changing tides. The gradual change from high tide to low tide takes a little more than 6 hours; and it takes a little more than 6 hours for the water to rise from low tide to high tide again.

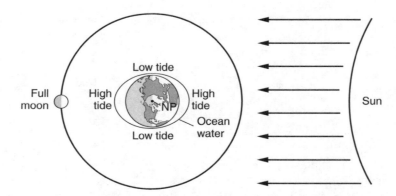

**Figure 9-16.** High tides occur at positions on Earth facing directly toward or away from the moon. Low tides occur at positions halfway between the high tides.

When the sun, Earth, and moon are lined up, the gravity of the sun and moon combine to produce exceptionally high and low tides. When they are not lined up, the tides are less extreme.

## SKILLS ACTIVITY 3

### PREDICTING THE PHASES OF THE MOON

The phases of the moon go through a complete cycle every 29½ days. There are eight named moon phases; it takes about 3⅔ days for the moon to slowly change from one phase to the next (refer to Figure 9-14). When you know the date of a given phase of the moon, you can predict the upcoming dates of future phases. Based on this information and on the calendar below, answer the following questions.

| July 2002 | | | | | | | August 2002 | | | | | | |
|---|---|---|---|---|---|---|---|---|---|---|---|---|---|
| Su | M | T | W | Th | F | Sa | Su | M | T | W | Th | F | Sa |
| | 1 | 2 | 3 | 4 | 5 | 6 | | | | | 1 | 2 | 3 |
| 7 | 8 | 9 | 10 | 11 | 12 | 12 | 4 | 5 | 6 | 7 | 8 | 9 | 10 |
| 14 | 15 | 16 | 17 | 18 | 19 | 20 | 11 | 12 | 13 | 14 | 15 | 16 | 17 |
| 21 | 22 | 23 | 24 | 25 | 26 | 27 | 18 | 19 | 20 | 21 | 22 | 23 | 24 |
| 28 | 29 | 30 | 31 | | | | 25 | 26 | 27 | 28 | 29 | 30 | 31 |

## Questions

1. Brad knew there was a full moon on July 24, 2002. He wanted to camp out in his yard on the night of the next full moon. On what date should Brad have camped out? Explain.

2. Calculate the dates of the last quarter, new moon, and first quarter phases in August.

3. Draw a diagram to show what the moon would have looked like on August 5, 2002. Explain.

4. The Perseid meteor shower occurred on August 12, 2002. How much did the moonlight interfere with Brad's ability to observe the meteor shower? Explain your answer.

## Question Set 2

*Multiple Choice*

1. Eva wanted to photograph a full moon on January 1, but the night was cloudy. When will be her next opportunity to take a picture of a full moon?
   A. January 15
   B. January 30
   C. February 10
   D. February 18

2. The moon shines by means of
   A. its own light
   B. radioactivity
   C. light reflected off Earth
   D. reflecting the sunlight

3. As it revolves around Earth, the moon
   A. always has the same side facing Earth
   B. does not rotate at all on its axis
   C. has its far side facing Earth
   D. does not reflect any sunlight

Refer to the diagram below to answer questions 4 and 5.

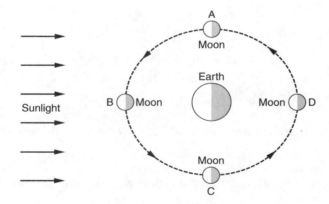

4. The moon's shadow may fall on Earth, causing a solar eclipse, when the moon is in
   A. position *A*
   B. position *B*
   C. position *C*
   D. position *D*

5. At which position in its orbit can all of the moon's lighted side be seen from Earth?
   A. position *A*
   B. position *B*
   C. position *C*
   D. position *D*

6. Diagram (a) shows how the moon looked on three nights in May. Which figure in diagram (b) shows how the moon would most likely appear on the night of May 15?

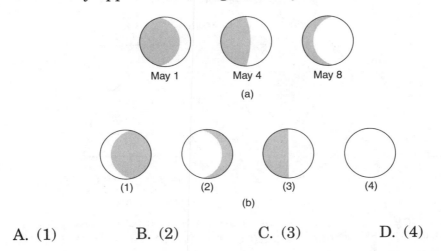

May 1          May 4          May 8

(a)

(1)          (2)          (3)          (4)

(b)

A. (1)          B. (2)          C. (3)          D. (4)

## Open Ended

7. Kareem saw the moon over a tree at 9:00 P.M. (position *A* in the diagram). An hour later, the moon had moved to position *B*. What caused this apparent change in position?

8. The table below shows the times at which high tides and low tides occurred over a two-day period. Based on the pattern in the table, predict the time of the next low tide.

### TIDAL DATA TABLE

| Day | Time | Tide | Day | Time | Tide |
|---|---|---|---|---|---|
| *April 1* | 4:20 A.M. | Low | *April 2* | 5:10 A.M. | Low |
| | 10:35 A.M. | High | | 11:25 A.M. | High |
| | 4:45 P.M. | Low | | 5:35 P.M. | Low |
| | 11:00 P.M. | High | | 11:50 P.M. | High |

9. The diagram below compares how the sun's gravity and the moon's gravity affect Earth's tides. Which object has a greater effect on Earth's tides? Explain why.

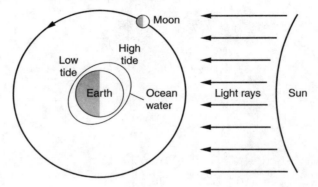

10. During what phase of the moon can a solar eclipse occur? Describe the moon's location relative to the sun and Earth. (Draw a diagram to illustrate your answer.)

# Chapter 10

# Organisms and Their Environment

**Macro Statement:** Recognize the environment as a system of interdependent components affected by human activity and natural phenomena.

## KNOWLEDGE STATEMENTS

**A.** Personal and societal activities impact the environment.

**B.** Human practice affects the use and management of natural resources.

**C.** Individuals and groups may have differing points of view on environmental issues.

**D.** In an ecosystem, living communities and their physical environment function together as an interdependent and relatively stable system.

## CHAPTER OUTLINE

**Organisms and Ecosystems**

**Human and Natural Impacts on Ecosystems**

# ORGANISMS AND ECOSYSTEMS

 **Living Things**

Look at Figure 10-1. How can we classify all the things that are shown in the diagram into two categories? One way is to separate the living things from the nonliving things. For example, birds, fish, plants, and insects are living things; water, rocks, air, and soil are nonliving things. Living things are called *organisms*. They share certain characteristics that set them apart from nonliving things. In particular, organisms carry out life processes (discussed in detail in Chapter 3).

**Figure 10-1.** Living things have characteristics that set them apart from nonliving things.

Living things interact constantly with their surroundings, called the ***environment***. An organism's environment includes all living and nonliving things around it. Organisms obtain food, water, and oxygen from the environment. In turn, they release wastes, such as carbon dioxide. Thus, there is a continual exchange of materials between an organism and its environment. The study of the interaction between organisms and their environment is called ***ecology***.

 **Communities and Ecosystems**

The particular environment in which an organism normally lives is called its ***habitat***. There are many different types of habitats in the world, including such diverse kinds as desert, salt marsh, lake, coral reef, stream, prairie, rain forest, and tundra. Habitats vary in the amounts of water, light, temperature, and wind that they receive. As a result, different types of organisms live in the various habitats, but they all depend on other organisms for survival. All the different

**Figure 10-2a.** All the different species living in this habitat make up the lake community.

species within a habitat make up a ***community***, such as that seen in the lake habitat in Figure 10-2a.

When you set up an aquarium that contains plants, snails, and guppies, you also create a small community (see Figure 10-2b). To set up an aquarium, you must provide more than just the animals and plants. You need water, a source of additional oxygen (air bubbles), gravel, and light. You must also maintain a proper water temperature.

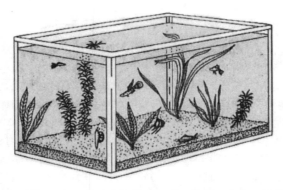

**Figure 10-2b.** All the different species living in the tank make up the aquarium community.

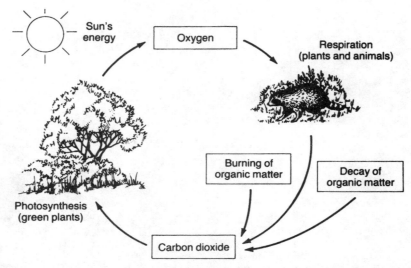

**Figure 10-3.** Oxygen and carbon dioxide are constantly recycled within an ecosystem.

Just as in a lake habitat, these nonliving factors along with the living members of the community make up an **ecosystem**. The living members of a community get the materials they need to survive from the ecosystem. In return, they give back materials, such as waste products and their dead, decaying bodies. Materials are constantly recycled within an ecosystem. Figure 10-3 shows how oxygen and carbon dioxide are recycled. Energy, however, is not recycled; it must be continually provided by an outside source, mainly the sun. In a lake, water is replenished by rain through the water cycle (discussed in Chapter 8). But in an aquarium, the water is not recycled; it is lost to the environment through evaporation. You need to replace the water that has evaporated.

 **Nutrition**

Every organism needs food to stay alive. Food provides an organism with **nutrients**, which are used for growth and repair and for producing energy. Energy can be stored in chemical bonds. The energy stored in the food's chemical bonds is released to provide an organism with energy for life processes. Plants (and algae) make their own food through the process called *photosynthesis* (see Figure 10-4). Plants use energy from sunlight to convert carbon dioxide and water taken from their environment into sugar (glucose). The sun's energy is thereby stored in the sugar. Photosynthesis also produces oxygen, which is released into the environment. The green pigment chlorophyll, present in plant

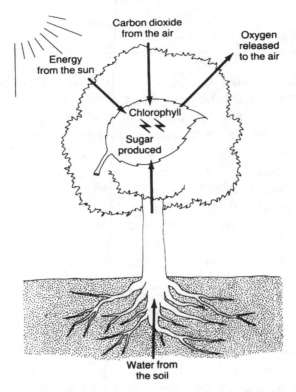

**Figure 10-4.** Green plants use the energy of sunlight to make their food.

leaves, is necessary for this process to take place. Animals obtain nutrients by eating plants or other animals that feed on plants. Animals use the sugar in plants to produce energy. The original source of all energy in food is the sun. Figure 10-5 shows one way to get food energy from the sun.

**Figure 10-5.** Food energy from the sun is transferred from plants to animals (including humans).

 **Food Chains**

Plants make their own food, so they are called ***producers***. Animals have to ingest their food, so they are called ***consumers***. Plant-eating animals, or ***herbivores***, get their energy from the plants they eat. Meat-eating animals, or ***carnivores***, also get energy from plants, but indirectly. For instance, when a lion eats a zebra, it obtains nutrients from the zebra's meat. The lion gets its energy from these nutrients. The zebra had obtained these nutrients from the plants that it ate. Animals that hunt and kill their food, such as the lion, are called ***predators***. The animals that they hunt, such as the zebra, are called their ***prey***. Both the lion and the zebra depend on other organisms for their food. Animals that eat plants and animals are ***omnivores***.

Nearly every animal depends, either directly or indirectly, on green plants for food and oxygen. The nutrients in plants get passed along from one organism to another in a feeding sequence called a ***food chain*** (see Figure 10-6). For example, grass produces food during the process of photosynthesis; a rabbit eats the grass to get its nutrients; and then a hawk eats the rabbit. When the hawk dies, its body decays. Special organisms called ***decomposers*** break down the hawk's remains and return its nutrients to the soil. Plants, such as grass, can then use these nutrients again. Decomposers include fungi, such as mushrooms and molds, and some bacteria. Fungi and decay bacteria cannot make their own food. Therefore, they depend on other living things for food. Decomposers are the last link in any food chain. Suppose that, suddenly, there were no more rabbits. How would the hawk get its nutrients? A hawk can also eat other types of animals. If the rabbits were gone, the hawk would eat more of another animal, such as mice. Thus, the removal of one species from a food chain would affect other species.

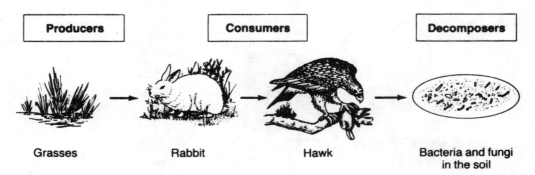

**Figure 10-6.** In a food chain, nutrients in plants get passed along from one organism to another.

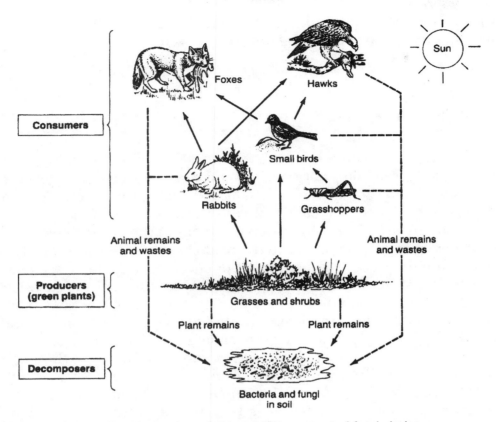

**Figure 10-7.** A food web consists of several interconnected food chains.

## Food Webs

Most ecosystems contain a number of food chains that are interconnected to form a *food web*, as shown in Figure 10-7. Energy (in the form of nutrients) flows through a food web from organism to organism. An ecosystem must contain a constant supply of energy that is available to all organisms within it. There is a delicate balance in an ecosystem among the producers, consumers, decomposers, and the environment. Even the lives of animals that do not prey on one another may be connected. For example, both the fox and the hawk, shown in the food web, prey on small birds and rabbits. The fox and the hawk are in *competition* for the same food items. A decrease in the numbers of foxes would increase the food supply available to the hawks, and vice versa.

Suppose the predator in an ecosystem is destroyed, perhaps due to people's actions. What would happen to the prey in that ecosystem? If a predator were removed from an ecosystem, the population of its prey would increase. This, in turn, would affect the amount of vegetation. The increased number of prey animals would require more vegetation to feed them. As the amount of vegetation decreased from overgrazing, other consumers would be affected as well.

 ## Energy in the Food Web

What happens to you when you exercise? Exercising causes you to "burn" a lot of food for energy. As you do this, your body temperature increases. Heat is being created and lost to the environment. Every organism uses some of the energy it consumes and stores the rest. The energy that is used is lost to the environment in the form of heat. Only the stored energy is available to the next consumer in the food chain. This results in a decreasing amount of energy available at each successive step of the food chain. Which of the organisms in Figure 10-7 would provide the smallest amount of energy per gram consumed? The hawk and the fox are carnivores that eat other consumers. Not all of the energy from the grass is passed along to the fox. The rabbit uses some of this energy to stay alive. The fox and the hawk have the smallest amount of available energy per gram.

As you move up the food chain, the amount of available energy in the same amount of food becomes less and less. This can be represented by a pyramid, which gets smaller and smaller toward the top. Figure 10-8 illustrates an energy, or food, pyramid. What type of organism is always at the base? A food pyramid always has plants or algae (producers) at its base.

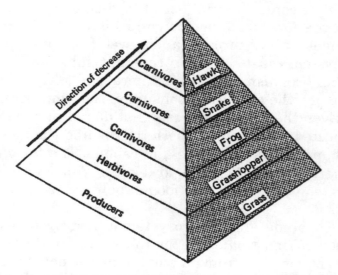

**Figure 10-8.** A food pyramid shows the relationship of producers to consumers; the producers (plants and algae) are always at its base.

## SKILLS ACTIVITY **1**

## ORGANIZING DATA

A student observes the animals in an environment and reports the following: There are trees and grasses. The rabbits and deer eat the grass; and the deer, squirrels, and small birds eat the fruits, berries, and leaves of the trees. Foxes hunt for the rabbits and squirrels. Large birds also eat the rabbits.

1.  Copy the diagram below into your notebook. Fill in (within their correct spaces) each of the organisms from the food web described above.

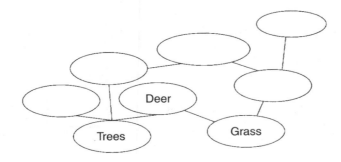

2.  Draw an arrow showing the direction in which energy flows in this food web.
3.  What might happen to this food web if a disease killed most of the rabbits?
4.  Copy the table below into your notebook. Based on the food web, identify each of the organisms as a producer, herbivore, or carnivore by checking the appropriate space. The first organism has been identified for you.

| Organism | Producer | Herbivore | Carnivore |
|----------|----------|-----------|-----------|
| Grasses | ✓ | | |
| Foxes | | | |
| Rabbits | | | |
| Deer | | | |
| Small birds | | | |
| Trees | | | |
| Large birds | | | |
| Squirrels | | | |

## Question Set 1

*Multiple Choice*

To answer questions 1 through 3, use the following diagram, which represents a food chain.

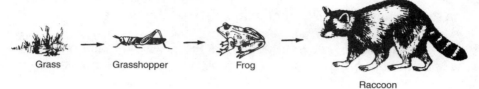

1. Which organism is the producer in this food chain?
   A. grass
   B. grasshopper
   C. frog
   D. raccoon

2. In this food chain, the frog is a
   A. producer
   B. consumer
   C. decomposer
   D. herbivore

3. Which type of organism is *not* shown in this diagram?
   A. producer
   B. consumer
   C. decomposer
   D. green plant

Use the following diagram, which represents a food web, to answer questions 4 through 7.

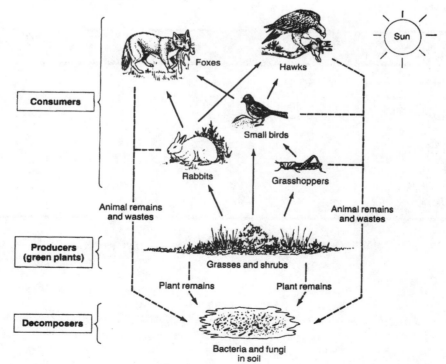

**4.** A decrease in the number of small birds would most likely result in an increase in the number of
   A. rabbits
   B. hawks
   C. foxes
   D. grasshoppers

**5.** The organisms that return nutrients to the soil are the
   A. producers
   B. consumers
   C. decomposers
   D. green plants

**6.** The producers in this ecosystem get their energy from the
   A. rabbits
   B. consumers
   C. decomposers
   D. sun

**7.** Animals that eat only plants are called herbivores. Animals that eat only meat are called carnivores. Animals that can eat both meat and plants are called omnivores. According to the food web, which organism may be considered an omnivore?
   A. grasshopper
   B. small bird
   C. hawk
   D. fox

Base your answer to question 8 on the diagram below, which represents a food pyramid.

**8.** Which organism would be considered a producer?
   A. the human, because it is at the top of the pyramid
   B. the pig, because it changes the energy in plants into food
   C. the corn, because it changes energy from the sun into food
   D. the corn and the pig, because they both can be eaten

**9.** Which of these organisms makes its own food?
   A. frog      B. bird      C. tree      D. snake

**10.** Photosynthesis is the process by which plants make their own food. The energy for photosynthesis comes from
   A. the sun      B. oxygen      C. water      D. wind

11. All of the organisms that live in a pond make up
    A. a habitat
    B. a community
    C. the environment
    D. an ecosystem

Base your answers to questions 12 and 13 on the following diagram, which illustrates a small ecosystem.

12. All animals need oxygen to live, even animals that live in the water. The main source of oxygen in this ecosystem would be the
    A. water
    B. fish
    C. snails
    D. green plants

13. Many important, nonliving factors within an ecosystem are recycled, although some are not. The survival of this community depends upon a constant external supply of
    A. energy
    B. oxygen
    C. carbon dioxide
    D. plants

Base your answers to questions 14 and 15 on the diagram below, which represents a food pyramid.

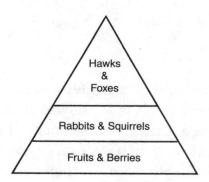

14. Based on this food pyramid, which would provide the greatest quantity of energy per pound when eaten?
    A. apples    B. rabbits    C. hawks    D. foxes

15. Which organism can be considered a carnivore?
    A. rabbits, because they eat berries
    B. berries, because they produce sugar from the sun's energy

   C. squirrels, because they eat acorns
   D. hawks, because they eat animals

**16.** Which of the following is the most likely outcome when a predator has been eliminated from an ecosystem?
   A. The number of prey decreases, while the vegetation increases.
   B. The number of prey increases, while the vegetation decreases.
   C. Both the number of prey and vegetation will decrease.
   D. Both the number of prey and vegetation will increase.

**17.** Which statement describes the energy changes that occur in an ecosystem?
   A. The larger animals provide energy for the smaller animals and plants.
   B. The sun's energy is made available to other organisms through the plants.
   C. Energy for the plants and animals comes from the remains of dead organisms.
   D. The smaller animals provide energy for the larger animals and plants.

## Open Ended

**18.** Explain why green plants (or algae) must be part of every food web.

Base your answers to questions 19 through 22 on the following diagram, which illustrates a food web.

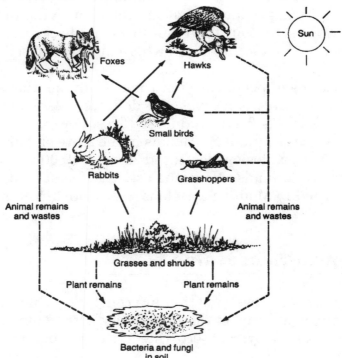

19. Which species are producers?

20. Which species are predators?

21. Explain how two other species would be affected by a decrease in the number of rabbits.

22. How might the disappearance of the small birds from this food web cause a decrease in the rabbit population?

# HUMAN AND NATURAL IMPACTS ON ECOSYSTEMS

 ## Upsetting the Balance of Nature

The interactions between predator and prey, and the competition between species for food, water, and shelter, create a delicate balance in nature. If this balance is disturbed, it may change the entire ecosystem. Human activities can have a negative impact on the environment that affects wildlife populations. For example, early settlers in the northeastern United States killed all the wolves in the region because they preyed on their farm animals. However, the wolves were the only natural predators that ate the deer living in the area. Without the wolves to hold their numbers in check, the deer increased their population to the point where many starved to death each winter.

The actions of people are not the only things that can disturb the balance of nature. Sometimes, the delicate balance is upset by natural events, such as floods and forest fires. For example, in May 1980, the large volcano Mount St. Helens in the state of Washington erupted violently. The explosion destroyed almost 40,000 hectares of forest, killing many animals. Nevertheless, the forest and its inhabitants have returned to Mount St. Helens, reestablishing a natural balance.

 ## Ecological Succession

Ecosystems are systems that are constantly changing, resulting in changes to the makeup of the community. After a forest fire or volcanic eruption has destroyed an ecosystem, the soil becomes enriched with

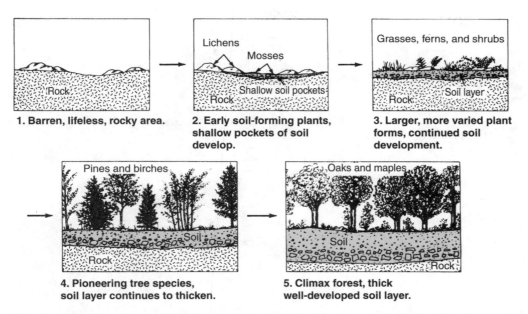

1. Barren, lifeless, rocky area.

2. Early soil-forming plants, shallow pockets of soil develop.

3. Larger, more varied plant forms, continued soil development.

4. Pioneering tree species, soil layer continues to thicken.

5. Climax forest, thick well-developed soil layer.

**Figure 10-9.** The diagrams illustrate ecological succession on land, from barren rock to climax forest.

minerals from the decaying remains of the plants and animals that had lived there. Soon, small new plants sprout. These become the homes and food for insects and small animals. Eventually, these plants die and are replaced by other, larger plants. Each new community changes the environment, making it more suitable for the next community. Finally, a community emerges that is not replaced, called the ***climax community***.

On Mount St. Helens, the climax community was the forest of spruce and fir trees, along with the animals that lived there, which existed before the eruption. The natural process by which one community is replaced by another in an orderly, predictable sequence is called ***ecological succession***. Figure 10-9 illustrates the ecological succession of a barren area into a forest. Even a pond or a lake can undergo a series of changes that eventually results in a forest community. Silt and other sediments that are washed into a lake fill it in over time. As this occurs, plants and fish that prefer the warmer, shallower water replace the previous community. Eventually the lake dries up. First water plants, then land plants establish themselves in the dry lakebed (see Figure 10-10).

 **Natural Resources**

A forest is an important *natural resource*. It supplies wood and oxygen, conserves soil and water, and provides a habitat for wildlife and

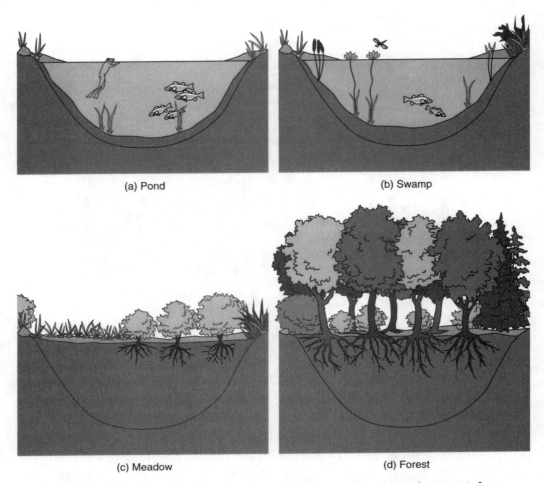

(a) Pond

(b) Swamp

(c) Meadow

(d) Forest

**Figure 10-10.** The diagrams illustrate succession in an aquatic environment, from pond to forest.

recreation for people. Forests that are destroyed can be replaced, although renewal takes a long time. This means that trees are ***renewable resources***; they can be planted and grown again. When plants and animals die and decay, their nutrients are returned to the soil. Therefore, given enough time, soil is also a renewable resource. Water too is renewable, since it is constantly recycled through the environment (see Figure 10-11).

Aluminum, like other minerals, is not replenished by nature. Minerals and other materials that are not naturally replaced are ***nonrenewable resources***. To guarantee an adequate supply of these valuable materials for the future, we must conserve and recycle them today. Although natural processes do recycle water, soil, and plant materials, people often deplete them faster than nature can replace them. Therefore, it is important to conserve renewable resources as well, or they too may be in short supply in the future.

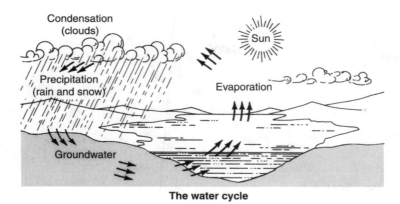

**The water cycle**

**Figure 10-11.** Water is constantly recycled through the environment by the processes of evaporation, condensation, and precipitation.

 # Geologic Events

Some geologic events, such as volcanic eruptions, earthquakes, and tsunami waves, can completely devastate an ecosystem, or disrupt the environment and cause an ecosystem to change. You have read how the explosion on Mount St. Helens destroyed almost 40,000 hectares of forest. In addition, this event caused mudslides, flooding, and the blanketing of land by volcanic ash for many kilometers downwind. Nearby communities on land and in the water were destroyed or disrupted. Many large animals, such as deer, elk, and bear, perished, as did many smaller animals, including birds. However, some animals, like rodents, frogs, and insects, survived the disaster because they lived underground. Soon after the eruption, life started to return to the mountain. Plant roots began to sprout, and seeds that were spared destruction started to germinate. Living communities, in all stages of succession, reappeared around the mountain.

 # Climate Change

Climate is the average condition of the atmosphere over a large region for a period of many years. Life on Earth is well adapted to the varied climatic conditions of the planet; thus, a wide variety of ecosystems exist. However, climate changes can affect communities of living organisms within an ecosystem.

About 18,000 years ago, glacial ice covered a large portion of North America. Fossil evidence indicates that, during this glacial episode, organisms such as the mastodon, woolly mammoth, and saber-toothed

**Figure 10-12.** The woolly mammoth and the saber-toothed cat were adapted to North America's ice-age conditions; they became extinct when the glaciers retreated about 11,000 years ago.

cat lived near the ice sheet (see Figure 10-12). Today, these animals are gone—most likely the victims of a major extinction event that took place across North America about 11,000 years ago, when the glaciers retreated. The warming climate seriously disrupted ecosystems and was probably partly responsible for the extinction of these mammals.

 ## Floods and Droughts

*Floods* occur when there is excessive water on land. Heavy rainfall and rapidly melting snow and ice are the most common causes of flooding. Low-lying land areas near the ocean are commonly flooded by storm surges and exceptionally high tides. Flooding may also upset fish, birds, and invertebrates living in or near rivers and streams.

*Droughts* are caused by a lack of precipitation for extended periods of time. Droughts commonly cause many plants to die, thereby removing the main food source for herbivores in a community. The lack of water can also upset lake and stream ecosystems.

 ## Storms

Thunderstorms, hurricanes, and tornadoes can seriously affect ecosystems. **Thunderstorms** may ignite fires, which can destroy large areas of forest; they may even produce hail that is large enough to destroy crops and other plant life. **Hurricane** storm surges along coasts destroy beach ecosystems for nesting birds and spawning fish. **Tornadoes** are capable of severely disrupting life in a narrow strip of land (see Figure 10-13). In addition, **winter storms** (blizzards and ice storms), consisting of blowing snow, severe cold, and high winds, can cause animals to starve and many living things to freeze to death.

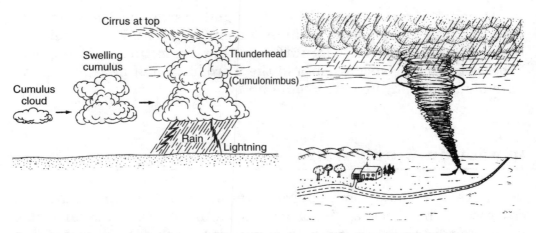

**Figure 10-13.** Thunderstorms and tornadoes can have a devastating impact on an ecosystem.

 ## Forest Fires

Forest fires, or wildfires, destroy large areas of timber each year. In addition to the trees that are destroyed, many other living things die, too. Forest fires may be started by humans or by natural events like lightning strikes. Table 10-1 lists the most common causes of recent U.S. forest fires.

| TABLE 10-1. | CAUSES OF WILDFIRES IN THE U.S. (1984–1990) |
| --- | --- |
| **Cause** | **Percent of Total Number** |
| Arson | 30 |
| Debris burning | 25 |
| Lightning | 11 |
| Miscellaneous | 11 |
| Cigarette smoking | 6 |
| Children | 5 |
| Equipment | 5 |
| Campfires | 3 |
| Railroads | 3 |

Although forest fires can take lives and destroy property, natural wildfires play an important role in the environment. Ecosystems are renewed by the carbon and nutrients that are returned to the soil. Processes such as succession and the introduction of new plants and animals replenish the living community.

 ## Impact on Biodiversity

You have read how some environmental conditions can change an ecosystem. The effects on living species within an ecosystem can range from limiting their diversity, to endangering them, to even causing their extinction—the ultimate destruction of life.

*Biodiversity* describes the variety of different species that exist. There is great value to having a high number of species on Earth. We should protect and preserve biodiversity—not only because complex ecosystems are usually the most stable ones, but also because we depend on a great variety of organisms for our food, clothing, medicine, and industry. Tropical rain forests and coral reefs are examples of ecosystems with great species diversity that are also threatened. Table 10-2 gives an idea of the biodiversity in the world's major coral reefs.

**TABLE 10-2. BIODIVERSITY IN MAJOR CORAL REEFS**

| Coral Reef | Coral Species | Fish Species |
|---|---|---|
| Philippines | 400 | 1500 |
| Great Barrier Reef | 350 | 1500 |
| New Caledonia | 300 | 1000 |
| French Polynesia | 168 | 800 |
| Aqaba (Gulf of) | 150 | 400 |

There are thought to be millions of species alive on Earth that have not yet been identified. Some of these organisms might have unique traits that could be used to develop new sources of food or cures for diseases. Failure to preserve the interconnected diversity of life on Earth could limit our ability to solve future problems and may even limit our own future on Earth.

## Endangered Species

An ***endangered species*** is a group of organisms that appears close to extinction. More and more species are being added to the government's list of endangered species. Many of these plants and animals are endangered because of human activities. Organizations concerned with this problem are developing strategies to save species from extinction. Endangered animal species include the manatee, rhinoceros, elephant, snow leopard, tiger, mountain gorilla, California condor, whooping crane, giant panda, and blue whale (see Figure 10-14a). There are also endangered plant species. Some reasons why species decline and may become extinct include the following:

- Loss of habitat

- Introduced species

- Overgrazing of lands

- Development of area

- Low gene-pool diversity

- Heavy predation (overhunting)

- Vegetation changes

- Competition among species

- Clearing of forests

- Heavy equipment effects

In 1840, the buffalo (bison) population of North America was estimated to be between 30 and 40 million strong. As settlers moved across the plains, massive slaughter of these animals occurred. Professional

(a) Blue whale

**Figure 10-14a.** The blue whale is an endangered species due to overhunting by people.

(b) Bald eagle

**Figure 10-14b.** The bald eagle has recovered from being endangered, but is still protected as a threatened species.

hunters killed buffalo in great numbers for sport and hides. Often, the bodies were left to rot. In the early 1870s, it was estimated that 2.5 million buffalo were killed each year. The last large herd was slaughtered in 1883. By 1900, only 500 American buffalo remained. Since then, various organizations and parks have protected the buffalo, and today the number is back up to about 200,000. The American bald eagle was once thought to be in danger of extinction, too. However, thanks to the efforts of conservationists, the bald eagle is no longer endangered; but it is still officially protected as a *threatened species* (see Figure 10-14b*)*.

 ## Extinction of Species

Extinction occurs when a species dies out. This usually happens when some essential part of its living or nonliving environment is removed. Common natural causes of extinction include climate change and habitat invasion by a predator. Humans also cause extinction by excessive hunting and by pollution of land, air, and water. Some animals known to have become extinct include woolly mammoths, dodo birds, passenger pigeons, and the dinosaur species.

*Dinosaurs.* About 70 percent of all animal species, including all the dinosaurs, became extinct about 65 million years ago. Many theories have been proposed for this great extinction of life on Earth. However, scientists are still not exactly sure what caused it. Theories about the demise of the dinosaurs include climate change, impact of a large asteroid or comet, massive volcanic eruptions, or even some combination of these events. Certainly, their extinction was natural and had nothing to do with human interference, since humans did not even exist yet. Some mammals existed on Earth during the heyday of the dinosaurs. After the dinosaurs' extinction, mammals diversified and became the dominant large land animals (see Figure 10-15).

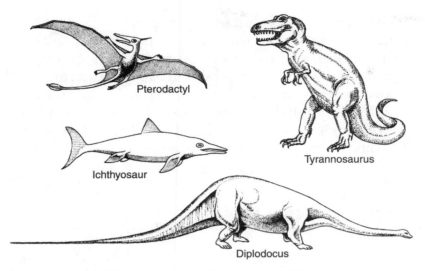

**Figure 10-15.** The extinction of the many dinosaur species resulted from natural causes.

*Passenger Pigeons.* Early in the 1800s, millions of passenger pigeons lived throughout eastern North America. They fed on acorns and beechnuts in forests. Passenger pigeons became a popular food of people and were killed in great numbers. By 1880, the huge flocks were gone, and the pigeon's numbers were decreasing rapidly. The last wild passenger pigeon was seen in 1889, and the last captive one died in the Cincinnati Zoo in 1914. Their extinction was directly due to the overhunting by people.

 **Destruction of Habitats**

As the human population increases, its need for land grows. The land is used to build homes, businesses, and roads; provide water supplies; provide recreation areas; grow food; and provide for waste disposal. When land is changed to meet human needs, the local ecosystem is often disrupted or destroyed. How can the growing human population meet its needs without harming the environment? People can change the land without completely destroying ecosystems; they can focus on living in harmony with nature by not completely removing the ecosystem as they build. In some cases, people have been able to restore damaged ecosystems. An example follows:

In 1941, in order to meet its water demands, the city of Los Angeles began diverting the streams that flowed into Mono Lake. This quickly lowered the water level of the lake and increased its salt content. The rapid change in environment caused the lake's ecosystem to falter. Algae, which were the base of the food chain for all living things in and around the lake, began to die. The brine shrimp population decreased. A lowering of the lake's water level exposed land bridges to islands, which animals could then cross to prey on the lake's bird population. Stream ecosystems deteriorated, and air quality worsened due to organic decay around the lake. In 1984, restoration processes began to reverse some of the stresses placed on Mono Lake and its ecosystems. Today, the living communities in and around the lake are slowly recovering, and people are learning better ways to meet their needs while maintaining natural ecosystems.

 ## Introduction of New Species

Throughout history, humans have transported plants and animals as they traveled. When "foreign" organisms are introduced to a new location, they may upset the existing ecosystem. They often compete for food and space with the local or "native" species, and they may disrupt the entire ecosystem.

For example, in 1788, European settlers introduced rabbits to Australia for the first time. The rabbits multiplied rapidly because they had few natural enemies in the ecosystem. By the mid-1800s, the grasslands were being stripped of vegetation by the rabbits, reducing the available food for native species. Cattle (also an introduced species) found it difficult to find food, too, and were faced with starvation. Scientists introduced a disease-causing virus that killed many of the rabbits. The grasslands recovered and the settlers' cattle were saved.

 ## Pollution of the Environment

For hundreds of years, humans showed little or no concern for the environment. Human activities have put stresses on many ecosystems, and sometimes destroyed them. Factories, power plants, cars, and airplanes all produce harmful substances called ***pollutants***. Pollutants in smoke from factories and vehicles can increase the acidity of the moisture in clouds. When the moisture falls to Earth as *acid rain*, it can harm lakes and forests and the living things in them (see Figure 10-16).

Many industries and most forms of transportation produce carbon dioxide. Many scientists fear that a buildup of carbon dioxide in the atmosphere, caused by human activities, may lead to a rise in worldwide average temperatures, or *global warming*. This could have disastrous effects on many ecosystems by making climates warmer. The higher temperatures might cause some melting of the polar ice caps, resulting in sufficient changes in sea level to flood many coastal cities. Global warming is one example of how individuals or groups may have

**Figure 10-16.** Pollutants in acid rain can harm forests and the organisms living in them.

differing points of view on environmental issues. Some people feel that the amount of carbon dioxide being emitted by factories should be dramatically reduced. Others feel that this will have little effect on the rate of global warming. The debate continues.

Other examples of human activities that cause pollution and affect the environment are the burial and burning of garbage and toxic materials, and the release of sewage into rivers and lakes. Today, many people are showing a concern for the environment and the ecosystems that it supports. As a result, there are sewage-treatment plants and regulations for garbage disposal.

 ## Chemicals in the Environment

Shortly before World War II, the discovery of a very effective pesticide, called *DDT*, gave human beings a powerful weapon in their fight against disease-carrying insects. During the war, DDT protected American troops from typhus, a disease carried by lice. It is estimated by the World Health Organization that roughly 25 million lives have been saved by the use of DDT and similar pesticides. Yet, DDT has been banned from use in the United States since 1972. It was found that, when introduced into the environment, DDT eventually finds its way into the food that is consumed by birds and fish. As fish-eating

## SKILLS ACTIVITY 2
### READING FOR UNDERSTANDING

Although many animal species in the U.S. became endangered during the previous century, only a few became extinct. The efforts of many people have successfully increased the numbers of several animals, such as the bison and bald eagle. One species that may have disappeared, however, is the ivory-billed woodpecker.

Unlike the passenger pigeon, which was hunted to extinction, the ivory-billed woodpecker was seldom deliberately killed. Yet its numbers have decreased, perhaps to zero. Scientists blame the disappearance of this beautiful woodpecker on loss of habitat. The ivory-billed woodpecker feeds on beetles that are found in decaying hardwood trees. As human populations have increased in the southeastern U.S., marshlands have been "cleaned up" and dead and decaying logs have been removed. Deprived of its principal food source, the ivory-billed woodpecker has disappeared in the states. Every now and then, someone claims to have seen one, which creates great excitement among biologists. But, unfortunately, most biologists believe this great bird is extinct.

## Questions

1. Based on this passage, you could conclude that efforts to save endangered species are

    A. always successful

    B. usually successful

    C. always unsuccessful

    D. usually unsuccessful

2. Excessive hunting caused the extinction of the

    A. bald eagle

    B. bison

    C. passenger pigeon

    D. manatee

3. The major cause for the disappearance of the ivory-billed woodpecker seems to be

    A. water pollution

    B. destruction of habitat

    C. introduction of a new species

    D. introduction of chemicals into the environment

birds, such as eagles and ospreys, accumulated DDT in their bodies, the chemical entered and weakened their eggshells, making the birds unable to hatch offspring. (Refer to Figure 10-14b.)

So great were the declines in the population of certain birds, that biologist and author Rachel Carson wrote a book called *Silent Spring*, which warned of the possible extinction of many species. Although DDT has probably saved more human lives than any single chemical substance, today we weigh the benefits to humans against the damage to other species. We can always search for another insecticide, but the extinction of another species cannot be undone.

More recently, scientists have become concerned about the destruction of the ozone layer. The ozone layer is an area in the upper atmosphere that filters out harmful ultraviolet radiation. Without this filter, there would be a dramatic increase in the occurrence of skin cancer. The ozone layer has been reduced due to chemicals called *chlorofluorocarbons*, or *CFCs*. These CFCs were once used as the propellants in aerosol cans, and as coolants in refrigerators and air conditioners. Although, at the time, it was thought that the small amount of CFCs in the environment could not make any difference, it was demonstrated in 1986 that CFCs have had a definite impact on the atmosphere. The propellants used in air conditioners, refrigerators, and spray cans have since been changed to more "environment-friendly" substances. Through increased awareness of ecological interactions, people try to prevent continued disruptions of the environment and to counteract the negative results of past actions.

## Question Set 2

*Multiple Choice*

1. As the population of old shrubs decreases in a changing ecosystem, the population of new trees increases. The old community
   A. destroys the new ecosystem
   B. prepares the ecosystem for the new community
   C. is the climax community
   D. does not provide nutrients to the soil

Brief case histories of three species are presented below. Read each of the cases; then answer questions 2 through 4.

*Case 1:* In 1598, Portuguese sailors discovered the dodo on the island of Mauritius, in the Indian Ocean. Having no natural enemies, the birds lacked fear of the sailors and were easy prey. Those birds that survived were killed by the dogs and pigs introduced to the island by the sailors. By 1681, the dodo was completely eliminated (see illustration).

*Case 2:* The elimination of the dodo disrupted the delicate balance of the environment on Mauritius. The calvaria tree stopped sprouting seedlings soon after the extinction of the dodo and it, too, seemed doomed. It appears that the calvaria seeds needed to be eaten, digested, and eliminated by the dodo. Fortunately, turkeys were found to do the same thing, and the calvaria tree was saved.

*Case 3:* The Iowa Pleistocene snail is a small land snail about 0.6 centimeter in diameter. The brown to greenish snail lives in cool leaf litter at about 30 sites in Iowa and Illinois. Fossil evidence indicates that the snails were much more widespread during the Ice Age. Although climate change appears to have been the most devastating cause of their population decline, human building activities have also contributed to the decrease in numbers.

2. Extinction occurs when a living species dies out. According to the case histories above, the organism that has become extinct is the
   A. dodo
   B. calvaria tree
   C. Iowa Pleistocene snail
   D. wild pig

3. An endangered species is a plant or animal that appears close to extinction. According to the case histories above, the organism that has become endangered is the
   A. dodo
   B. calvaria tree
   C. Iowa Pleistocene snail
   D. turkey

4. The two organisms that most nearly perform the same role in their ecosystems are
   A. humans and Iowa Pleistocene snails
   B. calvaria trees and turkeys

  C. wild dogs and dodos
  D. turkeys and dodos

Study the graph, which shows the relationships among the populations of three different species (frogs, grasshoppers, and snakes) in a natural community; then answer questions 5 through 7.

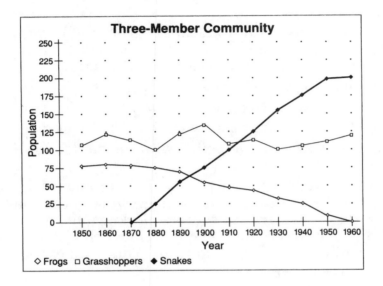

5. Which two species lived in a stable relationship in 1850?
   A. frogs and snakes
   B. frogs and grasshoppers
   C. grasshoppers and snakes
   D. none of the species listed

6. The decline in frogs appears to have been caused by the
   A. decline in the number of snakes
   B. introduction of the snakes
   C. decline in the number of grasshoppers
   D. change in climate

7. Based on the graph, by 1980 the snake population would probably have been
   A. greater than in 1960
   B. less than in 1960
   C. the same as in 1960
   D. the same as the grasshopper population

8. Which of the following is a nonrenewable resource?
   A. soil             C. water
   B. silver           D. forest

9.  In the northeastern U.S., thousands of lakes are so acidic they can hardly support any fish. This is probably due to
    A. humans doing too much fishing
    B. changing climate conditions
    C. rain mixing with air pollutants to form acid rain
    D. decaying of dead fish in the lakes

10. A lake is stocked with trout that feed on small minnows. Fishermen notice that the number of large bass in the lake has decreased. The best explanation for this is that
    A. there is not enough water for all the fish
    B. the trout are eating the large bass
    C. the trout are competing with the bass for food
    D. the minnows are competing with the bass for food

11. Tracy observed that the forest behind her house had many large trees, with some small trees growing in the shade of the larger trees. The large trees were blocking out the sunlight, and preventing the sun's energy from reaching the small trees. The small trees will eventually die. This is an example of
    A. a climax forest
    B. a balanced community
    C. competition
    D. an unbalanced community

12. All ponds change over time. Soil and decaying plants and animals tend to slowly fill in a pond. Fish, frogs, and swamp grasses die as the water depth decreases and soil forms. Grass and small land plants grow in the soil. The process may take tens or hundreds of years, depending on the climate, size of the pond, and other environmental conditions. This process is called
    A. competition                 C. the balance of nature
    B. succession                  D. a food chain

Questions 13 and 14 refer to the following short paragraph.

A decrease in the number of sea otters can lead to an increase in sea urchins. An increase in the sea urchin population results in less kelp (seaweed). Kelp "forests" provide fish with protection from predators.

13. This chain of events demonstrates how
    A. living things depend on nonliving factors
    B. living things grow
    C. living things do not depend on each other
    D. living things depend on each other

**14.** Humans harvest kelp for use in agricultural and chemical industries. What effect would the removal of kelp have on the species discussed above?

A. The populations of sea urchins and fish would both increase.

B. The populations of sea urchins and fish would both decrease.

C. The population of sea urchins would increase, while the population of fish would decrease.

D. The population of sea urchins would decrease, while the population of fish would increase.

**15.** Succession is the process by which one living community is replaced by a new community. Recently cooled lava in Hawaii forms a rock surface devoid of living organisms. The order of succession of living organisms on the rock surface would most likely be

A. trees, shrubs, grasses, mosses

B. grasses, shrubs, mosses, trees

C. mosses, shrubs, trees, grasses

D. mosses, grasses, shrubs, trees

**16.** The area that looks most like a climax community is

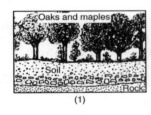 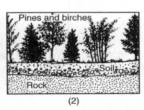 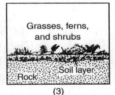 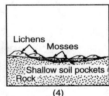

A. (1)         B. (2)         C. (3)         D. (4)

Questions 17 through 19 refer to the following paragraph.

In the winter of 1949, Lake Michigan froze and a pack of wolves made their way from the mainland to Isle Royal National Park. A study was conducted to investigate the wolf–moose relationship and its effect on the ecosystem. During the 1970s, there were several severe winters that led to starvation and malnutrition among the moose population. The wolves found the weak moose easy prey, and as the moose population decreased, the wolf population tripled.

**17.** The wolf–moose relationship at Isle Royal demonstrates the effects on an ecosystem of

A. human actions          C. geologic events

B. changes in weather     D. acid precipitation

**18.** If the moose population continues to decrease, the wolf's food supply will decrease. This will most likely cause the wolf population to

A. increase greatly
B. increase slightly

C. remain the same
D. decrease

**19.** Which graph best depicts the wolf–moose relationship during the 1970s?

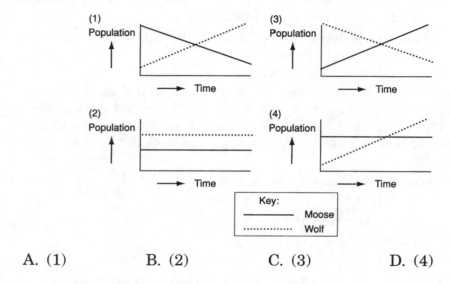

A. (1)        B. (2)        C. (3)        D. (4)

## Open Ended

**20.** When rabbits were introduced to Australia, their numbers increased dramatically and rapidly until they were a serious threat to agriculture. In England, the same rabbit species is only a minor nuisance. What factors might have been responsible for the dramatic population growth of rabbits in Australia?

**21.** If permitted, extensive use of DDT might greatly reduce the mosquito population in New Jersey. A reduction in the mosquito population could decrease the spread of such dangerous diseases as West Nile Virus. Why isn't this insecticide being used in New Jersey today?

**22.** One way in which New Jersey residents could help control the mosquito population is to eliminate or decrease the amount of standing water around their homes. Why might this procedure be effective?

# Practice Test 1

## SCIENCE—PART 1

**DIRECTIONS FOR QUESTIONS 1 THROUGH 15: For each of the questions or incomplete statements below, choose the best of the answer choices given. Write your answers on a separate sheet of paper.**

1. A group of cells working together to perform a particular task is best described as

   A. a system.   C. an organ.

   B. a tissue.   D. an organism.

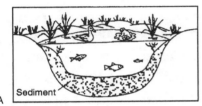

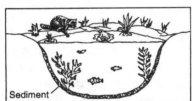

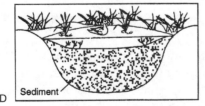

2. Using the drawings shown above, arrange the stages of succession in their proper sequence.

   A. B, A, D, C      C. C, B, A, D

   B. A, D, C, B      D. D, A, C, B

3. As the food source in a bird's environment changes from insects to seeds with hard shells, which adaptation would best enable the bird species to survive?

   A. webbed feet    C. thicker beaks

   B. longer wings   D. sharper talons

4. Tulip bulbs are produced through asexual reproduction. This process ensures that the next generation of plants will be

   A. identical to the parents.

   B. healthier than the parents.

   C. taller than the parents.

   D. a blend of the two parents' traits.

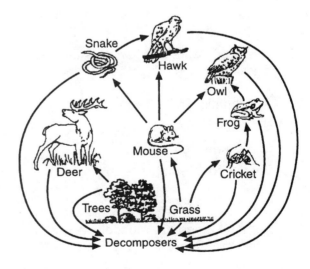

Questions 5 and 6 refer to the food web shown above, which illustrates the flow of energy among living things in an ecosystem.

5. Which organisms, if eliminated, would harm the survival of all other organisms in the web?

   A. frogs
   B. hawks
   C. crickets
   D. grass and trees

6. What can you conclude about the animals illustrated in the food web?

   A. They all eat other animals.
   B. They require only sunlight to survive.
   C. They obtain their energy by eating other organisms.
   D. They manufacture their own food.

7. Which taxonomic group includes all of the other groups?

   A. kingdom
   B. phylum
   C. genus
   D. species

8. Over 200 years ago, Carolus Linnaeus classified living things based on their

   A. genetic similarities.
   B. structural similarities.
   C. biochemical similarities.
   D. environmental similarities.

9. Human beings are most closely related to other animals that are in the same

   A. kingdom.
   B. phylum.
   C. class.
   D. order.

10. Which tool would be best to use for determining the volume of a small rock?

    A. a balance
    B. a microscope
    C. a graduated cylinder
    D. a spring scale

11. Which two tools would be most useful for determining the density of a liquid?

    A. a triple beam balance and a graduated cylinder
    B. a microscope and a spring scale
    C. a ruler and a triple beam balance
    D. a microscope and a ruler

12. A pack of wolves moved into an area that had a large population of deer. After several generations, the most likely change to be noticed in the surviving deer would be their

    A. thicker fur.
    B. faster running ability.
    C. brighter coloration.
    D. poorer hearing.

13. Organisms must transfer wastes from their cells to the environment. In humans, which two systems are most directly involved in this process?

    A. digestive and nervous
    B. excretory and circulatory
    C. digestive and circulatory
    D. skeletal and nervous

**GO ON TO THE NEXT PAGE.** ➡

14. The smallest particle of a compound that still has the properties of that compound is called

A. an atom.
B. a mixture.
C. a solution.
D. a molecule.

15. Which instrument would be the most useful for studying planets in our solar system?

A. a microscope
B. a telescope
C. a magnifying glass
D. an electroscope

**DIRECTIONS FOR QUESTION 16: Respond fully to the open-ended question that follows. Show your work and clearly explain your answer. You may use words, tables, diagrams, or drawings. Write your answer on a separate sheet of paper.**

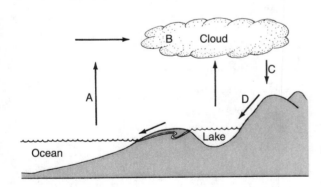

16. The diagram above illustrates how water moves in and out of the atmosphere during the hydrologic cycle.

- Describe the process that is occurring at position *A*.

- Describe the process that is occurring at position *B*.

- Explain how the hydrologic cycle helps purify water.

## SCIENCE—PART 2

**DIRECTIONS FOR QUESTIONS 17 THROUGH 31:** For each of the questions or incomplete statements below, choose the best of the answer choices given. Write your answers on a separate sheet of paper.

17. Which of the following techniques can be used to separate a mixture of salt and water?

    A. filtering
    B. settling
    C. mixing
    D. boiling

18. Which statement best describes the behavior of most solids?

    A. They contract when heated.
    B. They expand when heated.
    C. They melt when cooled.
    D. They expand when cooled.

19. When separating a mixture of salt, sand, and water, a student can use filter paper to remove the sand but not the salt. The best explanation for this fact is that the

    A. sand particles are too small to fit through the holes in the filter paper.
    B. salt particles are too small to fit through the holes in the filter paper.
    C. salt particles are large enough to be trapped by the filter paper.
    D. sand particles are large enough to be trapped by the filter paper.

20. A mixture of sugar, sand, and water is filtered. What is the composition of the substance that passes through the filter?

    A. sand, sugar, and water
    B. sand and water only
    C. sugar and water only
    D. water only

21. A class tests an unknown substance and observes the properties listed in the table below.

    | Property | Observation |
    | --- | --- |
    | Appearance | Yellow powder |
    | Electrical conductivity | Poor |
    | Melting point | Low |

    Based on these data, the students would most likely classify the substance as a

    A. metallic solid.
    B. metallic liquid.
    C. nonmetal.
    D. noble gas.

22. External forces on Earth are constantly wearing down the surface of the land. The processes associated with leveling the land surface are

    A. volcanoes and earthquakes.
    B. weathering and erosion.
    C. evaporation and condensation.
    D. precipitation and plate tectonics.

**GO ON TO THE NEXT PAGE.** ➡

23. Which scientific tool would be used to measure the mass of an object?

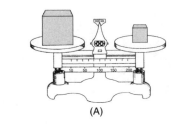

(A)

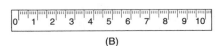

(B)

(C)

(D)

A. Tool *A*

B. Tool *B*

C. Tool *C*

D. Tool *D*

24. Wet clothes placed on a clothesline will eventually dry. The process that causes the wet clothes to dry is

A. condensation.    C. precipitation.

B. evaporation.    D. dripping water.

25. Ocean currents are strongly associated with Earth's

A. changing of seasons.

B. high air pressure systems.

C. planetary wind belts.

D. water temperature differences.

26. Weathering and erosion are two forces that affect Earth's surface. Generally, they can be described as

A. slow forces that level the land.

B. slow forces that uplift the land.

C. abrupt forces that level the land.

D. abrupt forces that uplift the land.

27. The average salinity of seawater is 35 parts per thousand. Which condition would cause the salinity of seawater to increase?

A. adding freshwater from land runoff

B. cooling the water in a polar region

C. evaporating the water in a tropical region

D. melting icebergs in a tropical region

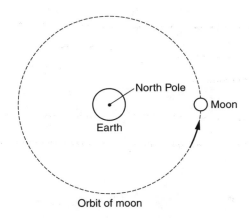

Orbit of moon

28. The diagram above shows the moon's orbit around Earth. About how much time does it take for the moon to complete its orbit?

A. 1 day    C. 60 days

B. 30 days    D. 365 days

**GO ON TO THE NEXT PAGE.** ➡

29. Which diagram shows the position of the sun, moon, and Earth that would cause the highest tides to occur along the New Jersey shore?

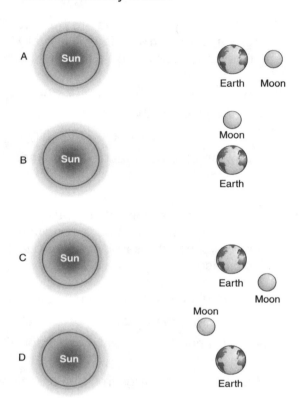

A. Diagram *A*  C. Diagram *C*
B. Diagram *B*  D. Diagram *D*

30. The diagram below shows the water at dockside changing from low tide to high tide. What was the period of time between these two consecutive events?

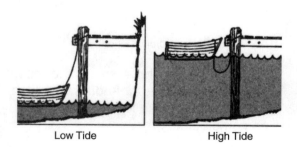

Low Tide          High Tide

A. about 12 hours  C. about 6 hours
B. about 24 hours  D. about 2 days

31. Which diagram correctly represents the relationship among the sun, Earth, and moon?

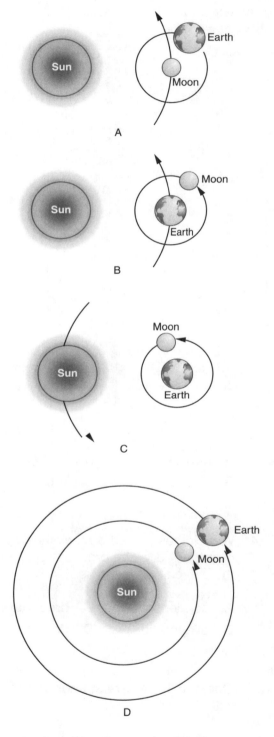

A. Diagram *A*  C. Diagram *C*
B. Diagram *B*  D. Diagram *D*

**GO ON TO THE NEXT PAGE.** ➡

**DIRECTIONS FOR QUESTION 32:** Respond fully to the open-ended question that follows. Show your work and clearly explain your answer. You may use words, tables, diagrams, or drawings. Write your answer on a separate sheet of paper.

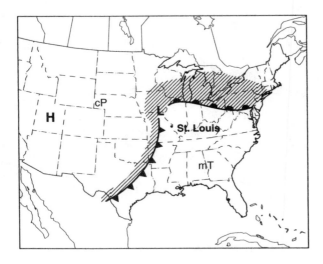

32.  The weather map shows a typical low-pressure system moving across the United States.

   • Describe the temperature and moisture characteristics of the cP air mass that formed over northern Canada.

   • Based on the map, predict the weather for the city of St. Louis.

   • Explain why the weather systems move from west to east in the United States.

**END OF PART 2**
You may check your work on this part only.
DO NOT GO TO THE NEXT PAGE.

## SCIENCE—PART 3

**DIRECTIONS FOR QUESTIONS 33 THROUGH 47: For each of the questions or incomplete statements below, choose the best of the answer choices given. Write your answers on a separate sheet of paper.**

33. The diagram below represents the molecules in a steel rod at 72°C. Which of the four choices best illustrates the change in the rod's molecules when its temperature is lowered to 50°C?

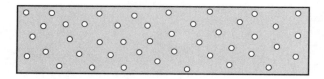

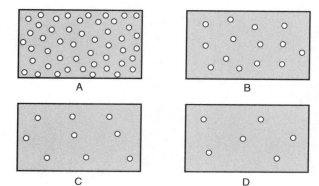

A. Diagram *A*

B. Diagram *B*

C. Diagram *C*

D. Diagram *D*

34. Sound is a form of energy produced by a vibrating object. How does sound travel?

A. in the form of sound waves, outward in all directions

B. in the form of sound waves, outward in a single direction

C. in the form of electromagnetic waves, outward in all directions

D. in the form of electromagnetic waves, outward in a single direction

35. In which beaker of water are the molecules vibrating fastest?

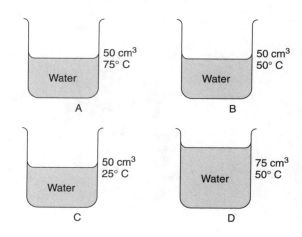

A. Beaker *A*

B. Beaker *B*

C. Beaker *C*

D. Beaker *D*

36. A boy observes a fish in a pond. He thinks the fish is at position *A*, but it is actually at position *B*. Why does the fish appear to be at position *A*?

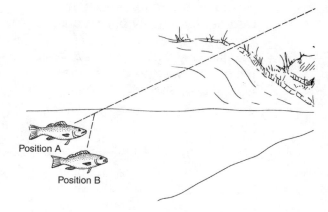

A. Light is reflected from the fish.

B. Light is absorbed by the water.

**GO ON TO THE NEXT PAGE.** ➡

C. Light is refracted when it passes from one medium to another.

D. Light is reflected when it passes from one medium to another.

37. A science textbook has the following statement: "Heat normally flows from high-temperature regions to low-temperature regions. It flows through all substances, even a vacuum." Heat flows through a vacuum by means of

A. conduction.

B. convection.

C. radiation.

D. absorption.

38. Heating a steel rod with a flame causes the molecules in it to

A. move slower.

B. move faster.

C. stop moving.

D. move closer together.

39. Newton's second law of motion states the relationship among force, mass, and acceleration as $F = m \times a$. According to the second law of motion,

A. the larger the mass, the greater the force necessary to accelerate it.

B. the larger the mass, the less the force necessary to accelerate it.

C. the smaller the mass, the greater the force necessary to accelerate it.

D. the greater the force applied to a mass, the less its acceleration.

40. April tries to pull a cart but cannot move it. When Mary helps April pull, they are able to move the cart. The reason for this result is that the total force on the cart is

A. the ratio of the two forces.

B. the product of the two forces.

C. the sum of the two forces.

D. the difference of the two forces.

41. A force is a push or a pull. A force can start motion, stop motion, change the speed of motion, or change the direction of motion. What is the purpose of the force a golfer applies to a golf ball when he hits the ball with the golf club?

A. start the ball's motion

B. stop the ball's motion

C. change the speed of motion

D. change the direction of motion

42. Engines lift rockets into space. What scientific principle is the basis for the rocket engine?

A. A body in motion remains in motion until an outside force acts on it.

B. Velocity is the product of mass times acceleration.

C. Every action has an equal and opposite reaction.

D. The force of gravity is a based on the mass and distance between two objects.

**GO ON TO THE NEXT PAGE.** ➡

43. Which diagram shows balanced forces acting on an object?

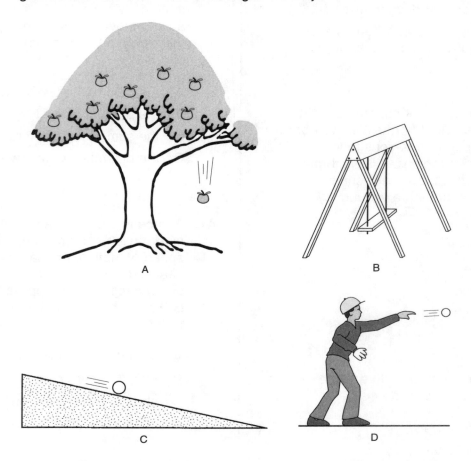

A. Diagram *A* (apple falling from a tree)  C. Diagram *C* (ball rolling down a ramp)
B. Diagram *B* (a motionless swing)  D. Diagram *D* (thrown baseball in motion)

44. The use of previously discovered scientific knowledge about magnetism and electricity to build the first telephone is an example of

A. a scientific discovery.
B. a technological development.
C. predicting future physical events.
D. observing the natural world.

**GO ON TO THE NEXT PAGE.** ➡

45. The following graph shows how the average life expectancy changed between the years 1910 and 2000. This change was most likely the result of

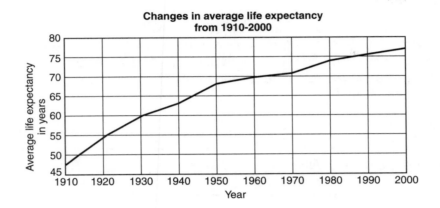

**Changes in average life expectancy
from 1910-2000**

A. advances in educational technology.

B. harmful effects of technology on the environment.

C. advances in medical technology.

D. advances in communication technology.

46. The search for knowledge is an important issue for many people, especially scientists. An example of the search for scientific knowledge is someone

A. building a telescope.

B. sailing a boat.

C. drawing a map of the moon.

D. exploring the bottom of the ocean.

47. NASA developed a special material for astronaut spacesuits; it is now being used to produce clothing for firefighters. This is an example of

A. how we gather scientific knowledge.

B. how space technology affects our lives.

C. how scientific knowledge affects our lives.

D. a new scientific discovery.

**DIRECTIONS FOR QUESTION 48: Respond fully to the open-ended question that follows. Show your work and clearly explain your answer. You may use words, tables, diagrams, or drawings. Write your answer on a separate sheet of paper.**

48. A solution's pH is a measure of its acidity. The lower the pH, the more acidic the solution. A student wanted to test the effect of pH on the growth of bean plants. He divided his plants into six groups, watering each group with solutions that were identical except for their pH. After three weeks, he recorded the average growth for each group of plants.
    (*Note:* A pH of 7 is neutral.)

| pH of solution: | 4 | 5 | 6 | 7 | 8 | 9 |
|---|---|---|---|---|---|---|
| Average growth (cm): | None (all plants died) | 5 cm | 9 cm | 8 cm | 8 cm | 6 cm |

- What result would you expect at a pH of 3? Explain your prediction.

- What result would you expect at a pH of 7.5? Explain your prediction.

- What result would you expect at a pH of 10? Explain your prediction.

**END OF PART 3**
You may check your work on this part only.

STOP

# Practice Test 2

## SCIENCE—PART 1

**DIRECTIONS FOR QUESTIONS 1 THROUGH 15:** For each of the questions or incomplete statements below, choose the best of the answer choices given. Write your answers on a separate sheet of paper.

1. Which of the following lists the terms in order of increasing complexity?

   A. tissue, organ, system, cell
   B. cell, system, tissue, organ
   C. cell, tissue, organ, system
   D. system, cell, tissue, organ

2. A student wishes to study the effect of a low-protein diet on weight loss. Which of the following statements would be a useful hypothesis for this study?

   A. What is the effect of a reduced protein intake on weight loss?
   B. If protein intake is reduced, there will be noticeable weight loss.
   C. Protein is necessary for the growth and repair of tissues.
   D. The control group consumed normal amounts of protein.

3. An organism is genetically identical to its parent. This organism most likely reproduces by

   A. sexual reproduction involving one parent.
   B. sexual reproduction involving two parents.
   C. asexual reproduction involving one parent.
   D. asexual reproduction involving two parents.

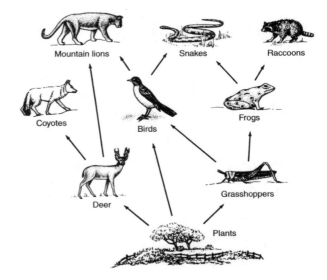

4. The food web above illustrates how energy flows through an ecosystem. Which of the following organisms does *not* provide energy for any of the other animals in this food web?

   A. Plants
   B. Snakes
   C. Deer
   D. Frogs

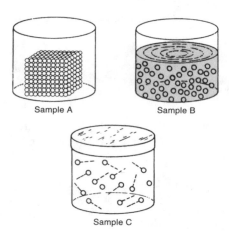

Sample A     Sample B

Sample C

5. Samples *A*, *B*, and *C* in the diagram above all represent molecules of the same substance. At high temperatures, the arrangement of molecules is most likely to resemble those seen in

   A. Sample *A*
   B. Sample *B*
   C. Sample *C*
   D. Samples *A* and *C*

6. Owners of Doberman pinschers clip the ears of their dogs to prevent ear infections. Which statement would be true about the offspring of a Doberman that has clipped ears?

   A. All of the offspring will be born with clipped ears.
   B. Some of the offspring will be born with clipped ears.
   C. None of the offspring will be born with clipped ears.
   D. It is not possible to predict the ears of the offspring.

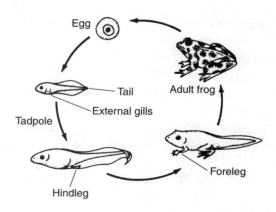

7. What is shown in the diagram above?

   A. an ecosystem
   B. a community
   C. a food chain
   D. a life cycle

8. Which of the following terms includes the other three?

   A. elements
   B. metals
   C. nonmetals
   D. noble gases

9. One atom of sulfur can react with exactly three atoms of oxygen to produce a molecule of sulfur trioxide. How many atoms are there in one molecule of sulfur trioxide?

   A. 1 atom     C. 3 atoms
   B. 2 atoms     D. 4 atoms

10. Which of the following correctly matches a tool with the quantity it measures?

    A. triple-beam balance—density
    B. graduated cylinder—volume
    C. ruler—mass
    D. spring scale—length

**GO ON TO THE NEXT PAGE.** ➡

11. To survive, animals need nutrients and oxygen, which are supplied by the digestive system and respiratory system, respectively. Which system is most directly involved in getting these materials to the cells where they can be used?

    A. excretory system
    B. nervous system
    C. circulatory system
    D. skeletal system

12. Which of the following represents the symbol of an element only?

    A. $H_2O$          C. $Cl_2$
    B. $C_6H_{12}O_6$   D. $CO_2$

13. Argon (Ar) does *not* take part in chemical reactions. Thus, argon is classified as a

    A. metal          C. noble gas
    B. nonmetal       D. compound

14. When oil and vinegar are mixed, they form separate layers, as shown in the diagram. Why does the layer of oil float on top?

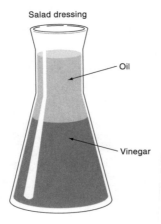

Salad dressing

Oil

Vinegar

    A. Oil is less dense than vinegar.
    B. Oil is denser than vinegar.

    C. Oil is thicker than vinegar.
    D. Vinegar is thicker than oil.

15. When electricity is passed through water, two gases are formed—one that burns and one that supports burning. This change can best be described as a

    A. physical change, because new substances were formed.
    B. physical change, because no new substances were formed.
    C. chemical change, because new substances were formed.
    D. chemical change, because no new substances were formed.

**GO ON TO THE NEXT PAGE.** ➡

**DIRECTIONS FOR QUESTION 16: Respond fully to the open-ended question that follows. Show your work and clearly explain your answer. You may use words, tables, diagrams, or drawings. Write your answer on a separate sheet of paper.**

16. The electromagnetic spectrum graphically shows the range of electromagnetic waves. Refer to the diagram below to complete this question.

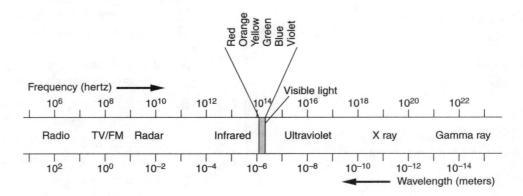

- Describe gamma rays in terms of their frequency and wavelength.

- Compare the frequency and wavelength of radio waves and X rays.

- Compare the frequency and wavelength of red light and violet light.

# SCIENCE—PART 2

**DIRECTIONS FOR QUESTIONS 17 THROUGH 31: For each of the questions or incomplete statements below, choose the best of the answer choices given. Write your answers on a separate sheet of paper.**

17. Humans and apes both belong to the order primates. Therefore, humans and apes must also belong to the same

    A. class.      C. genus.
    B. family.     D. species.

18. A sheep named Dolly was produced (by scientists) from a single cell of a female sheep in a process called *cloning*. Cloning can best be described as

    A. a natural form of asexual reproduction.
    B. an artificial form of asexual reproduction.
    C. a natural form of sexual reproduction.
    D. an artificial form of sexual reproduction.

19. Many materials are recycled in an ecosystem; but, for an ecosystem to survive, there must be a constant external source of

    A. water.      C. air.
    B. food.       D. energy.

20. When ecological succession takes place in central New Jersey, the most probable climax community would be

    A. barren, rocky land.
    B. lichens and mosses.
    C. small shrubs.
    D. a mature forest.

21. Which of the following natural events changes Earth's surface most abruptly?

    A. a melting glacier
    B. an erupting volcano
    C. a flowing river
    D. a breaking wave

22. Weathering is the breaking down of rocks into smaller pieces, and erosion is the process by which rock material on Earth's surface is removed and carried away. Which of the following processes is an example of erosion?

    A. plant roots expanding in the crack of a rock
    B. wind blowing sand off a beach dune
    C. oxygen changing iron to rust particles in a rock
    D. rainwater dissolving limestone rock

23. Which type of graph would best illustrate the following data?

    **Earth's Atmospheric Gases**

    | Gas | Percent |
    | --- | --- |
    | Nitrogen | 78 |
    | Oxygen | 21 |
    | Other gases (argon and carbon dioxide) | 1 |

    A. bar graph      C. line graph
    B. pie graph      D. pictograph

**GO ON TO THE NEXT PAGE.** ➡

24. Storms typically move across the United States from west to east because the

   A. prevailing easterlies blow from west to east.

   B. prevailing easterlies blow from east to west.

   C. prevailing westerlies blow from west to east.

   D. prevailing westerlies blow from east to west.

25. Why are there only a small number of earthquakes in New Jersey compared to the large number of earthquakes in California?

   A. California is on a tectonic plate, whereas New Jersey is not on a tectonic plate.

   B. New Jersey and California are on opposite sides of the same tectonic plate.

   C. California has more active volcanoes than New Jersey has.

   D. New Jersey is in the center of a tectonic plate, whereas California is on the edge of a tectonic plate.

26. The Statue of Liberty, which is located in New York Harbor, weighs about 200,000 kilograms. If the statue were to be placed about 10 kilometers above sea level, it would have the

   A. same weight but more mass than at sea level.

   B. same weight but less mass than at sea level.

   C. same mass but more weight than at sea level.

   D. same mass but less weight than at sea level.

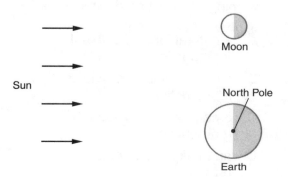

27. Base your answer on the diagram above. Which of the following choices shows how the moon would appear to a person in New Jersey?

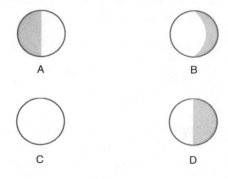

   A. Moon *A*

   B. Moon *B*

   C. Moon *C*

   D. Moon *D*

**GO ON TO THE NEXT PAGE.** ➡

28. Our sun is officially which of the following celestial objects?

   A. a comet

   B. a planet

   C. a moon

   D. a star

29. The tides occur because of the gravitational effects of the moon and sun on Earth. The effect of the moon's gravity is greater than the effect of the sun's gravity on Earth's tides because

   A. the moon is smaller than the sun.

   B. the moon is larger than the sun.

   C. the sun is closer to Earth than the moon is.

   D. the moon is closer to Earth than the sun is.

30. How would the size of the sun differ if viewed from Mars instead of from Earth?

   A. The sun would be the same size when viewed from Mars.

   B. The sun would be larger when viewed from Mars.

   C. The sun would be smaller when viewed from Earth.

   D. The sun would be smaller when viewed from Mars.

31. While looking at the night sky, Edith observed a short streak of light. Edith most likely observed

   A. a comet.

   B. a meteor.

   C. the birth of a star.

   D. an asteroid.

**DIRECTIONS FOR QUESTION 32: Respond fully to the open-ended question that follows. Show your work and clearly explain your answer. You may use words, tables, diagrams, or drawings. Write your answer on a separate sheet of paper.**

32. The four land profiles illustrate how a portion of Earth's surface changed over a long period of time.

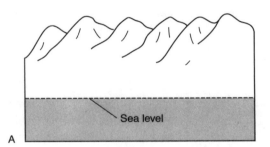

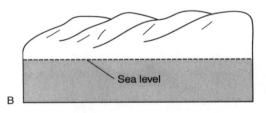

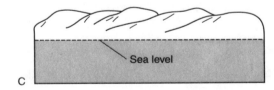

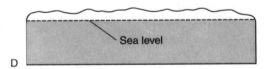

   • What processes were involved in producing profile *A*?

   • Describe the processes that changed the profile of the land.

   • Predict how the land will change if the same processes continue.

**END OF PART 2**
You may check your work on this part only.
DO NOT GO TO THE NEXT PAGE.

## SCIENCE—PART 3

**DIRECTIONS FOR QUESTIONS 33 THROUGH 47:** For each of the questions or incomplete statements below, choose the best of the answer choices given. Write your answers on a separate sheet of paper.

33. Heat energy from the sun reaches Earth by the process of

    A. conduction.
    B. radiation.
    C. convection.
    D. refraction.

34. The sun produces energy by a process called nuclear fusion, which combines hydrogen atoms to produce helium atoms and energy. What type of energy does the sun produce from nuclear fusion?

    A. light energy only
    B. heat energy only
    C. light and heat energy
    D. mechanical energy

35. Sound waves travel fastest through a

    A. vacuum.
    B. gas.
    C. liquid.
    D. solid.

36. The diagram shows how heat can be transferred by conduction, convection, and radiation. Each method of heat transfer is numbered. Based on the diagram, which numbering system is correctly identified?

    A. (1) conduction, (2) convection, (3) radiation
    B. (1) convection, (2) radiation, (3) conduction
    C. (1) radiation, (2) conduction, (3) convection
    D. (1) convection, (2) conduction, (3) radiation

37. The diagram shows what happens to a ray of light when it passes through a glass lens. This event is caused by the

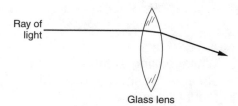

    A. absorption of light
    B. reflection of light
    C. refraction of light
    D. conduction of light

**GO ON TO THE NEXT PAGE.** ➡

38. What type of energy transformation is represented by the illustration?

A. light energy to chemical energy

B. chemical energy to light and heat energy

C. heat energy to light energy

D. light and heat energy to chemical energy

39. Velocity is determined by dividing the *distance* traveled by the *time* that it takes to travel that distance. The formula $v = d/t$ describes the relationship of these three factors. A goose flies south a distance of 30 kilometers in 2 hours. At what velocity did the goose travel?

A. 15 kilometers/hour

B. 60 kilometers/hour

C. 30 miles/hour

D. 30 kilometers/hour

40. Friction is a force that

A. acts in the same direction as the motion of an object.

B. acts in an opposite direction to the motion of an object.

C. is unrelated to the direction of motion of an object.

D. acts perpendicular to the motion of an object.

41. A baseball player hits a high fly ball that takes 4 seconds to be caught. Which graph shows the relationship between the acceleration of the ball and the time it took to be caught?

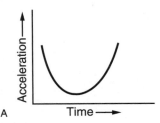

A

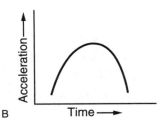

B

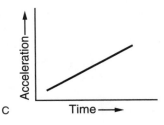

C

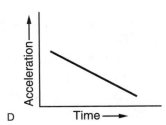

D

A. Graph A

B. Graph B

C. Graph C

D. Graph D

GO ON TO THE NEXT PAGE. ➡

42. The diagram shows two people pulling a cart in opposite directions. The person on the right is pulling the cart eastward with a force of 300 newtons; the person on the left is pulling the cart westward with a force of 200 newtons. The total force on the cart is

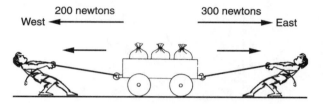

A. the sum of the two forces—500 newtons to the east.

B. the difference of the two forces—100 newtons to the east.

C. the difference of the two forces—100 newtons to the west.

D. equal to zero—the opposite forces cancel out.

43. How can you determine which one of several objects has the greatest inertia?

A. The object with the largest volume has the greatest inertia.

B. The object with the largest mass has the greatest inertia.

C. The object with the greatest height has the greatest inertia.

D. The object with the smallest mass has the greatest inertia.

44. By using scientific knowledge from many fields, engineers built a space probe and sent it to Jupiter in 1979. The probe sent data back to Earth, adding to our scientific knowledge of Jupiter. Which statement best describes this interaction of fields?

A. New technology sometimes builds on past technology.

B. Advances in technology cause some changes in society.

C. Technology has an impact on our natural environment.

D. Science knowledge and technology advance each other.

45. Developments in microelectronics and computer science are changing the United States from a largely industrial nation into one more dependent on information services. This is an example of

A. science helping technology to advance.

B. society affecting science and technology.

C. science and technology affecting society.

D. science and technology solving society's problems.

46. The development of a major techno-logical device such as the computer is usually made by

A. one person over a short period of time.

B. many people over a short period of time.

C. one person over a long period of time.

D. many people over a long period of time.

47. Which of the following scientific tools can be used to measure the width of a plant cell most accurately?

A. a triple-beam balance and a metric ruler

B. a compound microscope and a graduated cylinder

C. a metric ruler and a compound microscope

D. a graduated cylinder and a metric ruler

**GO ON TO THE NEXT PAGE.** ➡

**DIRECTIONS FOR QUESTION 48: Respond fully to the open-ended question that follows. Show your work and clearly explain your answer. You may use words, tables, diagrams, or drawings. Write your answer on a separate sheet of paper.**

48.  When a toy car is released from point *A* at the top of a ramp, it rolls down the ramp and then stops at point *B* (see diagram). The total motion of the car takes 4 seconds.

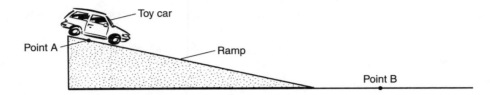

-  Explain why the toy car stops its motion at point *B*.

-  How can the distance that the toy car travels be increased?

-  Describe what would happen if you placed sandpaper on the ramp and then released the toy car from point *A*.

# Practice Test 3

**DIRECTIONS FOR QUESTIONS 1 THROUGH 15: For each of the questions or incomplete statements below, choose the best of the answer choices given. Write your answers on a separate sheet of paper.**

1. The information needed to produce the next generation is carried in an organism's

    A. chloroplasts.
    B. cell membrane.
    C. blood cells.
    D. genetic material.

2. Members of the same phylum must also be members of the same

    A. kingdom.
    B. class.
    C. order.
    D. genus.

3. Which one of the following traits is most likely to be passed on to the children of a heavyweight boxer?

    A. a broken nose
    B. big muscles
    C. brown hair
    D. scars over the eyes

4. Organs that work together to perform a particular function are organized into

    A. cells.
    B. tissues.
    C. systems.
    D. organisms.

5. The aquarium illustrated below represents a small ecosystem. Which of the following must constantly be supplied to this ecosystem?

    A. carbon dioxide
    B. energy
    C. water
    D. oxygen

6. Plants need carbon dioxide to carry out photosynthesis. Which of these is a source of carbon dioxide in the aquarium's ecosystem?

    A. water          C. light
    B. fish           D. gravel

7. The total number of elements that have been identified by scientists is closest to

    A. 50.            C. 150.
    B. 100.           D. 200.

8. A substance that is malleable, ductile, and conducts electricity would most likely be a

   A. metal.
   B. nonmetal.
   C. noble gas.
   D. compound.

9. Which of the following is a heat-releasing process?

   A. evaporation
   B. boiling
   C. freezing
   D. melting

10. Which of these is a physical change only?

    A. Charcoal burns to produce carbon dioxide.
    B. Ice melts to form liquid water.
    C. Iron forms rust when exposed to water.
    D. Sugar produces carbon dioxide and water during respiration.

11. In the reaction $2H_2 + O_2 \rightarrow 2H_2O$, comparing the reactants to the products, there are

    A. equal numbers of substances but different numbers of atoms.
    B. equal numbers of atoms but different numbers of substances.
    C. different numbers of substances and different numbers of atoms.
    D. equal numbers of substances and equal numbers of atoms.

12. Which of the following results in offspring that are *not* identical to their parents?

    A. sexual reproduction involving one parent
    B. sexual reproduction involving two parents
    C. asexual reproduction involving one parent
    D. asexual reproduction involving two parents

**Use the following table to answer questions 13 through 15. The table represents the number of goldfinches seen each year in New Jersey during the annual winter bird count.**

| Year | Count |
|------|-------|
| 1993 | 3770 |
| 1994 | 3553 |
| 1995 | 2377 |
| 1996 | 3616 |
| 1997 | 4229 |
| 1998 | 5258 |
| 1999 | 3914 |
| 2000 | 5841 |

13. What is the range for the number of birds counted?

    A. about 4070          C. 2377–5841
    B. 1993–2000          D. 3770–5841

14. The birdwatchers probably used which tool to collect their data?

    A. microscope
    B. binoculars
    C. magnifying glass
    D. radio telescope

**GO ON TO THE NEXT PAGE.** ➡

15. Which statement is best supported by the data in the table?

A. The number of goldfinches in New Jersey is steadily increasing.

B. The number of goldfinches in New Jersey is steadily decreasing.

C. The number of goldfinches in New Jersey was greater in the last four years than in the first four years.

D. The number of goldfinches in New Jersey was lower in the last four years than in the first four years.

**DIRECTIONS FOR QUESTION 16: Respond fully to the open-ended question that follows. Show your work and clearly explain your answer. You may use words, tables, diagrams, or drawings. Write your answer on a separate sheet of paper.**

16. The arrows on the map show the ocean currents that flow across the North Atlantic Ocean.

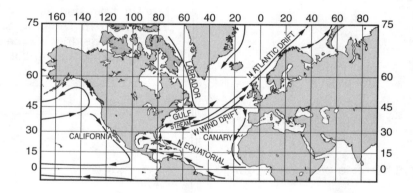

- Explain why the Labrador Current is a cold current.

- Why do the Gulf Stream and North Atlantic Drift cross the Atlantic Ocean from west to east?

- Explain how the North Atlantic Drift affects the climate of Great Britain.

**END OF PART 1**
You may check your work on this part only.
DO NOT GO TO THE NEXT PAGE.

## SCIENCE—PART 2

**DIRECTIONS FOR QUESTIONS 17 THROUGH 31: For each of the questions or incomplete statements below, choose the best of the answer choices given. Write your answers on a separate sheet of paper.**

17. There has been a recent increase in the deer population in a national park. One possible cause for the increase could be

    A. a decrease in the wolf population.
    B. an increase in the wolf population.
    C. a decrease in the plant population.
    D. an increase in the annual snowfall.

18. A flock of migrating birds is exposed to a chemical that causes mutations. When they settle to breed, some of the birds lay eggs that have very soft shells, which makes them break when the parent bird sits on them. This mutation is probably

    A. a beneficial change that will appear in future generations.
    B. a harmful change that will appear in future generations.
    C. a beneficial change that will not appear in future generations.
    D. a harmful change that will not appear in future generations.

19. A natural disaster completely destroys a forest environment. The first new plants to appear in the recovering environment would probably be the

    A. pine trees.
    B. maple trees.
    C. small shrubs.
    D. moss and grass.

20. When exercising, a person's muscles need an additional supply of oxygen. Which two systems are directly involved in bringing oxygen to the muscle cells?

    A. respiratory and circulatory
    B. nervous and skeletal
    C. digestive and respiratory
    D. circulatory and nervous

21. Many species of birds have webbed feet. What do these different birds probably have in common with each other?

    A. They live mainly on or near water.
    B. They live mainly on land and in trees.
    C. They all live in tropical climates.
    D. They all live in polar climates.

22. Which of the following natural events changes Earth's surface most slowly?

    A. an advancing glacier
    B. an erupting volcano
    C. a flowing river
    D. a breaking wave

**GO ON TO THE NEXT PAGE.** ➡

23. Ice water placed in a dry glass on a warm summer day will cause water to appear on the outside of the glass. The process that forms water on the outside of the glass is

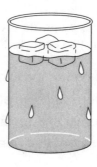

   A. evaporation.
   B. condensation.
   C. precipitation.
   D. melting.

24. On a hot summer day, uneven heating along the shore causes a cool breeze to form during the day. In which direction does the cool daytime breeze flow along the shore?

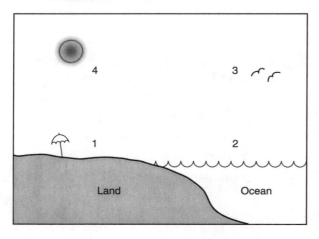

   A. from position 1 to position 2
   B. from position 2 to position 1
   C. from position 1 to position 3
   D. from position 4 to position 1

25. Which two processes are opposite in terms of their effect on Earth's surface?

   A. water erosion and volcanoes
   B. glaciers and wind erosion
   C. earthquakes and volcanoes
   D. weathering and erosion

26. Mountains on Earth are produced by the uplift of land. The processes associated with mountain formation are

   A. weathering and erosion
   B. glaciation and running water
   C. volcanoes and earthquakes
   D. physical and chemical weathering

27. What scientific principle is demonstrated by the use of a mercury barometer?

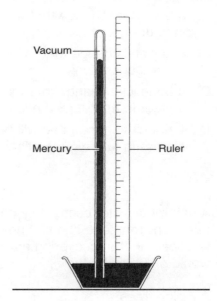

   A. that air has weight
   B. that substances expand when they are heated
   C. that warm air rises
   D. that a body at rest remains at rest until a force acts on it

**GO ON TO THE NEXT PAGE.** ➡

28. Chrysanthemums start to blossom in New Jersey during September. A student wants to test a possible hypothesis to explain this. Which is the best way for the student to state his hypothesis?

A. Chrysanthemums only blossom in New Jersey during the fall.
B. Chrysanthemums never blossom during the summer months.
C. When air temperatures cool, chrysanthemums start to blossom.
D. Why do chrysanthemums start to blossom in the fall?

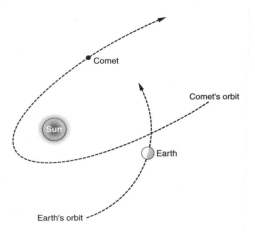

29. The diagram above shows part of Earth's orbit around the sun and part of a comet's orbit. Which choice shows how the comet would appear when viewed from Earth?

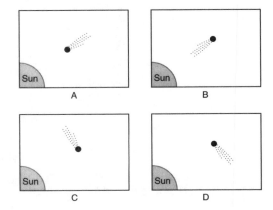

A. Diagram *A*
B. Diagram *B*
C. Diagram *C*
D. Diagram *D*

30. The same side of the moon always faces Earth because the moon

A. rotates at the same rate that it revolves.
B. revolves around Earth but does not rotate.
C. rotates but does not revolve around Earth.
D. always stays on the same side of Earth.

31. The mass of the moon is about 1/80 that of Earth. If the mass of the moon were 1/160 that of Earth, how would our tides be affected?

A. low tide would be higher
B. high tide would be higher
C. high tide would be lower
D. there would be no more tides

**GO ON TO THE NEXT PAGE.** ➡

**DIRECTIONS FOR QUESTION 32: Respond fully to the open-ended question that follows. Show your work and clearly explain your answer. You may use words, tables, diagrams, or drawings. Write your answer on a separate sheet of paper.**

32. The table below shows the times of high tides and low tides during a two-day period.

| Day | Time | Tide |
|-----|------|------|
| September 18 | 2:20 A.M. | Low |
| | 8:35 A.M. | High |
| | 2:45 P.M. | Low |
| | 8:58 P.M. | High |
| September 19 | 3:10 A.M. | Low |
| | 9:20 A.M. | High |
| | 3:35 P.M. | Low |
| | 9:48 P.M. | High |

- Approximately what is the time period between each high tide and low tide?

- At what time will the next low tide occur on September 20th?

- Explain why Earth's high tides and low tides are predictable events.

**END OF PART 2**
You may check your work on this part only.
DO NOT GO TO THE NEXT PAGE.

STOP

# SCIENCE—PART 3

**DIRECTIONS FOR QUESTIONS 33 THROUGH 47: For each of the questions or incomplete statements below, choose the best of the answer choices given. Write your answers on a separate sheet of paper.**

33. A car engine converts chemical energy in the form of gasoline into mechanical energy in the form of moving parts. Also produced, but not needed, is another type of energy. The undesired additional energy is

A. nuclear energy
B. heat energy
C. light energy
D. magnetic energy

34. A pot of water heating on a stove demonstrates which process?

A. the water losing energy
B. the water gaining energy
C. the water losing then gaining energy
D. the water gaining then losing energy

35. The diagram illustrates what happens to a beam of white light that passes through a glass prism. The colors of the spectrum become visible because, as it passes through, the light is

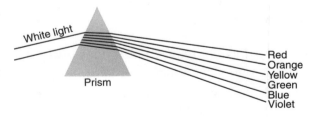

A. reflected.
B. refracted.
C. absorbed.
D. expanded.

| Temperature | Speed (m/s) |
|---|---|
| 0°C | 331 |
| 20°C | 343 |
| 40°C | 355 |

36. The table above shows the speed of sound waves through the air at three different temperatures. According to the data, the relationship can be described as follows:

A. An increase of 1°C increases the speed of sound waves in air by 1 m/s.
B. An increase of 10°C increases the speed of sound waves in air by 6 m/s.
C. An increase of 20°C increases the speed of sound waves in air by 6 m/s.
D. An increase of 40°C increases the speed of sound waves in air by 12 m/s.

37. The tides, eclipses, and phases of the moon

A. are predictable events.
B. are random events.
C. are very rare events.
D. occur at the same time every year.

**GO ON TO THE NEXT PAGE.** ➡

38. In the diagram, a ray of white light strikes a red flower. The flower looks red to the girl because it reflects the red portion of the spectrum. What happens to the other colors of the spectrum?

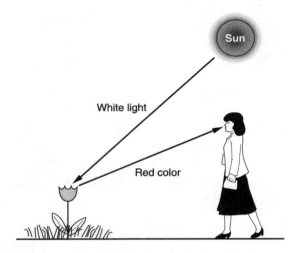

A. They are absorbed.

B. They are refracted.

C. They are reflected.

D. They are transmitted.

39. The mass of a bowling ball would be

A. greatest at sea level.

B. lowest on the moon.

C. greatest on top of Mt. Everest.

D. the same at all of these locations.

40. When a baseball is thrown, what forces affect its motion?

A. gravity and the push from the person throwing the ball

B. friction and the push from the person throwing the ball

C. gravity, friction, and the push from the person throwing the ball

D. gravity and friction only

41. If each of the balls listed below were thrown with the same force, which one would have the greatest acceleration of motion?

A. golf ball

B. baseball

C. basketball

D. bowling ball

42. The diagram shows two people pulling a cart in the same direction. One person is pulling with a force of 250 newtons and the other person is pulling with a force of 200 newtons. The total force on the cart is

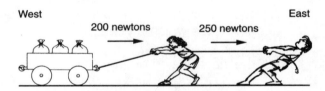

A. 250 newtons to the east.

B. 250 newtons to the west.

C. 450 newtons to the east.

D. 50 newtons to the east.

43. A man walking along the street steps onto a patch of ice. He is more likely to slip on the ice than on the sidewalk because the

A. friction between his shoes and the ice is increased.

B. friction between his shoes and the ice is decreased.

C. force between his shoes and the ice is increased.

D. force between his shoes and the ice is decreased.

**GO ON TO THE NEXT PAGE.** ➡

44. Early space exploration progressed from near-Earth projects to solar system projects. For example, spacecraft first orbited Earth, then landed on the moon, and later went to explore Mars. The most likely reason for this progression was the

   A. invention of larger rockets.
   B. increase in scientific knowledge only.
   C. improvement in space technology only.
   D. increase in science knowledge and improvements in technology.

45. In 1900, the number of known natural satellites that revolve around Jupiter was four. By 2002, the number of known satellites of Jupiter was up to 28. The reason for this change is that

   A. Jupiter acquired additional satellites between 1900 and 2002.
   B. advances in technology have improved our science knowledge.
   C. Jupiter moved closer to Earth between 1900 and 2002.
   D. Jupiter was more massive in 2002 than it was in 1900.

46. What scientific knowledge played a major role in the technological development of the microscope?

   A. Objects become larger the closer you get to them.
   B. White light is composed of the colors of the rainbow.
   C. Light rays are bent (refract) when they pass through a lens.
   D. Light rays travel at 300,000 kilometers per second.

47. The Hubble Space Telescope was placed in orbit around Earth in the early 1990s. As scientists analyzed the pictures taken with the telescope, they learned more about the universe. This is an example of

   A. science improving our knowledge of technology.
   B. technology improving our knowledge of science.
   C. science improving our society.
   D. technology improving our society.

GO ON TO THE NEXT PAGE. ➡

**DIRECTIONS FOR QUESTION 48: Respond fully to the open-ended question that follows. Show your work and clearly explain your answer. You may use words, tables, diagrams, or drawings. Write your answer on a separate sheet of paper.**

48. A flash of lightning and a clap of thunder are produced at the same time. Jane sees the lightning and six seconds later hears the thunder.

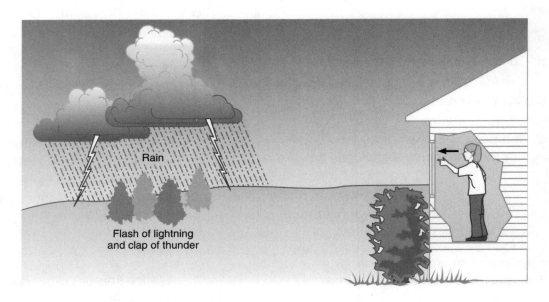

- Explain why Jane sees the lightning first and then hears the thunder.

- How does the sound of thunder travel from the lightning to Jane?

- How can Jane determine her distance from the flash of lightning?

# Glossary

**A**

***acceleration*** The rate of change in velocity.

***adaptation*** A characteristic that helps an organism survive in its habitat.

***air mass*** A large body of air that has a uniform temperature and humidity throughout.

***altitude*** The height above sea level of a place.

***amplitude*** The height of the crest or the depth of the trough of a wave measured from the undisturbed surface.

***asexual reproduction*** The form of reproduction that involves only one parent, producing offspring that are genetically identical to the parent.

***atmosphere*** The gases that surround Earth.

***atom*** The smallest particle of an element that has the properties of that element.

**B**

***bacteria of decay*** Microorganisms that break down dead organisms and return nutrients to the environment.

***bar graph*** Visual tool used to organize, illustrate, and compare observations.

***biodiversity*** Describes the great variety of species on Earth or within a habitat.

***boiling*** The rapid change in phase from liquid to gas, during which bubbles of gas form within the liquid.

***boiling point*** The temperature at which a substance changes rapidly from a liquid to a gas.

***buoyancy*** The tendency of an object to float.

**C**

***calorie*** A unit used to measure and compare the amount of heart energy in a substance; the amount of heat needed to raise the temperature of 1 gram of water 1°C.

***carnivore*** A meat-eating animal.

***cell*** The basic unit of structure and function of all living things.

***cell membrane*** The outer covering of the cell, which regulates the flow of materials into and out of the cell.

***chemical bond*** The link that joins one atom to another in a molecule.

***chemical change*** A change that results in the formation of one or more new substances; a chemical reaction.

***chemical energy*** The energy stored in certain substances because of their chemical makeup.

***chemical property*** A characteristic that a substance displays when it undergoes a change to a new substance or substances.

***chloroplast*** The organelle in plant (and algae) cells that contains chloro-phyll and in which photosynthesis takes place.

***climate*** The average condition of the atmosphere (weather) in an area over many years.

***climax community*** The final community that emerges and is not replaced after ecological succession.

*cold front* The boundary formed when a cool air mass pushes into and under a warm air mass.

*community* All the different populations of species that live within a habitat.

*competition* The interaction between organisms that require the same food and resources.

*compound* A substance that is formed when two or more different elements combine chemically.

*compound microscope* A microscope that uses two lenses.

*condensation* The changing of water vapor into droplets of liquid water; the change in phase from a gas to a liquid.

*conduction* The transfer of heat by direct molecular contact.

*conservation* The saving of natural resources through wise use.

*consumer* An organism that obtains nutrients by eating other organisms.

*convection* The transfer of heat by the flowing action within a liquid or gas.

*core* Earth's center, which is made up of an outer zone and an inner zone.

*corrosion* The chemical wearing away of a metal.

*crust* The outermost solid rock layer of Earth; contains all the surface features.

*cytoplasm* The fluid that fills a cell, in which most life processes occur.

### D

*decomposer* An organism that breaks down dead organisms and returns their nutrients to the environment.

*density* The quantity that compares of mass of an object to its volume; density = mass/volume.

*dependent variable* The variable you measure, which depends on the value of the independent variable.

*digestion* The breaking down of nutrients into a useable form.

*Doppler effect* The apparent change in the frequency of a sound wave that occurs when the source and/or the observer are in motion relative to one another.

### E

*earthquake* A shaking of Earth's crust, caused by the sudden movement of rocks sliding along a fault in the crust.

*eclipse* An event that occurs when the sun, moon, and Earth are in a straight line.

*ecological succession* The natural process by which one community of living things is replaced by another in an orderly predictable sequence, until a stable community appears.

*ecology* The study of the interaction between organisms and their environment.

*ecosystem* The living members of a community along with the nonliving elements of their environment.

*electrical energy* The energy produced by the flow of electrons from one point to another through a conductor.

*electromagnetic spectrum* The continuous band of waves formed by all the electromagnetic waves together.

*electromagnetic waves* Energy waves that travel at the speed of light and can move through a vacuum; include radio waves, infrared waves, microwaves, visible light, ultraviolet waves, X rays, and gamma rays.

*element* One of the basic substances that form the building blocks of all matter.

*elimination* The removal of undigested materials from the body.

*endangered species* A group of organisms that is in danger of extinction.

*energy* The ability to do work.

*environment* The surroundings in which an organism lives; includes both living and nonliving things.

*erosion* The process by which rock material at Earth's surface is physically worn away and carried away.

*evaporation* The changing of liquid water into water vapor (gaseous water); the change in phase from a liquid to a gas.

*evolution* The process by which a species changes over time to become a different species.

*excretion* The removal of the waste products of cellular respiration from the body.

*extinct* Species that no longer exist (either in the wild or in captivity).

## F

*faulting* The process by which internal forces cause Earth's crust to break and slide along fractures called faults.

*fertilization* The joining together of an egg and a sperm cell, during sexual reproduction, to produce a new individual.

*first law of motion* An object at rest will remain at rest and an object in motion will remain in motion unless an outside force acts on the object.

*folding* The process by which rock layers in Earth's crust are squeezed into wavelike patterns called folds.

*food chain* A sequence of organisms through which nutrients are passed along in an ecosystem.

*food web* A number of interconnected food chains.

*force* A push or a pull.

*fossil* The remains or traces of an ancient organism, usually found in sedimentary rock.

*freezing* The change in phase from a solid to a liquid.

*freezing point* The temperature at which a substance changes from a liquid to a solid.

*frequency* The number of waves that pass by a fixed point in a given amount of time.

*friction* A force that resists motion and must be overcome to start and/or keep an object moving.

*front* The boundary that forms between two different air masses.

*full moon* The phase of the moon that occurs when Earth is between the sun and the moon, so that all of the moon's lighted side can be seen from Earth.

## G

*gene* A piece of genetic information (on a chromosome) that influences a trait.

*greenhouse effect* The trapping of heat in Earth's atmosphere by carbon dioxide.

*growth* The increase in size of an organism.

## H

*habitat* The particular environment in which an organism lives.

*heat energy* The form of energy produced by the vibrating motion of molecules in a substance.

*herbivore* A plant-eating animal.

*hibernate* To enter a sleeplike state of reduced body activity; how some animals survive the winter.

**high-pressure system** A large area where air is sinking, causing high surface air pressure; also called a *high*.

**hurricane** A large, rotating storm that forms over the ocean in the tropics; has strong winds and heavy rains.

**hydrosphere** The liquid part of Earth.

**hypothesis** A possible answer to a scientific problem, based on observation and/or prior knowledge.

## I

**independent variable** The variable that you control in an experiment.

**inertia** The tendency of an object at rest to remain at rest or an object in motion to remain in motion.

**ingestion** The process of taking in food.

**inner core** Earth's center, it has a radius of 1200 kilometers; is thought to be solid because P-waves travel faster through it.

**insoluble** Not able to dissolve in a given solvent.

## K

**kingdom** The largest group in Linnaeus' classification system for living things.

## L

**latitude** The distance, measured in degrees, north or south of the equator.

**Law of Conservation Energy** Energy can be neither created nor destroyed.

**Law of Conservation of Mass** Mass can be neither created nor destroyed in a chemical reaction.

**Law of Conservation of Matter** Matter can be neither created nor destroyed in a chemical reaction.

**lens** A piece of transparent glass or plastic with curved surfaces that bend light rays.

**life cycle** The changes that an organism undergoes as it develops and produces offspring.

**light** A visible form of radiant energy that moves in waves, outward in all directions from its source.

**lithosphere** The solid part of Earth.

**longitude** The distance, measured in degrees, east and west of the prime meridian.

**longitudinal wave** An earthquake wave that travels along Earth's surface; an *L-wave*.

**low-pressure system** A large area where air is rising, causing low surface air pressure; also called a *low*.

## M

**mantle** The layer below Earth's crust; it is solid, but flows very slowly.

**mass** The amount of matter in an object.

**matter** Anything that has mass and takes up space.

**mechanical energy** The form of energy with which moving objects perform work.

**melting** The change in phase from a solid to a liquid.

**melting point** The temperature at which a substance changes from a solid to a liquid.

**metabolism** The sum of all the chemical reactions that take place in the body.

**metal** Describes shiny solids that conducts electricity; found at the left on the Periodic Table of the Elements.

**metamorphosis** The process of a complete change in body form during development from juvenile to adult stages.

**meteor** A rock fragment traveling through space that enters Earth's atmosphere and burns up, leaving a bright streak of light.

*meter* The standard SI unit for length.

*microorganism* A very small organism that usually cannot be seen without a microscope.

*migrate* To move from one environment to another, where conditions are more favorable; how some animals survive the change in seasons.

*mineral* A naturally occurring solid substance made of inorganic (nonliving) material.

*mixture* Forms when two or more materials are put together without forming a new substance.

*molecule* The smallest particle of a compound.

*motion* A change in the position of an object relative to another object, which is assumed to be at rest.

*mountain* A feature on Earth's surface that rises high above the surrounding landscape; produced by folding, faulting, or volcanic activity.

*multicellular* Describes a living thing that is composed of more than one cell.

*mutation* A change in the genetic material of an organism.

**N**

*natural selection* The process that favors those organisms that are best able to survive and reproduce.

*new moon* The phase of the moon that occurs when the moon is between Earth and the sun, so that the moon cannot be seen from Earth.

*noble gases* A group of gaseous elements that seldom react with other elements; found in the extreme right column on the Periodic Table of the Elements.

*nonmetal* Describes solids and gases that are poor conductors of electricity; found at the right on the Periodic Table of the Elements.

*nonrenewable resource* A resource, such as a mineral, that cannot be replaced by nature within a relatively short time span (i.e., within human history).

*nuclear energy* The energy stored within the nucleus of an atom; used by nuclear power plants to produce electricity.

*nucleus* (1) The structure within a cell that controls cell activities and contains genetic material. (2) The center of an atom.

*nutrients* Food substances that an organism uses for producing energy as well as for its growth and repair.

*nutrition* The process that includes ingestion, digestion, and elimination.

**O**

*observation* Anything we perceive through use of one or more of our five senses.

*omnivore* A consumer that can eat both plants and other animals.

*orbit* The path of an object in space that is revolving around another object.

*organ* A group of tissues that act together to perform a function.

*organism* A living thing.

*organ system* A group of organs that act together to carry out a life process.

*outer core* The layer that surrounds Earth's inner core, it is about 2300 kilometers thick; thought to be liquid because S-waves cannot travel through it.

## P

***phases*** (1) The changing apparent shape of the moon, as seen from Earth. (2) The three forms, or states, of matter—solid, liquid, and gas.

***photosynthesis*** The process by which plants use the energy from sunlight and carbon dioxide and water from the environment to manufacture sugar.

***physical change*** A change in the appearance of a substance that does not alter the chemical makeup of the substance.

***physical property*** A characteristic of a substance that can be determined without changing the identity of the substance.

***plain*** A broad, flat landscape region at a low elevation, usually made up of layered sedimentary rock.

***plateau*** A large area of Earth's surface made up of horizontally layered rocks, found at a relatively high elevation.

***plate tectonics*** The theory that Earth's crust is broken up into a number of large pieces, or plates, that move and interact, producing many of Earth's surface features.

***pollutants*** Harmful substances that contaminate the environment, often produced by human activities.

***population*** All the members of a particular species that live within a habitat.

***predator*** An animal that hunts and kills (another animal) for its food.

***prevailing winds*** The winds that commonly blow in the same direction at a given latitude.

***prey*** The animal hunted by a predator (to be its food).

***primary wave*** An earthquake wave that can travel through liquids and solids; a *P-wave.*

***problem*** a scientific query, always stated in the form of a question.

***producer*** An organism that makes its own food; algae and plants.

## R

***radiation*** The transfer of heat through space in the form of waves.

***regulation*** The process that helps an organism maintain a constant internal environment.

***renewable resource*** A resource that can be replenished by nature within a relatively short time span (i.e., within human history).

***reproduction*** The process by which an organism produces new individuals, or offspring.

***research*** The gathering of facts, data, and opinions on a scientific topic.

***respiration*** The process by which organisms use the energy stored in food—nutrients combine with oxygen, releasing energy (and carbon dioxide and water as waste products).

***revolution*** The movement of an object in space around another object, such as the revolution of the moon around Earth.

***rotation*** The spinning of an object around its axis; e.g., Earth makes one complete rotation on its axis each day.

## S

***satellites*** Solid objects in the solar system that revolve around planets; also called *moons.*

***science*** The study of the natural world.

***scientific method*** An organized, step-by-step approach to problem solving in science.

***secondary wave*** An earthquake wave that can travel only through solids; an *S-wave.*

*second law of motion* The relationship among force, mass, and acceleration; $F = m \times a$.

*sexual reproduction* The form of reproduction that involves two parents, producing offspring that are not identical to either parent.

*SI units* System of International Units, used by all scientists to express measurements.

*solar system* The sun and all the objects that revolve around it, including the planets and their moons, asteroids, comets, and meteors.

*solubility* The maximum amount of solute that can dissolve in a given amount of solvent at a given temperature.

*soluble* The ability of a substance to dissolve in a given solvent.

*solute* The substance that dissolves in the solvent.

*solution* A mixture in which the components remain evenly distributed.

*solvent* The substance (e.g., water) that dissolves the solute.

*sound* The form of energy produced by a vibrating object; moves in waves.

*species* A group of organisms of the same kind that can produce fertile offspring.

*speed* The distance traveled per unit of time; e.g., meters per second.

*statistical analysis* A rigorous, mathematical method of examining experimental data; also called *statistics*.

*system* A group of components, or parts, that work together for a common purpose.

**T**

*technology* The application of scientific knowledge and other resources to develop new products and processes.

*temperature* A measure of the average molecular motion of a substance.

*third law of motion* For every action there is an equal and opposite reaction.

*thunderstorm* A brief intense rainstorm that affects a small area and is accompanied by thunder and lightning.

*tides* The rise and fall in the level of the ocean's waters that take place twice each day.

*tissue* A group of similar cells that act together to perform a function.

*tornado* A violent whirling wind, sometimes visible as a funnel-shaped cloud.

*transport* The process of moving materials throughout an organism.

**U**

*unicellular* Describes a living thing composed of a single cell; e.g., an ameba.

**V**

*variable* The changeable condition that can affect the outcome of an experiment.

*velocity* The speed of an object in a certain direction.

*volcano* (1) An opening in Earth's surface through which hot, liquid rock flows from deep underground. (2) A mountain formed by a series of volcanic eruptions.

*volume* The amount of space an object occupies.

**W**

*warm front* The boundary formed when a warm air mass slides up and over a cool air mass.

*water cycle* The continuous movement of water between Earth's surface and the atmosphere by means of evaporation, condensation, and precipitation.

*wavelength* The distance from one point on a wave to the corresponding point on the next wave.

*weather* The changing conditions of the atmosphere, with respect to heat, cold, sunshine, rain, snow, clouds, and wind.

*weather forecasting* An attempt to make accurate predictions of future weather.

*weathering* The breaking down of rocks into smaller pieces; mostly caused by the movements of water, wind, and ice.

*wind* The movement of air over Earth's surface; blows from areas of higher air pressure to areas of lower air pressure.

*wind direction* The direction from which the wind is blowing.

*winter storms* Blizzards and ice storms.

*work* The moving of an object over a distance by force.

# Index